INTERSCIENCE TRACTS ON PHYSICS AND ASTRONOMY

Edited by R. E. MARSHAK

University of Rochester

Additional volumes in preparation

A. Einstein 1879–1955

GENERAL RELATIVITY
AND GRAVITATIONAL
WAVES

J. WEBER

*Professor of Physics, University of Maryland,
College Park, Maryland*

INTERSCIENCE PUBLISHERS, INC., NEW YORK
Interscience Publishers Ltd., London   **1961**

INTERSCIENCE PUBLISHERS, INC.

250 Fifth Avenue, New York 1, New York

For Great Britain and Northern Ireland:

INTERSCIENCE PUBLISHERS LTD.

88/90 Chancery Lane, London W.C. 2, England

PRINTED IN THE UNITED STATES OF AMERICA

ONULP

Preface

The renewed interest in general relativity is due to several factors. For the theorist, quantization of Einstein's gravitational field offers a challenging approach to a new theory of elementary particles and amelioration of the difficulties of quantum field theory. For the experimentalist the technological advances of the past two decades make possible some new gravitation experiments and more precise ways of doing the older ones.

A book of this length on general relativity cannot be complete. I have attempted to give a fairly thorough introduction to the foundations of the theory, to the Riemannian geometry and tensor calculus ordinarily required in this field, to the conservation laws, and to the classical experiments.

About a fourth of the book is mainly devoted to a treatment of the theoretical and experimental aspects of gravitational radiation. The last chapter gives a brief discussion of the deduction of the equations of motion, of unified field theories, of Friedman's solution of the cosmological problem, and of the Hamiltonian formulation of general relativity.

This tract is serving as a text for my relativity course in the Physics Department of the University of Maryland.

I wish to express appreciation to Professor John A. Wheeler for the very stimulating year I was privileged to spend with him, to Professor James Anderson in whose lectures I saw these field equations for the first time, to Professor Peter G. Bergmann for his many illuminating comments at the Stevens Institute of Technology colloquia, and to Dr. Charles Misner for his lucid remarks on a number of issues. Several sections of the book were substantially improved in consequence of discussions with a graduate

student, Mr. George Hinds. Professor C. J. Goebel read the
manuscript and gave valuable criticism.

The photograph of Einstein which appears here was
kindly made available by Mrs. T. Ehrenfest Afanassjewa.

My own research has had the support of the National
Science Foundation.

J. WEBER

Contents

CHAPTER 1

The Equivalence Principle

This assumption of exact physical equivalence makes it impossible for us to speak of the absolute acceleration of the system of reference, just as the usual theory of relativity forbids us to talk of the absolute velocity of a system. A. Einstein

1.1 The Eötvos Experiment

From the time of Newton it had been assumed that the ratio of the inertial mass to the weight (gravitational mass) of a body is the same for all substances. If we assume this and write the equations of motion for a body in the earth's gravitational field, the mass cancels out and all freely falling bodies have the same acceleration.

In 1890 Eötvos (1) performed an ingenious experiment designed to test the ratio of inertial mass to weight. Consider a mass on the earth's surface (Fig. 1.1). There is a gravita-

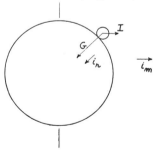

Fig. 1.1

tional force **G** acting toward the earth's center, and an inertial force **I** which is the centrifugal force associated with the earth's rotation. The ratio of the two magnitudes, and

1

of the corresponding components of these forces, depends on the ratio of the gravitational to the inertial mass. Eötvos suspended two masses from a torsion balance, as shown in Fig. 1.2, at a latitude about midway between the equator

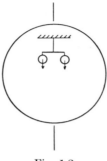

Fig. 1.2

and the pole. Suppose matters are arranged so that the balance is in equilibrium with the rod connecting the masses in the observer's horizontal plane and pointing in the east-west direction. We can first conclude that the net torque component resulting from the vertical components of the resultant forces $G + I$ on the two bodies is zero. If the ratio of inertial to gravitational mass is not the same for both, then the horizontal components of $G + I$ will give rise to a torque which is canceled by an opposite torque of the suspension wire. If now the entire apparatus is rotated through the angle π, the bodies are interchanged and the sign of the torque associated with the horizontal components of $G + I$ will reverse. The torque of the suspension wire, however, remains the same. The result is that an angular deflection of the rod and masses relative to the frame of the apparatus will be observed if the ratio of inertial to gravitational mass is not the same for both bodies.

Let the gravitational mass of one of the bodies be M_1 and let its inertial mass be m_1. Let $\mathbf{i}_r$ be a unit vector from the body to the center of the earth, and let $\mathbf{i}_m$ be a unit vector in the plane of the meridian, normal to the earth's axis of rotation. Let g_e be the magnitude of the earth's gravitational field. Then the gravitational force G_1 is given by

$$G_1 = g_e M_1 i_r \qquad (1.1)$$

Let a be the earth's radius, let ω be its angular velocity, and let φ be the latitude. Then the inertial (centrifugal) force I_1 is given by

$$I_1 = (m_1 a\omega^2 \cos \varphi)i_m \qquad (1.2)$$

Suppose the second body has gravitational mass M_2 and inertial mass m_2. We compare the forces on it with those on the first body, by means of the torsion balance. Assume that M_1 and M_2 are so chosen that the rod can be suspended in the center. Let the rod be represented by the vector b, and let the torque be denoted by T. We can write

$$T = \frac{b}{2} \times [G_1 - G_2] + \frac{b}{2} \times [I_1 - I_2] \qquad (1.3)$$

The resultant of the four forces must be in the direction of the thin wire which supports the rod, and is given by

$$F = G_1 + G_2 + I_1 + I_2 \qquad (1.4)$$

The component of the torque parallel to the supporting wire will tend to cause an observable rotation. Employing the preceding expressions enables us to write for the effective torque

$$T_\parallel = \frac{F \cdot T}{|F|}$$

$$\approx \frac{(g_e[M_1 + M_2]i_r + a\omega^2 \cos \varphi[m_1 + m_2]i_m) \cdot b \times [G_1 - G_2 + I_1 - I_2]}{2g_e(M_1 + M_2)} \qquad (1.5)$$

In (1.5) we have omitted the centrifugal force in the denominator since it is very small in comparison with the gravitational force. Evaluating (1.5) and making the substitutions,

$$\alpha_1 = M_1/m_1; \qquad \alpha_2 = M_2/m_2 \qquad (1.6)$$

gives, for the effective torque,

$$T_\parallel \approx \frac{a\omega^2 \cos \varphi \, m_1 m_2 (\alpha_1 - \alpha_2)[b \cdot i_r \times i_m]}{\alpha_1 m_1 + \alpha_2 m_2} \qquad (1.7)$$

Expression (1.7) vanishes if $\alpha_1 = \alpha_2$, and for $\alpha_1 \neq \alpha_2$ it will have a value which depends on the orientation of the rod **b**, with respect to the vector $\mathbf{i}_r \times \mathbf{i}_m$, which is normal to the meridian plane. It has its maximum when **b** points in the east-west direction. As we remarked earlier, the torsion balance is brought to equilibrium by turning it until the rod points in the east-west direction, in a plane tangent to the earth's surface. Then the apparatus is rotated through the angle π, reversing the sense of **b**; if $\alpha_1 \neq \alpha_2$ there will be a torque which may then give a rotation of the rod relative to the frame which supports the balance. Eötvos observed no rotation and concluded that within one part in 10^8, $\alpha_1 = \alpha_2$ for all the materials which were tested. This experiment has been repeated. (2, 3) The work of Southerns was done with pendulums and demonstrated the equality of α for radioactive materials. Professor R. H. Dicke (4) is now repeating the Eötvos experiment with greatly refined apparatus employing three bodies, and a threefold axis of symmetry, to minimize local disturbances. At this time his results agree with those of Eötvos, and the equality of α for certain substances is established to a few parts in 10^{10}.

The Eötvos experiment enables certain conclusions to be drawn concerning the elementary particles. The ratio of mass to weight for an electron plus a proton may be shown to be the same as for the neutron to one part in 10^7, and the reduction in mass of a nucleus resulting from nuclear binding forces can be shown to one part in 10^5 to be accompanied by a similar reduction in weight. With an accuracy of five parts in a thousand it can be concluded that the binding energy of the orbital electrons is accompanied also by a corresponding change in weight.

Bondi (5) notes a possible distinction between mass which is acted upon and mass which is the source of a gravitational field. The mass which is acted upon he calls passive gravitational mass, and a mass which is a source is called active gravitational mass. The Eötvos experiment, in this view, determines the equality of the ratio of inertial and passive gravitational mass.

1.2 Negative Mass

Nothing in either Newtonian or relativistic gravitation theory precludes the existence of negative mass, but it is an empirical fact that it has never been observed. Both Newtonian gravitation theory and general relativity indicate a quite different behavior for negative mass than for the corresponding situation in electrodynamics. If a small negative mass interacts with a large positive mass, again the (negative) mass cancels out on both sides of the equation of motion and the acceleration is still toward the positive mass. Thus a positive mass attracts all other masses, both positive and negative. A small negative mass would be expected to fall in the earth's gravitational field. Similarly a negative mass repels all other masses, regardless of their sign. For a pair of bodies, one with positive mass and one with negative mass, with magnitudes about equal, we should expect the positive mass to attract the negative mass and the negative mass to repel the positive mass so that one chases the other! If the motion is confined to the line of centers the pair is expected to move with uniform acceleration. This problem has been discussed by Bondi (5).

Schiff (6) has recently considered the possibility that the gravitational mass of an anti particle, the positron, might be negative. His arguments are based on the renormalized quantum electrodynamics. The Coulomb field of an atomic nucleus produces a polarization of the vacuum. This effect, first calculated by Uehling (7) for hydrogen, produces a 27 Mc contribution to the Lamb shift of the $2S$ state in hydrogen. The virtual electron-positron pairs associated with vacuum polarization would be expected to contribute to the renormalized mass of atoms. We know from experiment that the inertial mass of the positron is positive. If the gravitational mass were negative, different atoms would be expected to have slightly different ratios of inertial to (passive) gravitational mass. This follows because the relative contribution of virtual pairs to the mass would depend on the nuclear charge and its distribution. This would vary for different atoms. For the case where the gravitational rest mass of a positron is assumed equal in magnitude and opposite in sign to that of a negative electron, but its kinetic energy is acted upon normally by a gravitational field, the difference between gravitational mass and renormalized inertial mass is finite and approximately equal (6) to

$$(3m/8\pi)(Z/137)^2 \int_0^\infty \frac{|F(q)|^2 \, dq}{(q^2 + 4\mu^2)^{\frac{1}{2}}}$$

Here m is the electron mass, $\mu = mc/\hbar$, Z is the atomic number, and $F(q)$ is the Fourier transform for the nuclear charge distribution, normalized to unit total charge. This expression has a ratio to the atomic mass of 10^{-7}, 2×10^{-7}, and 4.3×10^{-7} for aluminum, copper, and platinum, respectively. Since these numbers are larger than the uncertainties in the mass ratios determined by Eötvos, Schiff concludes that the possibility that the gravitational mass of the positron is negative is ruled out.

It is likely that some experiment to see if anti neutrons fall in the earth's gravitational field may be attempted. As we remarked earlier, if existing theories of gravitation are accepted they will be expected to fall, in any case.

1.3 Equivalence of Different Frames of Reference

The empirical fact that the two kinds of mass are equivalent did not fit anywhere in theoretical physics until Einstein (5) pointed out that it could be understood in terms of the equivalence of different frames of reference. Einstein postulated that an accelerated frame in a region free of gravitational fields is equivalent[‡] to a rest frame in a given infinitesimal region [§] of a time-independent gravitational field. This is called the principle of equivalence. From this postulate the equivalence of gravitational and inertial mass can be

[‡] This implies that all observations made locally on a system in a uniform static gravitational field will be the same as that on a system subjected to a uniform acceleration.

[§] The nonuniformity of a real gravitational field precludes replacing it by a single accelerated frame over a large region.

shown to be a consequence, by the following (8) argument
(see Fig. 1.3). Here we have two systems Σ and Σ', whose
z axes coincide. The Σ frame is assumed so be at rest in a
gravitational field of strength g. The Σ' frame is assumed to

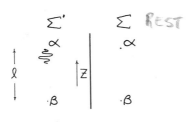

Fig. 1.3

have no gravitational field but it is being accelerated with
acceleration g, in the positive z direction. Let Σ' be at rest
at $t = 0$ when a light pulse of energy E_α is emitted from point
α. This light is absorbed at point β, at which time the velocity of Σ' is gl/c.

The light had energy E_α and momentum E_α/c. The
energy at point β can be obtained by use of the Lorentz transformation and is given by

$$E_\beta = E_\alpha \cos \psi + i E_\alpha \sin \psi \qquad (1.8)$$

where

$$\cos \psi = (1 - v^2/c^2)^{-\frac{1}{2}}; \qquad \sin \psi = (-iv/c)(1 - v^2/c^2)^{-\frac{1}{2}}$$

Evaluating (1.8) gives

$$E_\beta = E_\alpha[(c+v)/(c-v)]^{\frac{1}{2}} \approx E_\alpha(1+v/c) = E_\alpha + E_\alpha gl/c^2 \quad (1.9)$$

From the equivalence principle we assume that expression (1.9) holds for the same process taking place in the Σ
frame. Imagine a mass M to be initially at α, in Σ, then
moved to β. Light of energy E_α is emitted at α and absorbed
by M at β. The total gravitational mass of M plus the absorbed light is M'. Now lift M' back to α and re-emit light
so that the mass at α is again M. There is no net change of
energy during the process, so the change in energy going

from α to β can be set equal to the energy change on the return.

$$Mgl + E_\beta - E_\alpha = M'gl \qquad (1.10)$$

Making use of (1.9) then leads to

$$M' - M = E_\alpha/c^2 \qquad (1.11)$$

Expression (1.11) states that the increment in gravitational mass is the change in the inertial mass, and it therefore follows that the equivalence of mass and weight can be considered as a consequence of the equivalence of an accelerated frame to a gravitational field.

1.4 Gravitational Red Shift of Spectral Lines

It follows also from the equivalence principle that we should expect a gravitational red shift of spectral lines. For consider again the emission of light at α by an atom in accelerated frame Σ', which is momentarily at rest. The light of frequency ν is received by an observer at β who measures the frequency in units of his own proper time. The Doppler shift in the frequency at β gives rise to

$$\nu_\beta = \nu_\alpha[(c + v)/(c - v)]^{\frac{1}{2}} \qquad (1.12)$$

and

$$\nu_\beta \approx \nu_\alpha(1 + v/c) \qquad (1.13)$$

In the equivalent gravitational field, (1.13) again holds, and

$$E_\beta/E_\alpha = \nu_\beta/\nu_\alpha = 1 + gl/c^2 \qquad (1.14)$$

The quantity gl in (1.14) is the change in the gravitational potential, and we write the frequency shift $\nu_\beta - \nu_\alpha$ as

$$\Delta\nu = \nu(\varphi_\alpha - \varphi_\beta)/c^2 \qquad (1.15)$$

In (1.15) φ_β is the gravitational potential (a negative quantity) at the point where the light is received and φ_α is the gravitational potential at the point where the light is emitted. For light received on earth from a star, $\varphi_\beta > \varphi_\alpha$. If M is the star's mass, G is the gravitational constant, r_s is the star's radius, and m and r_e the mass and radius of the earth, respectively, (1.15) becomes

$$\Delta \nu \approx - \frac{\nu G}{c^2} \left[\frac{M}{r_s} - \frac{m}{r_e} \right] \qquad (1.16)$$

This predicts a red shift. In deriving (1.16) we have assumed that the frequency remains invariant in terms of the local proper time of the atom or molecule, even in a gravitational field. This assumption is really a statement about the atom. It would clearly not be valid for a pendulum clock but might be fulfilled at least approximately for a quartz oscillator clock,[‡] and more precisely for "atomic" clocks. In the absence of a complete quantum theory of atomic spectra which includes effects of all fields in interaction with a quantized gravitational field, it seems reasonable to suppose that (1.16) will be valid to a very good approximation. However, one might expect some effects due to the space derivatives of the gravitational field which would cause very small departures from (1.16) in some cases, even for an atomic or molecular system whose center of mass falls freely.[§] Additional discussion of the red shift is given in Chapter 5.

1.5 Further Remarks on the Equivalence Principle

Since an accelerated frame is equivalent to a certain gravitational field it follows that we can annul a gravitational field by an appropriate acceleration. For example, a freely falling elevator in a gravitational field appears to be an inertial frame insofar as gravitational forces are concerned. A body would move within it as though no gravitational field were present, and no observation made on the

---

[‡] A quartz oscillator at rest on earth is compressed by its own weight, thus altering its dimensions slightly from the free-fall value it would have in a satellite.

[§] The fact that the atom is in free fall implies that there are minimal stresses resulting from the gravitational field. An atom at rest in an accelerated frame might be perturbed by such stresses. These might lead to some observable (and calculable) effects for experiments which are carried out in accelerated frames. See, however, C. W. Sherwin(13).

body could enable a distinction to be drawn between an inertial frame and the space inside the elevator. It is not so clear that this will still be true if the body within the elevator is electrically charged. There have been a number of investigations of the possible radiation from a uniformly accelerated point charge (9, 10, 11, 12). Bondi and Gold, and Fulton and Rohrlich predict that such a charge does indeed radiate. The radiation reaction (for uniform acceleration) is zero and the issue of energy conservation is complicated by the infinite self energy. It may be that when the internal structure of elementary particles is properly taken into account, a charged particle will be found to radiate and have a non vanishing radiation reaction when falling in a uniform gravitational field. It would follow that by observing a charged and an uncharged body falling freely we can distinguish by local measurements whether we are in an inertial frame or falling freely in a gravitational field. The equivalence principle then becomes merely a guide for formulation of the equations of the gravitational field alone, and not a general law of nature.

References

1. R. V. Eötvos, *Math. u. naturw. Ber. Ungarn* 8, 65 (1890); *Beibl. Ann. Physik* 15, 688 (1891); *Ann. Phys.* 59, 354 (1896); *Ann. Physik* 68, 11 (1922).
2. L. Southerns, *Proc. Roy. Soc.* (*London*) 84, 325 (1910).
3. P. Zeeman, *Proc. Amsterdam Acad.* 20, 542 (1917).
4. R. H. Dicke, *Revs. Modern Phys.* 29, 3, 355 (1957). This does not discuss the new experiment but contains Dicke's ideas on the equivalence principle.
5. H. Bondi, *Revs. Modern Phys.* 29, 3, 423 (1957).
6. L. I. Schiff, *Phys. Rev. Letters* 1, 7, 254 (1958).
7. E. A. Uehling, *Phys. Rev.* 48, 55 (1935); R. Serber, *Phys. Rev.* 48, 49 (1935).
8. A. Einstein, *Ann. Physik* 35 (1911).
9. H. Bondi and T. Gold, *Proc. Roy. Soc.* (*London*) A229, 416–424 (1955).
10. B. DeWitt and R. W. Brehme, *Annals of Physics* 9, 220, (1960).
11. D. L. Drukey, *Phys. Rev.* 76, 543, (1949).
12. T. Fulton and F. Rohrlich, *Annals of Physics* 9, 499 (1960).
13. C.W. Sherwin, *Phys. Rev.* 120, 17(1960).

CHAPTER 2

Generalization of the Special Theory of Relativity

The general laws of nature are to be expressed by equations which hold good for all systems of coordinates, that is, are covariant with respect to any substitutions whatever (generally co-variant).   A. Einstein

2.1 The Idea of Covariance

Minkowski made the important discovery that transforming from one inertial frame to another moving with relative velocity v corresponds (1) to the rotation of axes in a four-dimensional space-time coordinate system. The requirements of special relativity are indeed met in a most elegant fashion by writing the laws of physics as relations among four-dimensional vectors. While this procedure is not essential, it does add elements of beauty and simplicity.

We employ coordinates labeled by superscripts. In the Minkowski space of special relativity we have the coordinates x, y, z, and ct, which we will denote x^1, x^2, x^3, and x^0. The important quantities are the relations between events. An event has no extension in space or time. It is a point in a four-dimensional space. The interval between two events a and b is denoted by the symbol s_{ab} and defined by

$$s_{ab}^2 = (x_a^0 - x_b^0)^2 - (x_a^1 - x_b^1)^2 - (x_a^2 - x_b^2)^2 - (x_a^3 - x_b^3)^2 \quad (2.1)$$

If we transform from one Minkowski system of coordinates to another, the interval between the same events remains invariant and in terms of new coordinates x'^1, x'^2, x'^3, x'^0 is given by

$$(s_{ab})^2 = (x'^0_a - x'^0_b)^2 - (x'^1_a - x'^1_b)^2 - (x'^2_a - x'^2_b)^2$$
$$- (x'^3_a - x'^3_b)^2 \quad (2.2)$$

11

While the magnitudes of some quantities such as s_{ab} are invariant, others such as $x_a{}^1 - x_b{}^1$ do change under these coordinate transformations, which constitute a group. The form of the relation for s_{ab} does not change, and such a relation is said to be covariant under the group of coordinate transformations (rotation of axes in Minkowski space). For two events separated by a differential interval we can write

$$ds^2 = dx^{0^2} - dx^{1^2} - dx^{2^2} - dx^{3^2} \qquad (2.3)$$

2.2 The Metric Tensor

We shall employ a great many sums and shall follow the summation convention that an index which is repeated represents a sum. This enables us to write (2.3) in the form

$$-ds^2 = g_{\mu\nu} dx^\mu dx^\nu \qquad (2.4)$$

The elements of $g_{\mu\nu}$ are represented by

$$g_{\mu\nu} = \begin{bmatrix} -1 & 0 & 0 & 0 \\ 0 & +1 & 0 & 0 \\ 0 & 0 & +1 & 0 \\ 0 & 0 & 0 & +1 \end{bmatrix} \qquad (2.5)$$

$g_{\mu\nu}$ is called the metric tensor and the expression (2.5), which retains its form under Lorentz transformations, is called a Lorentz metric.

In curvilinear coordinates, the metric tensor assumes a different form, but a coordinate transformation can transform it to the form (2.5), throughout the space, provided Euclidean geometry is valid there.

2.3 The Metric Tensor in Curved Spaces and Accelerated Frames

The curved two-dimensional space on the surface of a sphere is described by the squared line element

$$g_{\mu\nu} dx^\mu dx^\nu = r^2 d\theta^2 + r^2 \sin^2\theta \, d\varphi^2;$$
$$g_{\mu\nu} = \begin{vmatrix} r^2 & 0 \\ 0 & r^2 \sin^2\theta \end{vmatrix} \qquad (2.6)$$

Triangles composed of arcs of great circles have the sum of their angles greater than π and less than 3π. This non-Euclidean, curved character is implied by the metric (2.6), through relations involving the derivatives of $g_{\mu\nu}$. No coordinate transformation can reduce (2.6) everywhere to a diagonal form in which the diagonal elements are one. The concept of curvature will be discussed in more detail later.

Suppose now that we have a plane triangle in an inertial frame. If we measure from a different inertial frame, the shape of the triangle may change, but the sum of its angles remains π and the geometry will not have changed.

Consider a set of points which lie on a circle in an inertial frame. If we observe from a rotating frame of reference with center coinciding with the center of the circle and survey the same points, we find that the ratio of circumference to diameter now depends on our operational procedure for measuring length. To avoid, for the moment, the issue of clock synchronization within a rotating system, we assume that length is measured by bringing pairs of points into coincidence using the clocks of the inertial frame to define simultaneity. The ratio of circumference to radius using measuring rods at rest within the rotating system will exceed π. This follows because a rigid measuring rod would measure the same diameter as before, but when laid along the circumference it would be foreshortened by the Lorentz contraction. The metric tensor in the rotating frame now has to describe a non-Euclidean, curved space.

In the inertial frame we may set up a system of fixed synchronized clocks throughout the space. In the rotating frame clocks at different radii will have different time measures. Identical clocks at different radii are similar to identical clocks in different inertial frames. They cannot be synchronized. Suppose that coordinate time is measured by pulses emitted by a clock at the center of the rotating frame. A clock at each point in the rotating frame ticks intervals for an observer at that point. The relation between these intervals and the coordinate time differences corresponding to receipt of successive light pulses will be described by the g_{00} component of $g_{\mu\nu}$. This will now be a function of radius, and the metric (2.5) of special relativity does not apply.[‡]

The equivalence of a gravitational field to an accelerated[§] frame then implies that the special theory of relativity cannot be valid in an extended region (2) where gravitational fields are present. A curved-space metric is needed. To consider another example, suppose we make up a triangle in an inertial frame with sides which are light rays. The sum of the angles is π. If this is repeated in a gravitational field the sides of the triangle will become curved because of the action of gravitation on the energy of the photons. The sum of the angles of the triangle will now differ from π. In a covariant theory this is described by saying that the paths of light rays

[‡] An appropriate metric for the rotating frame is

$$-ds^2 = dr^2 + r^2\,d\varphi^2 + dz^2 + 2\omega r^2\,d\varphi dt - (c^2 - \omega^2 r^2)dt^2$$

[§] A few remarks on the clock paradox are in order. It was noted in Einstein's first paper on the electrodynamics of moving bodies that if we have two identical clocks and keep one at rest in an inertial frame and then move the other in a closed path which returns to the position of the first clock, the two clocks will no longer agree. Consider now a pair of twins. One remains at rest in an inertial frame and the other sets off in a rocket and then returns. The traveler will on returning find that the stay-at-home twin is older than he. Darwin has pointed out (C. G. Darwin, *Nature* **180**, 976 (1957)) that the entire problem may be understood within the framework of special relativity, for the acceleration times of the rocket may be short and the period of uniform motion extremely long. Then the result cannot depend on what happened during the short acceleration periods. If the velocity of the traveler relative to the twin at rest in an inertial frame is v then

$$t_r = t_m\,/\,\sqrt{1 - v^2/c^2}$$

where t_r is the elapsed time for the twin at rest and t_m is the elapsed time for the moving twin. This result follows immediately from special relativity, since we must carry out all calculations in the frame of the twin who remains fixed at all times in the inertial frame. The identical result may be obtained (see C. Møller, *The Theory of Relativity*, Oxford University Press, New York, 1952) if we calculate in the frame of the moving twin, using the formalism of general relativity, which is appropriate for frames that may undergo accelerations. There is, therefore, no paradox.

are always geodesics and that a curved-space metric is required in a gravitational field.

It has been pointed out (3, 4) that by suitably redefining, operationally, the measurement of length and time, the Lorentz metric may always be used. We could similarly insist that the earth's surface is flat. By suitably defining the operations of measurement as a function of latitude and longitude, internal consistency would be achieved with Euclidean geometry. This is not the point of view which we adopt in this tract.

2.4 General Covariance

If we consider gravitational fields alone, the equivalence principle denies us the possibility of distinguishing, by local measurements, between an inertial frame and a freely falling system in a gravitational field. There is then no a priori reason to give special significance to inertial frames. Also it is not possible to set up the required system of synchronized clocks throughout a gravitational field. For these reasons Einstein was led to postulate that all systems of coordinates are equally good for the description of nature and that the laws of physics should have the same form in all. This is the principle of general covariance.

If we adopt this principle the coordinates become nothing more than a bookkeeping system to label the events. The principle of general covariance has been a valuable guide in deducing correct equations. It leads us to avoid principles which seem simple only in certain coordinate systems, and to retain those which can be simply expressed in arbitrary systems of coordinates. It has been pointed out by Kretschmann (5) that any physical law can be written in a covariant form. The result is usually not simple. Kretschmann also pointed out that the principle of general covariance therefore has absolutely no necessary physical consequences. The requirements of simplicity of form plus covariance have nonetheless been a valuable guide in deducing equations which in a final analysis must stand or fall on the basis of comparison with experiment.

The treatment of generally covariant equations in a curved space is facilitated by the formalism of the tensor calculus.

References

1. H. Minkowski, address to the 80th Assembly of German Natural Scientists and Physicians, Cologne, 1908; reprinted in *The Principle of Relativity*, Dover Publications, New York, 1952.
2. A. Einstein, *Ann. Physik* **49**, 769 (1916).
3. N. Rosen, *Phys. Rev.* **57**, 147 (1949).
4. R. H. Dicke, *Revs. Modern Phys.* **29**, 363 (1957).
5. E. Kretschmann, *Ann. Physik* **53**, 575 (1917).

CHAPTER 3

Riemannian Geometry and Tensor Calculus

*The inner properties of surfaces are "most worthy of being
diligently exploited by geometers."*   C. F. Gauss

3.1 Some Ideas about Curvature

A more general kind of geometry, in which $g_{\mu\nu}$ is not
necessarily reducible by a coordinate transformation everywhere to the Lorentz metric, will now be discussed.

Gauss considered the following question. Suppose we
have a two-dimensional curved surface, inhabited by intelli-
gent two-dimensional animals. Can they determine that

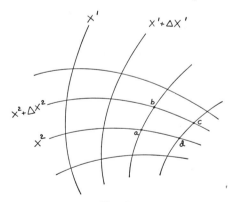

Fig. 3.1

their space is curved? Is it possible to determine the elements
of curvature by means of measurements made within the
surface alone? He found that this can indeed be done. First
we proceed by labeling the points of the surface in any

regular but nonetheless arbitrary way. Two arbitrary families of curves, $x^1 =$ constant and $x^2 =$ constant are the coordinate system (Fig. 3.1). Direct measurement of length between points a and b gives g_{22}; similarly by measuring lengths ac and ad we obtain g_{12} and g_{11}. Gauss gave formulas which allow the curvature to be written in terms of the $g_{\mu\nu}$, and their derivatives.

Curvature is an intrinsic property, at any given point the same value is obtained in every coordinate system. We shall see how the idea of curvature can be extended to more than two dimensions. Einstein's theory of gravitation relates the curvature of the space to the distribution of stress and energy. This follows in part the suggestion of Mach to the effect that the properties of the space-time continuum are determined by the distribution of energy.

3.2 Transformation Laws for Different Kinds of Tensors

Let us start our discussion with the assumption that we have M variables x^1, x^2, x^3, ..., x^M. A set of particular values of these variables is now regarded as a point in a hyperspace or manifold having M dimensions. The space is made up of all the points corresponding to the range of values which can be assumed by these variables. Suppose we employ a different labeling for the points x'^1, x'^2, x'^3, ..., x'^M, such that

$$x'^\alpha = f^\alpha(x^1, x^2, \ldots, x^M) \tag{3.1}$$

We assume that derivatives exist, and write

$$dx'^\alpha = \frac{\partial f^\alpha}{\partial x^\beta} dx^\beta = \frac{\partial x'^\alpha}{\partial x^\beta} dx^\beta \tag{3.2}$$

The coordinate differentials dx^α are said to be the components of a contravariant vector.[‡] Similarly, any set of quantities F^α are defined to be a contravariant vector if they obey the transformation law

‡ A vector is a tensor of the first rank, a scalar is a tensor of rank zero.

$$F'^{\alpha} = \frac{\partial x'^{\alpha}}{\partial x^{\beta}} F^{\beta} \tag{3.3}$$

Consider now quantities such as $\partial \varphi / \partial x^{\beta}$, where φ is some function of the variables $x^1, x^2, \ldots, x^M$:

$$\frac{\partial \varphi}{\partial x'^{\alpha}} = \frac{\partial \varphi}{\partial x^{\beta}} \frac{\partial x^{\beta}}{\partial x'^{\alpha}} \tag{3.4}$$

The quantities $\partial \varphi / \partial x^{\alpha}$ are seen to obey a different transformation law from (3.3) and any set of quantities transforming according to

$$K'_{\alpha} = \frac{\partial x^{\beta}}{\partial x'^{\alpha}} K_{\beta} \tag{3.5}$$

are said to form a covariant ‡ vector. Note that our definitions of covariant and contravariant vectors require the existence of derivatives on our manifold and not the existence of a metric. We are following the convention of denoting covariant vectors by subscripts and contravariant vectors by superscripts.

The product of two contravariant vectors A^{α} and B^{β} will satisfy the transformation law

$$A'^{\alpha} B'^{\beta} = \frac{\partial x'^{\alpha}}{\partial x^{\nu}} \frac{\partial x'^{\beta}}{\partial x^{\delta}} A^{\nu} B^{\delta} \tag{3.6}$$

A set of quantities $T^{\mu\nu}$, which obey the transformation law (3.6), are said to form a contravariant tensor of the second rank. Similarly a covariant second-rank tensor is one which obeys the transformation law

$$T'_{\mu\nu} = \frac{\partial x^{\alpha}}{\partial x'^{\mu}} \frac{\partial x^{\beta}}{\partial x'^{\nu}} T_{\alpha\beta} \tag{3.7}$$

A mixed tensor of any rank obeys the transformation

‡ The word covariant has two quite different meanings. A covariant theory or equation has the same form in all systems of coordinates. The word covariant is used also to signify that a tensor obeys the transformation law (3.5). Thus a covariant equation may contain contravariant tensors as well as covariant ones, and other objects which are not tensors.

law

$$T'^{\mu\nu\,\cdots}_{\epsilon\eta\,\cdots} = \frac{\partial x^\alpha}{\partial x'^\epsilon} \frac{\partial x^\beta}{\partial x'^\eta} \cdots \frac{\partial x'^\mu}{\partial x^\rho} \frac{\partial x'^\nu}{\partial x^\sigma} \cdots T_{\alpha\beta}{}^{\rho\sigma} \qquad (3.8)$$

Certain other quantities transform according to the law

$$T'^{\mu\,\cdots}_{\epsilon\,\cdots} = J^W \frac{\partial x'^\mu}{\partial x^\alpha} \frac{\partial x^\beta}{\partial x'^\epsilon} \cdots T^\alpha_\beta{}_{\cdots} \qquad (3.9)$$

J is the Jacobian determinant $|\partial x^\kappa/\partial x'^\iota|$. The superscript W is the power to which J is raised. $T^\mu_\nu{}_{\cdots}$ is said to be a tensor density of weight W.

A function S, which transforms to S', such that $S = S'$ at every point and in all coordinate systems is said to be an invariant, or scalar.

In all cases when a quantity is given, its form provides a prescription for getting it in other coordinate systems. Thus if $T_{\mu\nu} = A_\mu B_\nu$, then in a different system of coordinates $T'_{\mu\nu} = A'_\mu B'_\nu$.

The product $A_\lambda B^\lambda$ of a covariant and a contravariant vector transforms in the following way:

$$A'_\lambda B'^\lambda = \frac{\partial x^\mu}{\partial x'^\lambda} \frac{\partial x'^\lambda}{\partial x^\nu} A_\mu B^\nu = \delta_\nu{}^\mu A_\mu B^\nu = A_\nu B^\nu \quad (3.10)$$

This product is therefore a scalar. It also follows that the inner product (summation over upper-lower index pairs) is a scalar for tensors of higher rank. These notions may be employed to test for tensor character. Let B^μ be an arbitrary contravariant tensor and let A_μ be a set of quantities which may or may not have tensor character. Then if the product $A_\mu B^\mu$ is an invariant we can show that A_μ is a tensor, for

$$A_\mu B^\mu = A'_\mu B^\alpha \frac{\partial x'^\mu}{\partial x^\alpha} \qquad (3.11)$$

An index such as α or μ, over which a sum is to be carried out, may be given any convenient letter. This is an important aid in manipulation. We may then write (3.11) as

$$\left(A_\mu - A'_\nu \frac{\partial x'^\nu}{\partial x^\mu} \right) B^\mu = 0 \qquad (3.12)$$

It follows from (3.12) that A_μ transforms according to $A_\mu = A'_\nu \partial x'^\nu / \partial x^\mu$ and is therefore a covariant vector. The Kronecker delta, written as $\delta_\mu{}^\nu$, is a quantity which is unity if $\mu = \nu$ and zero if $\mu \neq \nu$. If we write

$$\delta_\mu{}^\nu = \frac{\partial x^\nu}{\partial x^\mu} = \frac{\partial x^\nu}{\partial x'^\alpha} \frac{\partial x'^\alpha}{\partial x^\mu} = \frac{\partial x^\nu}{\partial x'^\beta} \frac{\partial x'^\alpha}{\partial x^\mu} \delta'_\alpha{}^\beta \qquad (3.13)$$

it is evident that $\delta_\mu{}^\nu$ is a mixed tensor.

If a tensor $S^{\mu\nu\alpha} = S^{\nu\mu\alpha}$, it is said to be symmetric in the indices μ and ν. If $A^{\alpha\beta\gamma} = -A^{\beta\alpha\gamma}$, the tensor is said to be antisymmetric (or skew-symmetric) in the indices α and β. By writing out the transformation laws it becomes clear that the symmetry properties of a tensor are retained under coordinate transformations if the pair of indices are both subscripts or both superscripts. In general the symmetry properties are not retained if one index is a subscript and one a superscript. The symmetry properties are therefore meaningful only for the same kind of indices.

We may write any tensor $A^{\mu\nu}{}_\alpha{}^\delta$ as

$$A^{\mu\nu}{}_\alpha{}^\delta = \tfrac{1}{2}[A^{\mu\nu}{}_\alpha{}^\delta + A^{\nu\mu}{}_\alpha{}^\delta] + \tfrac{1}{2}[A^{\mu\nu}{}_\alpha{}^\delta - A^{\nu\mu}{}_\alpha{}^\delta] \qquad (3.14)$$

and it follows from (3.14) that any tensor may be considered as the sum of a part which is symmetric and a part which is antisymmetric in a given pair of upper or lower indices.

It follows from the transformation laws that if all components of a given tensor vanish in one coordinate system, then all components vanish in all coordinate systems. This fact is of great importance in theoretical physics. If a law is written in tensor form, for example by saying that one tensor equals another, the difference of the two tensors will vanish in all coordinate systems and the law has a validity independent of the coordinates which may be employed. Similarly, if we establish a tensor equation in a special coordinate system, it is valid in general.

We have seen that the derivatives of a scalar form a covariant vector. The derivatives of a covariant vector, on the other hand, do not have the required transformation law of tensors. For

$$\frac{\partial A_\rho}{\partial x^\sigma} = \frac{\partial}{\partial x^\sigma}\left(\frac{\partial x'^\alpha}{\partial x^\rho}A'_\alpha\right) = \frac{\partial x'^\alpha}{\partial x^\rho}\frac{\partial x'^\beta}{\partial x^\sigma}\frac{\partial A'_\alpha}{\partial x'^\beta} + A'_\alpha\frac{\partial^2 x'^\alpha}{\partial x^\sigma\,\partial x^\rho}\quad(3.15)$$

A new kind of derivative, the covariant derivative, does permit us to form tensors from the differentiation of other tensors. In order to see how this comes about, we must consider the concept of parallel displacement of a vector.

3.3 Parallel Displacement and Covariant Differentiation

It is possible to extend the idea of parallel displacement of a vector to curved spaces in a consistent way. We assume that there always exists a reference frame such that the geometry is Euclidean (or Minkowskian) in the immediate vicinity of a point ‡ P, and Cartesian coordinates are employed in that neighborhood. In such a coordinate system the idea of an infinitesimal parallel displacement of a vector simply means that none of its components change. Also the scalar product of two vectors A and B, $A_\mu B^\mu$, does not change under parallel displacement. For arbitrary coordinates we define the operation of infinitesimal parallel displacement of a vector A_μ from a point P to a neighboring point P' to be one which leaves the scalar product with an arbitrary vector B^μ invariant.

---

‡ We can always transform to a Lorentz metric at any given point where $g_{\mu\nu}$ is well defined. Suppose the space has n dimensions. The $g_{\mu\nu}$ at the point are a set of $n(n+1)/2$ numbers. Write $dx^\alpha = m^\alpha{}_\beta dx'^\beta$; for convenience assume $m^\alpha{}_\beta = m^\beta{}_\alpha$. Substitute this in ds^2 and set $g'_{\mu\nu} = \delta_{\mu\nu}$. This gives $n(n+1)/2$ equations for the same number of m's which are then determined. There are other ways of doing this. It cannot in general be done over a region, because the m's become functions rather than numbers, and the equations $dx^\alpha = m^\alpha{}_\beta dx'^\beta$ will not ordinarily be integrable to give the required coordinate transformation.

The idea of a parallel displacement along some given curve in a two-dimensional surface can be given an intuitive interpretation. Suppose the surface is developable. Then we can unroll it on to a plane and parallel-displace vectors in the plane. The surface is then rolled back and we have the required parallel-transported vector. If a given surface is not developable, we must first select a path for parallel transport, then erect a tangent plane at each point of the path. These tangent planes will envelope a developable surface. This new developable surface can then be unrolled and the operations of parallel transport and rerolling carried out. If the curve along which the parallel displacement is to be carried out happens to be a geodesic, it becomes a straight line when unrolled on to a plane. It is then clear that the angle between a geodesic and a vector remains unchanged in a parallel displacement. The angle between two vectors would also be expected to remain constant in a parallel displacement. We emphasize that the operation of parallel displacement from one point to another depends in general on the path which is specified between the points.

In curvilinear coordinates in both curved and flat spaces, the components of a vector A^ν would be expected to change, under a parallel displacement. Let δA^ν be this change, for an infinitesimal parallel displacement. δA^ν should be a linear function of the coordinate differentials and the components A^ν. It can be written

$$\delta A^\nu = -\Gamma^\nu_{\alpha\beta} A^\alpha \, dx^\beta \tag{3.16}$$

The quantities $\Gamma^\nu_{\alpha\beta}$ are coefficients whose properties are to be determined. First we show that $\Gamma^\nu_{\alpha\beta}$ is symmetric in α and β. Let A^ν be a coordinate differential dx^ν:

$$\delta(dx^\nu) = -\Gamma^\nu_{\alpha\beta} \, dx^\alpha \, dx^\beta \tag{3.17}$$

We now return to the local Cartesian coordinate system by the transformations

$$x^\alpha = f^\alpha(x'^1, x'^2, \ldots)$$
$$x'^\alpha = \varphi^\alpha(x^1, x^2, \ldots)$$

$$(3.18)$$

The primed coordinates are local Cartesian coordinates.

$$dx^\alpha = \frac{\partial f^\alpha}{\partial x'^\beta} \, dx'^\beta \qquad (3.19)$$

Under a parallel displacement, $\delta(dx'^\beta) = 0$ by definition, so that from (3.19) we can write

$$\delta(dx^\nu) = \frac{\partial^2 f^\nu}{\partial x'^\delta \, \partial x'^\gamma} \, dx'^\delta \, dx'^\gamma = \frac{\partial^2 f^\nu}{\partial x'^\delta \, \partial x'^\gamma} \frac{\partial \varphi^\delta}{\partial x^\alpha} \frac{\partial \varphi^\gamma}{\partial x^\beta} \, dx^\alpha \, dx^\beta$$

$$(3.20)$$

Comparing this expression with (3.17) it follows that

$$\Gamma^\nu_{\alpha\beta} = - \frac{\partial^2 f^\nu}{\partial x'^\delta \, \partial x'^\gamma} \frac{\partial \varphi^\delta}{\partial x^\alpha} \frac{\partial \varphi^\gamma}{\partial x^\beta} \qquad (3.21)$$

The right side of (3.21) is clearly symmetric in the indices α and β, so $\Gamma^\nu_{\alpha\beta}$ must be symmetric in α and β also. Earlier we stated that the use of upper or lower indices is employed to give the transformation properties of tensors. Unfortunately the index notation is also employed for quantities such as $\Gamma^\nu_{\alpha\beta}$, which, as we shall see, do not obey the transformation laws of tensors.

If the operation of parallel displacement from a given point to all other points in its neighborhood is defined for all vectors, the point is said to be affinely connected to its neighborhood.

It is desirable now to employ the metric tensor $g_{\mu\nu}$, which we defined earlier by

$$-ds^2 = g_{\mu\nu} \, dx^\mu \, dx^\nu$$

The tensor character of $g_{\mu\nu}$ follows from the invariance of the squared "length" ds^2, since all the coordinate transformations which are employed here leave unchanged the "lengths" of curves. If the $g_{\mu\nu}$ are arranged as a matrix and the inverse is taken, we obtain new quantities $g^{\alpha\beta}$, and

$$g_{\mu\nu}g^{\nu\alpha} = \delta_{\mu}{}^{\alpha} \qquad (3.22)$$

Since the Kronecker delta is a mixed tensor, it follows that $g^{\nu\alpha}$ is a contravariant tensor. The covariant and contravariant metric tensors are useful for raising and lowering indices ‡ to give new § tensors; i.e.,

$$A^{\alpha} = g^{\nu\alpha}A_{\nu} \qquad (3.23)$$

We derive formulas for the $\Gamma^{\nu}{}_{\alpha\beta}$ in terms of the metric tensor. From the definition for a parallel displacement,

$$\delta(A_{\mu}A^{\mu}) = g_{\mu\nu}\begin{pmatrix}\text{second}\\\text{point}\end{pmatrix}[A^{\nu} + \delta A^{\nu}][A^{\mu} + \delta A^{\mu}]$$

$$\qquad - g_{\mu\nu}\begin{pmatrix}\text{first}\\\text{point}\end{pmatrix}A^{\nu}A^{\mu} = 0 \qquad (3.24)$$

Carrying out these operations gives

$$\frac{\partial g_{\mu\nu}}{\partial x^{\alpha}}A^{\mu}A^{\nu}dx^{\alpha} + g_{\mu\nu}A^{\mu}\delta A^{\nu} + g_{\mu\nu}A^{\nu}\delta A^{\mu} = 0 \qquad (3.25)$$

Making use of (3.16) to eliminate δA^{μ} and δA^{ν} gives

$$\frac{\partial g_{\mu\nu}}{\partial x^{\alpha}} - g_{\mu\beta}\Gamma^{\beta}{}_{\nu\alpha} - g_{\nu\beta}\Gamma^{\beta}{}_{\mu\alpha} = 0 \qquad (3.26)$$

The symmetry of $\Gamma^{\beta}{}_{\nu\alpha}$ with respect to the lower indices allows permutation of the indices ν and α to obtain

$$\frac{\partial g_{\mu\alpha}}{\partial x^{\nu}} - g_{\mu\beta}\Gamma^{\beta}{}_{\nu\alpha} - g_{\alpha\beta}\Gamma^{\beta}{}_{\mu\nu} = 0 \qquad (3.27)$$

Similarly we write

$$\frac{\partial g_{\nu\alpha}}{\partial x^{\mu}} - g_{\nu\beta}\Gamma^{\beta}{}_{\mu\alpha} - g_{\alpha\beta}\Gamma^{\beta}{}_{\mu\nu} = 0 \qquad (3.28)$$

Solving (3.26), (3.27), and (3.28) gives, with the help of (3.22),

‡ Note that in arbitrary coordinates, $\delta_{\mu\nu}$ is replaced by $g_{\mu\nu}$, for $\delta_{\mu\nu} = g_{\mu\alpha}\delta_{\nu}{}^{\alpha} = g_{\mu\nu}$, also $\delta^{\mu\nu} \to g^{\mu\nu}$. Only $\delta_{\mu}{}^{\nu} = 1$ if $\mu = \nu$ and zero if $\mu \neq \nu$, in general.

§ In general $B_{\nu}{}^{\mu} \neq B^{\mu}{}_{\nu}$. The left to right order of indices must be preserved when raising and lowering them.

$$\Gamma^\gamma{}_{\mu\alpha} = \tfrac{1}{2}g^{\gamma\nu}\left[\frac{\partial g_{\nu\mu}}{\partial x^\alpha} + \frac{\partial g_{\nu\alpha}}{\partial x^\mu} - \frac{\partial g_{\mu\alpha}}{\partial x^\nu}\right] \qquad (3.29)$$

The three-index quantity

$$\tfrac{1}{2}\left[\frac{\partial g_{\nu\mu}}{\partial x^\alpha} + \frac{\partial g_{\nu\alpha}}{\partial x^\mu} - \frac{\partial g_{\mu\alpha}}{\partial x^\nu}\right] = \Gamma_{\nu,\mu\alpha}$$

is called the Christoffel symbol of the first kind and is often written as $[\mu\alpha, \nu]$. $\Gamma^\gamma{}_{\mu\alpha}$ is called the Christoffel symbol of the second kind and is often written as $\begin{Bmatrix}\gamma\\\mu\alpha\end{Bmatrix}$. As we remarked earlier the $\Gamma^\mu{}_{\alpha\beta}$ are not components of a tensor. By starting with the differentiated transformation law for $g_{\mu\nu}$ it is not too difficult to show that $[\mu\alpha, \nu]$ transforms according to

$$[\mu\alpha, \nu]' = \frac{\partial x^\beta}{\partial x'^\mu}\frac{\partial x^\gamma}{\partial x'^\alpha}\frac{\partial x^\delta}{\partial x'^\nu}[\beta\gamma, \delta] + g_{\beta\gamma}\frac{\partial x^\beta}{\partial x'^\nu}\frac{\partial^2 x^\gamma}{\partial x'^\mu \partial x'^\alpha} \qquad (3.30)$$

Making use of the transformation law for $g^{\alpha\beta}$ then leads to the transformation law for $\Gamma^\delta{}_{\beta\nu}$ as

$$\Gamma'^\delta{}_{\beta\nu} = \frac{\partial x'^\delta}{\partial x^\alpha}\frac{\partial x^\mu}{\partial x'^\beta}\frac{\partial x^\kappa}{\partial x'^\nu}\Gamma^\alpha{}_{\mu\kappa} + \frac{\partial x'^\delta}{\partial x^\kappa}\frac{\partial^2 x^\kappa}{\partial x'^\beta \partial x'^\nu} \qquad (3.31)$$

A study of (3.31) indicates that it is always possible to choose a coordinate system such that all the Christoffel symbols vanish at a point. One way to do this is the following. Suppose the given point is labeled P and the Christoffel symbols do not vanish there. Carry out the coordinate transformation

$$x'^\alpha = x^\alpha - x^\alpha{}_{(P)} + \tfrac{1}{2}\Gamma^\alpha{}_{\beta\delta(P)}(x^\beta - x^\beta{}_{(P)})(x^\delta - x^\delta{}_{(P)}) \qquad (3.32)$$

Here the subscript (P) refers to the value at point P. Making use of (3.31) to directly calculate the new values of $\Gamma^\iota{}_{\kappa\mu}$ shows that the new values vanish at point P. This constitutes a proof that the Christoffel symbols may be transformed away because (3.32) can always be carried out wherever the Christoffel symbols are not infinite. A coordinate system in which the Christoffel symbols vanish at point P is called a geodesic coordinate system: P is said to be the pole. It is also possible to transform away the Christoffel symbols along a curve (4).

We return to our main objective, which is the formation of new tensors by differentiation. As we saw earlier, the partial derivative of a vector is not a tensor. A new kind of derivative is formed in the following way. Let a vector at a given point be A^μ. At a neighbouring point the vector is $A^\mu + dA^\mu$. The vector resulting from parallel transport to the neighboring point is $A^\mu + \delta A^\mu$. Subtract these quantities to obtain

$$dA^\mu - \delta A^\mu = \left(\frac{\partial A^\mu}{\partial x^\sigma} + \Gamma^\mu{}_{\sigma\alpha} A^\alpha\right) dx^\sigma \tag{3.33}$$

(3.33) would be expected to be a vector since it is the difference of two vectors at the same point; the quantity

$$\frac{\partial A^\mu}{\partial x^\sigma} + \Gamma^\mu{}_{\sigma\alpha} A^\alpha$$

then, is a mixed tensor called the covariant derivative of A^μ and written

$$A^\mu{}_{;\sigma} = \frac{\partial A^\mu}{\partial x^\sigma} + \Gamma^\mu{}_{\sigma\alpha} A^\alpha \tag{3.34}$$

From $\delta(A_\mu A^\mu) = 0$ it follows, using (3.16), that

$$\delta A_\mu = \Gamma^\alpha{}_{\mu\beta} A_\alpha dx^\beta \tag{3.16a}$$

From this and a procedure similar to that of (3.33) and (3.34) we write the covariant derivative of A_μ as

$$A_{\mu;\,\sigma} = \frac{\partial A_\mu}{\partial x^\sigma} - \Gamma^\alpha{}_{\mu\sigma} A_\alpha \tag{3.35}$$

The tensor character of (3.34) and (3.35) can be formally established by showing that they obey the required transformation laws, employing (3.31). The contravariant derivative is formed by raising the index which denotes differentiation,

$$A^{\mu;\,\sigma} = g^{\sigma\alpha} A^\mu{}_{;\alpha} \tag{3.36}$$

The covariant derivatives of a second-rank tensor $C_{\beta\delta}$ may be obtained from the requirement that the $C_{\beta\delta}A^\beta B^\delta$ remain invariant under a parallel displacement for arbitrary A^β and B^δ. Setting $\delta(C_{\beta\delta}A^\beta B^\delta)$ equal to zero gives $\delta C_{\beta\delta}$, and the covariant derivatives may be written

$$C_{\beta\delta;\rho} = \frac{\partial C_{\beta\delta}}{\partial x^\rho} - \Gamma^\alpha{}_{\beta\rho}C_{\delta\alpha} - \Gamma^\alpha{}_{\delta\rho}C_{\beta\alpha} \qquad (3.37)$$

Similarly,

$$C^{\beta\delta}{}_{;\rho} = \frac{\partial C^{\beta\delta}}{\partial x^\rho} + \Gamma^\beta{}_{\alpha\rho}C^{\alpha\delta} + \Gamma^\delta{}_{\alpha\rho}C^{\beta\alpha} \qquad (3.38)$$

$$C^\beta{}_{\delta;\rho} = \frac{\partial C^\beta{}_\delta}{\partial x^\rho} + \Gamma^\beta{}_{\alpha\rho}C^\alpha{}_\delta - \Gamma^\alpha{}_{\delta\rho}C^\beta{}_\alpha \qquad (3.39)$$

The extension to higher-rank tensors is evident.

Consider the covariant derivative of the metric tensor $g_{\mu\nu}$. This is a tensor. In geodesic coordinates all components of this tensor must vanish. It therefore follows that

$$g_{\mu\nu;\sigma} = 0 \qquad (3.40)$$

in all other systems of coordinates.

3.4   The Curvature Tensor

Earlier we noted that if it is possible to carry out a coordinate transformation such that the metric tensor is a Lorentz metric everywhere, a region of space is said to be flat. A given vector may be parallel-displaced throughout such a space and give a constant vector field. Parallel displacement about a closed path results in a vector identical with the original one. In a curved space, parallel transport about a closed path does not, in general, yield the original vector. Consider, for example the surface of a sphere (Fig. 3.2) on which is a spherical triangle composed of geodesic curves. We start with the vector **A** and parallel transport it. It becomes **B**, then **C**, and finally **D**. Clearly **A** and **D** are not the same. We now proceed to calculate the change in components of a vector under a parallel displacement about an

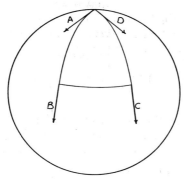

Fig. 3.2

infinitesimal closed path defined by four curves of the two-parameter set

$$x^\alpha = f^\alpha(u, v) \qquad (3.41)$$

The path to be considered is shown cross-hatched in Fig. 3.3, in which the sides are Δu at constant v and Δv at constant u.

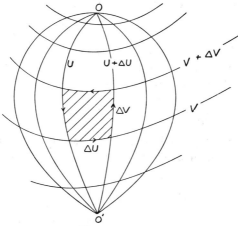

Fig. 3.3

The change in n^μ for the entire closed path is

$$\delta n^\mu = -\oint \Gamma^\mu{}_{\alpha\beta} n^\alpha \, dx^\beta \qquad (3.42)$$

Considering the algebraic sum of the contributions from opposite sides of the "parallelogram" and retaining terms only up to first order in Δu and Δv gives

$$\delta n^\mu = \frac{\partial}{\partial v} \left(\Gamma^\mu_{\alpha\beta} n^\alpha \right) \Delta v \, \frac{\partial x^\beta}{\partial u} \, \Delta u - \frac{\partial}{\partial u} \left(\Gamma^\mu_{\alpha\gamma} n^\alpha \right) \Delta u \, \frac{\partial x^\gamma}{\partial v} \, \Delta v \tag{3.43}$$

We carry out the operations indicated by (3.43), utilizing the expression for the change in n^α under parallel displacement. The result is then arranged in the form

$$\delta n^\mu = - \left[\frac{\partial \Gamma^\mu_{\alpha\gamma}}{\partial x^\beta} - \frac{\partial \Gamma^\mu_{\alpha\beta}}{\partial x^\gamma} + \Gamma^\mu_{\sigma\beta} \Gamma^\sigma_{\alpha\gamma} - \Gamma^\mu_{\sigma\gamma} \Gamma^\sigma_{\alpha\beta} \right]$$
$$n^\alpha \frac{\partial x^\gamma}{\partial v} \frac{\partial x^\beta}{\partial u} \Delta u \Delta v \tag{3.44}$$

Since only first-order terms have been retained it is more precise to write, from (3.44)

$$\lim_{\substack{\Delta u \to 0 \\ \Delta v \to 0}} \frac{\delta n^\mu}{\Delta v \Delta u} = - \left[\frac{\partial \Gamma^\mu_{\alpha\gamma}}{\partial x^\beta} - \frac{\partial \Gamma^\mu_{\alpha\beta}}{\partial x^\gamma} + \Gamma^\mu_{\sigma\beta} \Gamma^\sigma_{\alpha\gamma} - \Gamma^\mu_{\sigma\gamma} \Gamma^\sigma_{\alpha\beta} \right]$$
$$n^\alpha \frac{\partial x^\gamma}{\partial v} \frac{\partial x^\beta}{\partial u} \tag{3.45}$$

The left side of (3.45) is a vector. $\partial x^\beta / \partial u$ and $\partial x^\gamma / \partial v$ are vectors because u and v are parameters. It follows, therefore, that the quantity $R^\mu_{\alpha\beta\gamma}$ defined by

$$R^\mu_{\alpha\beta\gamma} = \frac{\partial \Gamma^\mu_{\alpha\gamma}}{\partial x^\beta} - \frac{\partial \Gamma^\mu_{\alpha\beta}}{\partial x^\gamma} + \Gamma^\mu_{\sigma\beta} \Gamma^\sigma_{\alpha\gamma} - \Gamma^\mu_{\sigma\gamma} \Gamma^\sigma_{\alpha\beta} \tag{3.46}$$

is a tensor. It is called the Riemann-Christoffel tensor, or simply the curvature tensor. For an infinitesimal closed path, then[‡],

$$\delta n^\mu = - R^\mu_{\alpha\beta\gamma} n^\alpha \frac{\partial x^\beta}{\partial u} \frac{\partial x^\gamma}{\partial v} \, du dv \tag{3.47}$$

[‡] This discussion implies that the result of two covariant differentiations depends, in general, on the order in which they are carried out. From (3.47) and (3.47a) it follows that

$$B^\mu_{;\alpha;\beta} - B^\mu_{;\beta;\alpha} = - B^\nu R^\mu_{\nu\alpha\beta}$$
$$B_{\mu;\alpha;\beta} - B_{\mu;\beta;\alpha} = B_\nu R^\nu_{\mu\alpha\beta}$$

Also for a parallel displacement $\delta(n_\mu n^\mu)$ vanishes. This leads to

$$\delta n_\mu = R^\alpha{}_{\mu\beta\gamma} n_\alpha \frac{\partial x^\beta}{\partial u} \frac{\partial x^\gamma}{\partial v} \, du \, dv \qquad (3.47\text{a})$$

From (3.47) and (3.47a) it follows that for any finite closed [t] path (requiring integration over u and v), the vanishing of $R^\mu{}_{\alpha\beta\gamma}$ guarantees that an arbitrary vector will not change under a parallel displacement.

For a Lorentz metric in a given region the curvature tensor vanishes because of the constant $g_{\mu\nu}$. If coordinate transformations are carried out in such a space, the transformed components of $R^\mu{}_{\alpha\beta\gamma}$ will still vanish in consequence of its tensor character. It follows that a necessary condition for the space to be flat is the vanishing of $R^\mu{}_{\alpha\beta\gamma}$. On the other hand, if $R^\mu{}_{\alpha\beta\gamma}$ vanishes everywhere, then a Lorentz metric may be generated by parallel propagation of a (Minkowski) set of axes because this is now a unique operation, independent of the path. The components of an arbi-

[t] Since n^α is a parallel-displaced vector, its value at any point within a given contour depends on the path taken. A meaning can be given to the integration of (3.47) or (3.47a) by carrying out the parametrization as indicated in Fig. 3.3. Suppose the initial point is 0. Parallel-displace n^α from 0 to 0′ along all the given curves. This generates a continuous vector field. The vanishing of (3.47) then guarantees no change in n^α as it is parallel-displaced around the (boundary) contour returning to 0. The entire matter can also be viewed using (3.16) alone. For a given contour, (3.16) may be written

$$\frac{dA^\mu}{ds} = -\Gamma^\mu{}_{\alpha\beta} A^\alpha \frac{dx^\beta}{ds}$$

This is a set of equations to determine A^μ as long as the tangent vector dx^β/ds is prescribed by specifying the path. If the change in A^μ is to vanish for all closed paths, the quantity $\Gamma^\mu{}_{\alpha\beta} A^\alpha dx^\beta$ must be an exact differential, and this leads to

$$\frac{\partial}{\partial x^\gamma} (\Gamma^\mu{}_{\alpha\beta} A^\alpha) = \frac{\partial}{\partial x^\beta} (\Gamma^\mu{}_{\alpha\gamma} A^\alpha)$$

Evaluating this with the condition that A^α is being parallel-displaced then gives the requirement that the right side of (3.46) has to vanish.

trary vector will not change on parallel-displacement anywhere. All the Christoffel symbols will vanish everywhere
and all first derivatives of the metric will vanish everywhere.
Since the metric was a Lorentz metric at the starting point it
is then clear that it is a Lorentz metric everywhere. It follows therefore that necessary and sufficient conditions for the
space to be flat are the vanishing of all components of $R^\mu{}_{\alpha\beta\gamma}$.
It is also clear that the vanishing of $R^\mu{}_{\alpha\beta\gamma}$ guarantees the
integrability of the set of equations (3.16).

Expression (3.46) tells us that $R^\mu{}_{\alpha\beta\gamma}$ is antisymmetric in
the indices β and γ. The tensor $R_{\delta\alpha\beta\gamma}$ is given[‡] by

$$R_{\delta\alpha\beta\gamma} = g_{\mu\delta} R^\mu{}_{\alpha\beta\gamma} = \frac{1}{2}\left(\frac{\partial^2 g_{\delta\gamma}}{\partial x^\alpha\,\partial x^\beta} + \frac{\partial^2 g_{\alpha\beta}}{\partial x^\delta\,\partial x^\gamma} - \frac{\partial^2 g_{\delta\beta}}{\partial x^\alpha\,\partial x^\gamma} - \frac{\partial^2 g_{\alpha\gamma}}{\partial x^\delta\,\partial x^\beta}\right)$$
$$+ g_{\mu\nu}(\Gamma^\mu{}_{\alpha\beta}\Gamma^\nu{}_{\delta\gamma} - \Gamma^\mu{}_{\alpha\gamma}\Gamma^\nu{}_{\delta\beta}) \qquad (3.48)$$

From (3.48) it follows that

$$R_{\alpha\delta\beta\gamma} = -R_{\delta\alpha\beta\gamma} = -R_{\alpha\delta\gamma\beta} = R_{\beta\gamma\alpha\delta} \qquad (3.49)$$

From (3.48) and (3.46) it may be verified that

$$R^\alpha{}_{\beta\gamma\delta} + R^\alpha{}_{\delta\beta\gamma} + R^\alpha{}_{\gamma\delta\beta} = 0$$
$$R_{\alpha\beta\gamma\delta} + R_{\alpha\delta\beta\gamma} + R_{\alpha\gamma\delta\beta} = 0 \qquad (3.50)$$

3.5   The Bianchi Identities

An important differential identity may now be proved.
Select at a point, a geodesic coordinate system; then the
Christoffel symbols vanish and the covariant derivative of
$R^\mu{}_{\delta\beta\gamma}$ becomes

$$R^\mu{}_{\delta\beta\gamma;\nu} = \frac{\partial^2 \Gamma^\mu{}_{\delta\gamma}}{\partial x^\beta\,\partial x^\nu} - \frac{\partial^2 \Gamma^\mu{}_{\delta\beta}}{\partial x^\gamma\,\partial x^\nu} \qquad (3.51)$$

‡ The rearrangement of (3.48) can be done by writing out $g_{\mu\delta} R^\mu{}_{\alpha\beta\gamma}$,
then noting that

$$g_{\mu\delta}\frac{\partial \Gamma^\mu{}_{\alpha\beta}}{\partial x^\gamma} = \frac{\partial}{\partial x^\gamma}(g_{\mu\delta}\,\Gamma^\mu{}_{\alpha\beta}) - \Gamma^\mu{}_{\alpha\beta}\frac{\partial g_{\mu\delta}}{\partial x^\gamma}$$

$$g_{\mu\delta}\,\Gamma^\mu{}_{\alpha\beta} = [\alpha\beta,\delta] \qquad \text{and} \qquad \frac{\partial g_{\mu\delta}}{\partial x^\gamma} = [\mu\gamma,\delta] + [\delta\gamma,\mu]$$

From (3.51) it then follows that

$$R^\mu{}_{\delta\beta\gamma;\nu} + R^\mu{}_{\delta\nu\beta;\gamma} + R^\mu{}_{\delta\gamma\nu;\beta} = 0 \qquad (3.52)$$

The left side of (3.52) is a tensor which we have calculated in a particular coordinate system and found all components to be zero. The result must therefore be valid in all other coordinate systems. The relations (3.52) are known as the Bianchi identities.

A mixed tensor of the second rank or higher can be summed over an upper and a lower index to give a tensor two ranks lower. This operation is called contraction. The tensor $R_{\mu\nu}$ is formed by contraction of $R^\alpha{}_{\mu\beta\nu}$,

$$R_{\mu\nu} = R^\alpha{}_{\mu\alpha\nu} = \frac{\partial \Gamma^\alpha{}_{\mu\nu}}{\partial x^\alpha} - \frac{\partial \Gamma^\alpha{}_{\mu\alpha}}{\partial x^\nu} + \Gamma^\alpha{}_{\mu\nu}\Gamma^\beta{}_{\alpha\beta} - \Gamma^\alpha{}_{\mu\beta}\Gamma^\beta{}_{\nu\alpha} \quad (3.53)$$

and is called[‡] the Ricci tensor. Its symmetry is evident. The scalar formed by contraction of $R_{\mu\nu}$ according to

$$g^{\mu\nu}R_{\mu\nu} = R \qquad (3.54)$$

is called the curvature scalar.[§]

Multiplication of (3.52) by $g^{\delta\beta}\delta_\mu{}^\gamma$ gives

$$g^{\delta\beta}[R^\gamma{}_{\delta\beta\gamma;\nu} + R^\gamma{}_{\delta\nu\beta;\gamma} + R^\gamma{}_{\delta\gamma\nu;\beta}] = 0 \qquad (3.55)$$

The covariant derivative of $g^{\delta\beta}$ vanishes; also from (3.46) we have $R^\nu{}_{\delta\beta\gamma} = -R^\nu{}_{\delta\gamma\beta}$. Equation (3.55) may then be written

$$(R_\gamma{}^\nu - \tfrac{1}{2}\delta_\gamma{}^\nu R)_{;\nu} = G_\gamma{}^\nu{}_{;\nu} = 0 \qquad (3.56)$$

(3.56) is the contracted Bianchi identity. The tensor

[‡] Contraction on the first and second indices gives zero, since $R^\alpha{}_{\alpha\beta\gamma} = g^{\iota\kappa}R_{\iota\kappa\beta\gamma}$ and this vanishes because $R_{\iota\kappa\beta\gamma}$ is antisymmetric in ι and κ. Contraction on the first and fourth index gives the negative of (3.53).

[§] In a two-dimensional space the following relations are valid at any given point:

$$\frac{R_{1212}}{g} = \frac{R}{2} = \frac{1}{r_1 r_2} = \lim_{s\to 0} \frac{\Delta\theta}{S}$$

Here g is the determinant of $g_{\mu\nu}$, r_1 and r_2 are the principal radii of curvature, S is the area of a small geodesic quadrilateral at the point, and $\Delta\theta$ is the excess of the sum of its angles over four right angles.

$G_\gamma{}^\nu = R_\gamma{}^\nu - \frac{1}{2}\delta_\gamma{}^\nu R$ is called the Einstein tensor.

3.6   Geodesics

Suppose we ask what is the equation of the curve defined by the requirement that each element of it is a parallel displacement of the preceding element. The equations of any curve are the one-parameter family of points

$$x^\alpha = f^\alpha(s) \tag{3.57}$$

The tangent vector is dx^α/ds, and the new tangent vector which results from a parallel displacement is

$$T'^\rho = \frac{dx^\rho}{ds} - \Gamma^\rho{}_{\alpha\beta} \frac{dx^\alpha}{ds} dx^\beta \tag{3.58}$$

The new tangent vector T'^ρ is also given by

$$T'^\rho = \frac{dx^\rho}{ds} + \frac{d}{ds}\left(\frac{dx^\rho}{ds}\right) ds \tag{3.59}$$

Setting (3.58) equal to (3.59) gives the equations of the curve whose elements are parallel-displaced preceding ones, as

$$\frac{d^2 x^\rho}{ds^2} + \Gamma^\rho{}_{\alpha\beta} \frac{dx^\alpha}{ds} \frac{dx^\beta}{ds} = 0 \tag{3.60}$$

As might be expected, (3.60) represents the equations of the curves of extremal length, called geodesic curves. To show this we seek the relations which must be satisfied to give a stationary value to the integral

$$\int ds = \int \sqrt{-g_{\mu\nu} dx^\mu dx^\nu} \tag{3.61}$$

We introduce a parameter k and write

$$\int ds = \int \sqrt{-g_{\mu\nu} \frac{dx^\mu}{dk} \frac{dx^\nu}{dk}}\, dk \tag{3.62}$$

Let

$$L^2 = -g_{\mu\nu} \frac{dx^\mu}{dk} \frac{dx^\nu}{dk} \tag{3.63}$$

The condition for a stationary value for (3.61) becomes[‡]

$$\delta \int L\,dk = 0 \qquad (3.64)$$

k may be chosen to be the length s along the geodesic. It is not the length for the other curves.

Accordingly, (3.64) becomes

$$\delta \int L\,ds = \int \left[\frac{\partial L}{\partial x^\iota}\,\delta x^\iota + \frac{\partial L}{\partial \left(\dfrac{dx^\iota}{ds}\right)}\,\delta\left(\frac{dx^\iota}{ds}\right) \right] ds \qquad (3.65)$$

The second term of the integrand may be written as the two terms

$$\frac{d}{ds}\left(\frac{\partial L}{\partial \left(\dfrac{dx^\iota}{ds}\right)}\,\delta x^\iota \right) - \frac{d}{ds}\left(\frac{\partial L}{\partial \left(\dfrac{\partial x^\iota}{\partial s}\right)} \right)\delta x^\iota$$

and on integration the first of these contributes nothing because the variations vanish at the end points. The Euler-Lagrange equations for this problem are then

$$\frac{d}{ds}\frac{\partial L}{\partial \left(\dfrac{dx^\iota}{ds}\right)} - \frac{\partial L}{\partial x^\iota} = 0 \qquad (3.66)$$

We note that $L = 1$ along the geodesic.
Making use of (3.63) gives

$$\frac{d}{ds}\frac{\partial L}{\partial \left(\dfrac{dx^\kappa}{ds}\right)} = -\left[\frac{dg_{\kappa\nu}}{ds}\frac{dx^\nu}{ds} + g_{\kappa\nu}\frac{d^2x^\nu}{ds^2} \right]; \quad \frac{\partial L}{\partial x^\kappa} = -\frac{\partial g_{\mu\nu}}{\partial x^\kappa}\frac{dx^\mu}{ds}\frac{dx^\nu}{ds}\Big/2$$

and (3.66) becomes

‡ Here δ means a variation corresponding to change in coordinates and the vector dx^ι/dk as we go from one possible path to another; k merely labels corresponding points on different paths.

$$g_{\kappa\nu}\frac{d^2 x^\nu}{ds^2} - \left[\frac{1}{2}\frac{\partial g_{\mu\nu}}{\partial x^\kappa} - \frac{\partial g_{\kappa\nu}}{\partial x^\mu}\right]\frac{dx^\mu}{ds}\frac{dx^\nu}{ds}$$

$$= g_{\kappa\nu}\frac{d^2 x^\nu}{ds^2} + \frac{1}{2}\left[\frac{\partial g_{\kappa\nu}}{\partial x^\mu} + \frac{\partial g_{\kappa\mu}}{\partial x^\nu} - \frac{\partial g_{\mu\nu}}{\partial x^\kappa}\right]\frac{dx^\mu}{ds}\frac{dx^\nu}{ds} = 0 \quad (3.67)$$

Multiplying (3.67) by $g^{k\alpha}$ and summing then leads to the geodesic equation

$$\frac{d^2 x^\alpha}{ds^2} + \Gamma^\alpha{}_{\mu\nu}\frac{dx^\mu}{ds}\frac{dx^\nu}{ds} = 0 \qquad (3.68)$$

(3.68) and (3.60) are identical.

If we are dealing with the propagation of light, we have null geodesics. The deduction as given above cannot be applied because ds vanishes throughout. Clearly the argument leading to (3.60) remains valid. It is therefore consistent to define the geodesic equation as the appropriate one for the null case, with the important proviso that the variable s is a parameter along the geodesic other than the length.

3.7   Some Useful Calculational Aids

We complete this section by giving a number of useful aids in manipulation of tensor quantities. First consider the covariant divergence $A^\mu{}_{;\mu}$:

$$A^\mu{}_{;\mu} = \frac{\partial A^\alpha}{\partial x^\alpha} + \Gamma^\mu{}_{\alpha\mu}A^\alpha \qquad (3.69)$$

From (3.29) we obtain

$$\Gamma^\mu{}_{\alpha\mu} = \tfrac{1}{2}g^{\mu\nu}\frac{\partial g_{\mu\nu}}{\partial x^\alpha} \qquad (3.70)$$

(3.70) can be written in terms of the determinant of $g_{\mu\nu}$, which we denote by g. The rule for expansion of a determinant leads to the relation

$$\frac{\partial g}{\partial g_{\mu\nu}} = \Delta^{\mu\nu} \qquad (3.71)$$

In (3.71) $\Delta^{\mu\nu}$ is the cofactor of the element $g_{\mu\nu}$. From the rule for obtaining the inverse of a determinant, and from the definition of $g^{\mu\nu}$, (3.71) may be written

$$\frac{\partial g}{\partial g_{\mu\nu}} = gg^{\mu\nu} \qquad (3.72)$$

$$dg = gg^{\mu\nu} dg_{\mu\nu} = -gg_{\mu\nu} dg^{\mu\nu} \qquad (3.72a)$$

The expression on the far right of (3.72a) follows from $d(g_{\mu\nu}g^{\mu\nu}) = 0$. We then have

$$\frac{\partial g}{\partial x^{\alpha}} = gg^{\mu\nu} \frac{\partial g_{\mu\nu}}{\partial x^{\alpha}} = -gg_{\mu\nu} \frac{\partial g^{\mu\nu}}{\partial x^{\alpha}} \qquad (3.73)$$

The use of (3.73) enables us to write (3.70) in the forms

$$\Gamma^{\mu}{}_{\alpha\mu} = -\tfrac{1}{2}g_{\mu\nu} \frac{\partial g^{\mu\nu}}{\partial x^{\alpha}} = \frac{1}{2g} \frac{\partial g}{\partial x^{\alpha}} = \frac{\partial}{\partial x^{\alpha}} (\ln \sqrt{-g}) \qquad (3.74)$$

Expression (3.74) is now employed to write the covariant divergence (3.69) as

$$A^{\mu}{}_{;\mu} = \frac{1}{\sqrt{-g}} \frac{\partial}{\partial x^{\mu}} (A^{\mu}\sqrt{-g}) \qquad (3.75)$$

For a contravariant tensor of the second rank, (3.38) and (3.74) give

$$C^{\alpha\beta}{}_{;\beta} = \frac{1}{\sqrt{-g}} \frac{\partial}{\partial x^{\beta}} (C^{\alpha\beta}\sqrt{-g}) + \Gamma^{\alpha}{}_{\beta\sigma}C^{\beta\sigma} \qquad (3.76)$$

and for a mixed tensor, (3.39) leads to

$$C_{\alpha}{}^{\beta}{}_{;\beta} = \frac{1}{\sqrt{-g}} \frac{\partial}{\partial x^{\beta}} (C_{\alpha}{}^{\beta}\sqrt{-g}) - \Gamma^{\beta}{}_{\alpha\sigma}C_{\beta}{}^{\sigma} \qquad (3.77)$$

For an antisymmetric tensor $F^{\alpha\beta}$, the last term of (3.76) vanishes and the covariant divergence is

$$F^{\alpha\beta}{}_{;\beta} = \frac{1}{\sqrt{-g}} \frac{\partial}{\partial x^{\beta}} (F^{\alpha\beta}\sqrt{-g}) \qquad (3.78)$$

For a symmetric tensor $S^{\alpha\beta}$, rearrangement of the last term of (3.77) leads to

$$S_\alpha{}^\beta{}_{;\beta} = \frac{1}{\sqrt{-g}} \frac{\partial}{\partial x^\beta} (S_\alpha{}^\beta \sqrt{-g}) - \tfrac{1}{2} \frac{\partial g_{\mu\nu}}{\partial x^\alpha} S^{\mu\nu} \qquad (3.79)$$

The Levi Civita symbol $\varepsilon_{\alpha\beta\gamma\delta}$ is often useful in performing calculations. It is defined by the statement that $\varepsilon = 0$ if any two of the four indices are identical. It changes sign on interchange of any pair of indices, and $\varepsilon_{0123} = 1$. A convenient way of expressing the expansion of the determinant K of the tensor $K_{\mu\nu}$ is

$$K\varepsilon_{\alpha\beta\gamma\delta} = \varepsilon_{\iota\kappa\lambda\mu} K_{\iota\alpha} K_{\kappa\beta} K_{\lambda\gamma} K_{\mu\delta} \qquad (3.80)$$

The transformation law

$$K_{\mu\nu} = \frac{\partial x'^\beta}{\partial x^\mu} \frac{\partial x'^\alpha}{\partial x^\nu} K'_{\alpha\beta}$$

may now be employed in (3.80) and the result rearranged to show that the determinants (K) and (K') are related by

$$K' = \left[J \left(\frac{\partial x}{\partial x'} \right) \right]^2 K \qquad (3.81)$$

Employing (3.80), (3.81), and the transformation law for $K_{\mu\nu}$ then gives

$$\varepsilon'_{\alpha\beta\gamma\delta} = \left(J \left(\frac{\partial x}{\partial x'} \right) \right)^{-1} \frac{\partial x^\iota}{\partial x'^\alpha} \frac{\partial x^\kappa}{\partial x'^\beta} \frac{\partial x^\lambda}{\partial x'^\gamma} \frac{\partial x^\mu}{\partial x'^\delta} \varepsilon_{\iota\kappa\lambda\mu} \qquad (3.82)$$

(3.82) tells us that $\varepsilon_{\alpha\beta\gamma\delta}$ is a tensor density of weight -1. Also it can be similarly shown that $\varepsilon^{\alpha\beta\gamma\delta}$ is a tensor density[‡] of weight $+1$. Note that this treatment requires the total number of indices on ε to be equal to the number of dimensions in the space if ε is to be a tensor density in the given space. We now let $K_{\mu\nu} = g_{\mu\nu}$ and from (3.81) conclude that the determinant of $g'_{\mu\nu}$ is related to that of $g_{\alpha\beta}$ by

$$(-g')^{\frac{1}{2}} = J \left(\frac{\partial x}{\partial x'} \right) (-g)^{\frac{1}{2}} \qquad (3.83)$$

[‡] The metric tensor cannot be used to raise or lower indices of ε since $\varepsilon_{\alpha\beta\gamma\delta}$ and $\varepsilon^{\alpha\beta\gamma\delta}$ have different weights.

A four-dimensional volume element d^4x' is related to d^4x according to the Jacobi rule

$$d^4x = J\left(\frac{\partial x}{\partial x'}\right) d^4x' \qquad (3.84)$$

Combining (3.83) and (3.84) gives

$$\sqrt{-g}\, d^4x = \sqrt{-g'}\, d^4x' \qquad (3.85)$$

the quantity $\sqrt{-g}\, d^4x$ is seen to be an invariant.

3.8 Length Measurements

We have been dealing with coordinates and intervals. In the special theory of relativity we deal also with lengths. A rod at rest in a given Lorentz frame has a well-defined length. The world lines of the ends of the rod are parallel to the time axis. In a different Lorentz frame with coordinates x'^{α}, the increment of length is given by

$$(\Delta x'^1)^2 + (\Delta x'^2)^2 + (\Delta x'^3)^2 \qquad (3.86)$$

$\Delta x'^1$ refers to the difference of x'^1 coordinates at the two points where the hyperplane $x'^0 = $ constant intersects the world lines of the ends of the rod (see Fig. 3.4). If we have

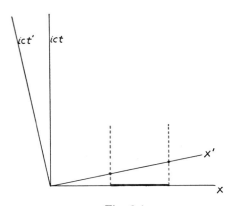

Fig. 3.4

a pair of events we proceed differently and project each space-time point normally onto the hyperplane $x'^0 =$ constant, again using (3.86).

In a curved space we can define length in the same way. Let the coordinates be x^0, x^1, x^2, and x^3, with metric $g_{\mu\nu}$. Introduce at a given point a local Lorentz frame with coordinates x'^0, x'^1, x'^2, x'^3. Let x'^0 be parallel to x^0, so that

$$\frac{\partial x'^i}{\partial x^0} = 0; \qquad \frac{\partial x'^0}{\partial x^0} \neq 0$$

The index i refers to a space coordinate. For a pair of events we *define*

$$dl^2 = dx'^i dx'^i = \frac{\partial x'^i}{\partial x^\mu} \frac{\partial x'^i}{\partial x^\nu} dx^\mu dx^\nu \tag{3.87}$$

The transformation law for the metric tensor is written

$$g_{jk} = \frac{\partial x'^i}{\partial x^j} \frac{\partial x'^i}{\partial x^k} - \frac{\partial x'^0}{\partial x^j} \frac{\partial x'^0}{\partial x^k}$$

$$g_{00} = - \frac{\partial x'^0}{\partial x^0} \frac{\partial x'^0}{\partial x^0}; \qquad g_{0j} = - \frac{\partial x'^0}{\partial x^0} \frac{\partial x'^0}{\partial x^j} \tag{3.88}$$

Use of (3.88) in (3.87) then gives

$$dl^2 = \left(g_{jk} - \frac{g_{0j} g_{0k}}{g_{00}} \right) dx^j dx^k = \gamma_{jk} dx^j dx^k \tag{3.89}$$

with γ_{jk} defined by

$$\gamma_{jk} = \left(g_{jk} - \frac{g_{0j} g_{0k}}{g_{00}} \right) \tag{3.90}$$

γ_{jk} can be shown[‡] to be the reciprocal of the three-by-three matrix g^{jk}. The determinant of the $g_{\mu\nu}$ (four-by-four) is related to the (three-by-three) determinant

‡ Write

$$g^{ij} g_{jk} + g^{i0} g_{0k} = \delta_i{}^k; \qquad g^{ij} g_{j0} + g^{i0} g_{00} = 0$$

then eliminate g^{i0} to obtain $g^{ij} \gamma_{jk} = \delta_i{}^k$.

of γ_{jk}, which we denote by γ, according[‡] to

$$g = g_{00}\gamma \qquad (3.91)$$

For a pair of events we may similarly define the time differential by its value in the locally Lorentz frame as

$$(dx'^0)^2 = dl^2 - g_{\mu\nu}dx^\mu dx^\nu$$

Employing (3.89), and extracting the square root gives

$$dx'^0 = (-g_{00})^{\frac{1}{2}}dx^0 - (-g_{00})^{-\frac{1}{2}}g_{0i}dx^i$$

3.9 Determination of the Metric Tensor

If we have a bendable (but not stretchable) rod and a "natural" clock which ticks at invariant intervals, these may be used to obtain the $g_{\mu\nu}$ at a given point by direct measurement, using suitably chosen pairs of events, with known coordinates. No rigid rods exist, but ordinary ones may be used if the departure from complete rigidity is calculable.

An alternative procedure makes use of a locally Lorentz frame and knowledge of the coordinates of events in both the original frame and the Lorentz frame. The squared lengths may be measured with rods in the Lorentz frame. No correction for lack of rigidity is needed since the rods are in free fall and are not stressed. Measurements on six pairs of events then allows us to calculate γ_{ij} using (3.89).

Suppose the original time coordinate is established by the receipt of radio signals, and we have a caesium beam clock at the given point where the $g_{\mu\nu}$ are desired. Comparison with the time signals gives g_{00}. To determine g_{01} we arrange radio receivers at two points which differ in their x^1

[‡] First set

$$\gamma = \frac{1}{g_{00}} \begin{vmatrix} g_{00} & 0 & 0 & 0 \\ g_{10} & \gamma_{11} & \gamma_{12} & \gamma_{13} \\ g_{20} & \gamma_{21} & \gamma_{22} & \gamma_{23} \\ g_{30} & \gamma_{31} & \gamma_{23} & \gamma_{33} \end{vmatrix}$$

Add (g_{10}/g_{00}) times the first column to the second column. Similar operations involving the third and fourth columns then lead to (3.91).

coordinate. We then arrange to transmit a pulse of radiation from one receiver to the other, measuring the times of arrival in terms of the time coordinate signals.

$$ds^2 = 0 = g_{11}[dx^1]^2 + 2g_{10}\,dx^0\,dx^1 + g_{00}[dx^0]^2 \quad (3.92)$$

from (3.89) we have

$$(dl^1)^2 = \left(g_{11} - \frac{(g_{01})^2}{g_{00}}\right)[dx^1]^2 \quad (3.93)$$

(3.93) is then used to eliminate g_{11} from (3.92), giving

$$(dl^1)^2 + \frac{(g_{01})^2[dx^1]^2}{g_{00}} + 2g_{10}\,dx^0\,dx^1 + g_{00}[dx^0]^2 = 0 \quad (3.94)$$

Everything in (3.94) is known except g_{01}, which is therefore determined. Similarly g_{02} and g_{03} are determined. Knowledge of these plus the fact that the γ_{ij} were measured then gives all the remaining components of $g_{\mu\nu}$.

References

1. T. Levi Civita, *The Absolute Differential Calculus*, Blackie and Son, London, 1927.
2. J. L. Synge and A. Schild, *Tensor Calculus*, University of Toronto Press, 1952.
3. B. Spain, *Tensor Calculus*, Interscience, New York, 1953.
4. E. Fermi, *Atti accad. nazl. Lincei* 31, 21, 51 (1922).

CHAPTER 4

Field Equations of General Relativity and Electromagnetism

Gravitation occupies an exceptional position with regard to other forces, particularly the electromagnetic forces, since the ten functions representing the gravitational field at the same time define the metrical properties of the space measured. A. Einstein

4.1 The Gravitational Field Equations

In Chapter 2 we discussed a rotating frame of reference. In consequence of the acceleration a Riemannian metric was needed. A nonuniform gravitational field is equivalent, within each small region, to an appropriate accelerated frame. A Riemannian metric would therefore be expected also to give a description of a gravitational field. The square of the line element is given by

$$- ds^2 = g_{\mu\nu} \, dx^\mu \, dx^\nu \tag{4.1}$$

We identify the metric tensor $g_{\mu\nu}$ as the gravitational field. This identification, which has followed from the equivalence principle, is perhaps the most important new feature of general relativity. The task now is to formulate the differential equations which relate $g_{\mu\nu}$ to the distribution of matter energy. The starting point is Newton's law of gravitation, described by the Poisson equation for the gravitational potential φ as

$$\nabla^2 \varphi = 4\pi G \rho_M \tag{4.2}$$

Here G is the constant of gravitation, ρ_M is the mass per unit volume.

The left side of (4.2) may be made at least Lorentz-invariant by writing

$$\Box \varphi = 4\pi G \rho_M \tag{4.3}$$

(4.3) is similar to the set of equations for the four potential in electrodynamics. There, the electric charge density is one component of a four vector in consequence of the invariance of total electric charge. Mass, however, is not an invariant, so the right side of (4.3) is not a component of a four vector. It is a component of the second-rank stress-energy tensor already known from the special theory of relativity. This second-rank tensor character leads to a more complex theory than electrodynamics. Also the particles of zero rest mass associated with the gravitational field, the gravitons, will have spin two, again in consequence of the second-rank tensor character of the gravitational "potentials," $g_{\mu\nu}$.

We recall the conservation laws. For a fluid in non-relativistic mechanics the conservation of mass is expressed by the equation of continuity

$$\frac{\partial(\rho v^i)}{\partial x^i} + c\,\frac{\partial \rho_M}{\partial x^0} = 0 \tag{4.4}$$

v^i is the velocity, and the summation over i includes the three space coordinates. (4.4) can be multiplied by $dx^1\,dx^2\,dx^3$ and integrated over a given volume. The first three terms are readily transformed to an integral over the closed surface bounding the volume. The result then states that the time derivative of the total mass within the region of integration equals that carried in through the surface.

The special relativity generalization of (4.4) is

$$\frac{\partial T_\mu{}^\nu}{\partial x^\nu} = 0 \tag{4.5}$$

$T_\mu{}^\nu$ is the stress energy tensor.

For the remainder of this tract we shall usually indicate the operation $\partial/\partial x^\alpha$ by a comma followed by α. Thus (4.5) becomes $T_\mu{}^\nu{}_{,\nu} = 0$.

In the theory of fields of special relativity a procedure is available for obtaining $T_{\mu\nu}$ from the Lagrangian density L, which is assumed to be a function of the field variables q^α and their first derivatives $q^\alpha{}_{,\beta}$. The action function is the four-volume integral of L/c, and the principle of stationary action states that for variations of the field variables which vanish on the boundary,

$$\delta \int L d^4 x = 0 \qquad (4.6)$$

Here the symbol δ is taken in the usual sense, and it is assumed that the field variables q^α and $q^\alpha_{,\beta}$ are functions of a parameter. If the parameter is k, δ means $dk(\partial/\partial k)$, with $\partial/\partial k$ meaning x^μ is constant. Thus the order of differentiation involving a coordinate and k may be interchanged. (4.6) can be expressed as

$$
\begin{aligned}
0 = \delta \int L d^4 x &= \int \left(\frac{\partial L}{\partial q^\alpha} \delta q^\alpha + \frac{\partial L}{\partial q^\alpha_{,\gamma}} \delta q^\alpha_{,\gamma} \right) d^4 x \\
&= \int \left(\frac{\partial L}{\partial q^\alpha} - \frac{\partial}{\partial x^\gamma} \frac{\partial L}{\partial q^\alpha_{,\gamma}} \right) \delta q^\alpha d^4 x + \int \frac{\partial}{\partial x^\beta} \left(\frac{\partial L}{\partial q^\alpha_{,\beta}} \delta q^\alpha \right) d^4 x
\end{aligned}
\qquad (4.7)
$$

The last term on the right of (4.7) is then written as a surface integral which is zero since δq^α are assumed to vanish on the boundary of the region. (4.7) has to hold for arbitrary variations and the field equations

$$\frac{\partial}{\partial x^\gamma} \frac{\partial L}{\partial q^\alpha_{,\gamma}} - \frac{\partial L}{\partial q^\alpha} = 0 \qquad (4.8)$$

follow. We multiply (4.8) by $q^\alpha_{,\beta}$, and note that

$$\frac{\partial L}{\partial x^\beta} = \frac{\partial L}{\partial q^\alpha} \frac{\partial q^\alpha}{\partial x^\beta} + \frac{\partial L}{\partial q^\alpha_{,\rho}} \frac{\partial q^\alpha_{,\rho}}{\partial x^\beta}$$

also that $q^\alpha_{,\gamma,\beta} = q^\alpha_{,\beta,\gamma}$. The result is then rearranged to give

$$\left[\delta_\beta{}^\gamma L - q^\alpha_{,\beta} \frac{\partial L}{\partial q^\alpha_{,\gamma}} \right]_{,\gamma} = 0 \qquad (4.9)$$

From (4.9) and (4.5) it follows that

$$T_\beta{}^\gamma = \delta_\beta{}^\gamma L - q^\alpha_{,\beta} \frac{\partial L}{\partial q^\alpha_{,\gamma}} \qquad (4.10)$$

From classical mechanics we recognize $-T_0{}^0$ as the energy density, since the $q^\alpha_{,0}$ correspond to velocities. A study of (4.9) and (4.10) indicates that the definition (4.10) does not make $T_\beta{}^\gamma$ unique. Any quantity $\Phi_\beta{}^{\gamma\alpha}{}_{,\alpha}$ can be added to $T_\beta{}^\gamma$ provided $\Phi_\beta{}^{\gamma\alpha}{}_{,\alpha}$ is antisymmetric in γ and α. It has been customary to select the function Φ in such a way that the resulting tensor $T_{\beta\gamma}$ (both indices raised or lowered) is symmetric (1, 2). The reason for this is the desirability of having the angular momentum density, defined by

$$M_{\alpha\beta\gamma} = T_{\alpha\beta}x_\gamma - T_{\alpha\gamma}x_\beta \tag{4.11}$$

satisfy a conservation law

$$M_{\alpha\beta\gamma}{}^{,\alpha} = 0 \tag{4.12}$$

Carrying out the differentiation indicated by the left side of (4.12) shows that (4.12) is indeed satisfied by a symmetric $T_{\alpha\beta}$.

For a fluid, $T_{\mu\nu}$ is given in terms of the four velocity U_μ, by

$$T_{\mu\nu} = (p + E)U_\mu U_\nu + \delta_{\mu\nu}p \tag{4.13}$$

Here p is the pressure and E is the total (mass) energy density, evaluated at each point in the rest frame of the local matter. Equation (4.13) is the four-dimensional generalization of the three-dimensional stress[‡] tensor T_{ij}, which gives the force dF_i transmitted across the element of surface ds^i as

$$dF_i = T_{ij}ds^j \tag{4.14}$$

(4.4) gave the conservation of mass; (4.5) includes the conservation of both total energy and momentum. The momentum and energy are given by the space and time components of P_α, with

$$P_i = \int T_i{}^0\, dx^1\, dx^2\, dx^3; \qquad P_0 = \int T_0{}^0\, dx^1\, dx^2\, dx^3$$

P_α transforms like a four vector, under Lorentz transformations.

[‡] Historically this is where the stress energy tensor had its origins. In elasticity T_{ij} is symmetric in consequence of the balance of turning moments on volume elements.

In electrodynamics[‡] the stress energy tensor is given in terms of the field tensor $F_{\mu\alpha}$ by

$$T_\mu{}^\nu = \frac{1}{4\pi}\,(F_{\mu\alpha}\,F^{\nu\alpha} - \tfrac{1}{4}F_{\alpha\beta}\,F^{\alpha\beta}\,\delta_\mu{}^\nu) \qquad (4.15)$$

This follows from (4.10) by using the Lagrangian density for the Maxwell field which is given later in this chapter. The term

$$-\frac{1}{4\pi}\,(A_\mu F^{\nu\alpha})_{,\alpha}$$

was added to make $T_{\mu\nu}$ symmetric.

These expressions were obtained from arguments appropriate for Lorentz frames. However (4.13) and (4.15) are tensor equations and are therefore valid in arbitrary coordinates. Any result obtained from (4.10) will either be in tensor form or can be readily modified (for example by changing ordinary derivatives to covariant derivatives) so that it transforms as a tensor. A manifestly covariant expression for $T_{\mu\nu}$ is given later in this chapter.

We return now to (4.3) and note that the right side of it is identified as the zero-zero component of $T_{\mu\nu}$. This suggests that the gravitational field equations be formulated as a second-rank tensor relation set equal to the stress energy tensor associated with the other fields. The left side of the tensor field equations should reduce to the D'Alembertian operator in a certain level of approximation. The number of possibilities for this tensor is reduced by the requirements that it be formed from $g_{\mu\nu}$ and contain no higher than second derivatives of $g_{\mu\nu}$. It should reduce to the D'Alembertian for weak fields. To guarantee this and to obtain dimensional consistency in a simple way it is reasonable to require that the equations at least be linear in the second derivatives of the $g_{\mu\nu}$.

Suppose then that a given tensor does not contain higher derivatives of $g_{\mu\nu}$ than the second and it is linear in these.

‡ We are using C.G.S. absolute units.

Introduce geodesic coordinates so that the Christoffel symbols vanish. From (3.48) we see that the second derivatives of $g_{\mu\nu}$ can in these coordinates always be written as linear functions of the curvature tensor. If a second-rank tensor is needed, its most general form must therefore be

$$C_1 R_{\mu\nu} + C_2 g_{\mu\nu} R + C_3 g_{\mu\nu} = B_{\mu\nu} \qquad (4.16)$$

C_1, C_2, and C_3 are constants. The first two terms of (4.16) are linear combinations of curvature tensor components. Since (4.16) is a tensor equation, it is valid in any system of coordinates. The requirements of general covariance, a second-rank tensor, linearity in the second derivatives of $g_{\mu\nu}$, plus absence of higher derivatives, have given us the form (4.16).

An argument of Mach (3) and Hilbert (4) is useful at this point. Suppose the laws are in the form of a relation

$$B_{\mu\nu} = T_{\mu\nu} \qquad (4.17)$$

between symmetric tensors. Assume that a solution is obtained, which gives the $g_{\mu\nu}$ as a function of the coordinates. Coordinate transformations can be carried out by introducing the four functions

$$x'^{\mu} = F^{\mu}(x) \qquad (4.18)$$

These functions may be selected in such a way that $g'_{\mu\nu} = g_{\mu\nu}$ and the first derivatives of $g_{\mu\nu}$ are everywhere equal to those of $g'_{\mu\nu}$ at some initial time or on a spacelike surface.‡ Because of the covariance of (4.17), the transformed field equations will have exactly the same form as the original ones. Therefore since the equations do not have higher derivatives of $g_{\mu\nu}$ than the second, it follows that $g_{\mu\nu} = g'_{\mu\nu}$ everywhere. This would be in contradiction to

$$g'_{\mu\nu} = \frac{\partial x^{\beta}}{\partial x'^{\nu}} \frac{\partial x^{\alpha}}{\partial x'^{\mu}} g_{\alpha\beta} \qquad (4.19)$$

It was therefore concluded by Hilbert that a four di-

‡ Consider for example $x'^0 = x^0$, $x'^1 = x^1 + a(x^0)^3$, $x'^2 = x^2$, $x'^3 = x^3$; then $g'^{\mu\nu} = g^{\mu\nu}$ everywhere at $x^0 = 0$, and all first space and time derivatives of $g^{\mu\nu}$ are the same at $x^0 = 0$.

mensional covariant expression such as (4.17) should not be ten independent equations, but that four identities would have to hold such that the set consists only of six independent equations. In this case the solutions would contain four arbitrary functions which become uniquely specified when the coordinate system is singled out in some noncovariant way. A clue to the four identities which have to be satisfied by (4.17) comes from the fact that with a Lorentz metric the stress energy tensor which forms the right side of (4.8) satisfies the conservation law

$$T_\mu{}^\nu{}_{,\nu} = 0 \tag{4.20}$$

The logical extension of (4.20) for a generally covariant theory is

$$T_\mu{}^\nu{}_{;\nu} = 0 \tag{4.21}$$

It was shown (Eq. (3.56)) that the Bianchi identities give

$$(R_\mu{}^\nu - \tfrac{1}{2}\delta_\mu{}^\nu R)_{;\nu} = 0 \tag{4.22}$$

These identities apply if the constants in (4.16) are suitably chosen. From these arguments it follows that the field equations must be given by

$$R_\mu{}^\nu - \tfrac{1}{2}\delta_\mu{}^\nu R - \lambda\delta_\mu{}^\nu = KT_\mu{}^\nu \tag{4.23}$$

Here λ and K are constants. Experience (5) and logical simplicity have indicated that λ may be set equal to zero. Einstein's original (7) formulation included the statement that the motion of particles in a gravitational field is described by the covariant generalization of Newton's laws, which gives the geodesic equation

$$\frac{d^2 x^\alpha}{ds^2} + \Gamma^\alpha{}_{\beta\gamma} \frac{dx^\beta}{ds} \frac{dx^\gamma}{ds} = 0 \tag{4.24}$$

Later it was shown that the equations of motion are in fact already contained within the field equations (4.23) and do not need to be postulated separately. According to (4.24) the force per unit mass on a body at rest is given by the three components $-c^2\Gamma^i{}_{00}$. In the weak field approximation the

$g^{i\alpha}$ are very close to the Lorentz metric values, and for a time-independent metric

$$F^i = -c^2 \Gamma^i{}_{00} \approx \tfrac{1}{2}c^2 \nabla_i g_{00}$$

By analogy with other fields, it is then natural to regard $\tfrac{1}{2}c^2 g_{\mu\nu}$ as the gravitational potentials. For weak fields, (4.23) should reduce to the Poisson equation,[‡] (4.2). This can be accomplished by choosing the constant K in (4.23) equal to $8\pi G/c^4$ where G is the gravitational constant. $G = 6.67 \times 10^{-8}$ cm^3 gm^{-1} sec^{-2}. The field equations then become

$$R_{\mu\nu} - \tfrac{1}{2}g_{\mu\nu} R = \frac{8\pi G}{c^4} T_{\mu\nu} \qquad (4.25)$$

4.2   Variational Principle Deduction of the Field Equations

We start with the action function I, given by

$$I = I_G + I_F = \frac{1}{c} \int (L_G + L_F)\sqrt{-g}\, d^4x \qquad (4.26)$$

Here I_G is the gravitational part and I_F is the part of the action function due to all other fields, L_G is the Lagrangian density for the gravitational field, and L_F is the Lagrangian density for all other fields. For L_G we select the curvature scalar R times a dimensional factor $c^4/16\pi G$. The principle of stationary action then gives

$$(c^3/16\pi G)\delta \int R\sqrt{-g}\; d^4x + \delta I_F = 0 \qquad (4.27)$$

For the variation of the gravitational part of the action function we have then

$$\delta I_G = (c^3/16\pi G) \left[\int \delta R_{\mu\nu} g^{\mu\nu} \sqrt{-g}\, d^4x + \int R_{\mu\nu}\, \delta(\sqrt{-g}\, g^{\mu\nu})d^4x \right] \tag{4.28}$$

We recall that

$$R_{\mu\nu} = \Gamma^\alpha{}_{\mu\nu,\alpha} - \Gamma^\alpha{}_{\mu\alpha,\nu} + \Gamma^\alpha{}_{\mu\nu}\Gamma^\beta{}_{\alpha\beta} - \Gamma^\alpha{}_{\mu\beta}\Gamma^\beta{}_{\nu\alpha}$$

First let us choose a geodesic coordinate system; then we may (6) write

‡ The weak-field treatment is carried through in Chapter 7.

$$\delta R_{\mu\nu} = (\delta \Gamma^\alpha{}_{\mu\nu})_{;\alpha} - (\delta \Gamma^\alpha{}_{\mu\alpha})_{;\nu} \qquad (4.29)$$

This is a tensor equation which is therefore valid in all coordinate systems. The variation of $-g$ is needed. (3.72) gives

$$\delta(-g) = -g g^{\mu\nu} \delta g_{\mu\nu} = g g_{\mu\nu} \delta g^{\mu\nu} \qquad (4.30)$$

Expressions (4.29) and (4.30) and the vanishing of the covariant derivative of the metric tensor enable us to express (4.28) in the form

$$\delta I_G = (c^3/16\pi G) \left[\int [g^{\mu\nu} \delta \Gamma^\alpha{}_{\mu\nu} - g^{\mu\alpha} \delta \Gamma^\beta{}_{\mu\beta}]_{;\alpha} \sqrt{-g}\, d^4x \\ + \int [R_{\mu\nu} - \tfrac{1}{2} g_{\mu\nu} R] \delta g^{\mu\nu} \sqrt{-g}\, d^4x \right] \qquad (4.31)$$

The first integral in (4.31) will now be shown to vanish (6). The quantity $g^{\mu\nu} \delta R_{\mu\nu}$ is a scalar; from (4.29) it follows then that the quantity $g^{\mu\nu} \delta \Gamma^\alpha{}_{\mu\nu} - g^{\mu\alpha} \delta \Gamma^\beta{}_{\beta\mu}$ is a vector. Expression (3.75) then gives

$$\int [g^{\mu\nu} \delta \Gamma^\alpha{}_{\mu\nu} - g^{\mu\alpha} \delta \Gamma^\beta{}_{\mu\beta}]_{;\alpha} \sqrt{-g}\, d^4x \\ = \int (\sqrt{-g}\, [g^{\mu\nu} \delta \Gamma^\alpha{}_{\mu\nu} - g^{\mu\alpha} \delta \Gamma^\beta{}_{\beta\mu}])_{,\alpha}\, d^4x \qquad (4.32)$$

Gauss' theorem may be used to convert the right side of (4.32) to a surface integral which is zero in consequence of the vanishing of the variations on the boundary. (4.31) becomes

$$\delta I_G = \left(\frac{c^3}{16\pi G}\right) \int [R_{\mu\nu} - \tfrac{1}{2} g_{\mu\nu} R] \delta g^{\mu\nu} \sqrt{-g}\, d^4x \qquad (4.33)$$

This result was obtained without making entirely definite statements concerning what (in addition to $g^{\mu\nu}$) are the variables. For the remainder of the action function it will be assumed that no higher than first derivatives of the $g^{\mu\nu}$ are present. For the variation of I_F we have

$$\delta I_F = \frac{1}{c} \int \left[\frac{\partial (L_F \sqrt{-g})}{\partial g^{\mu\nu}} \delta g^{\mu\nu} + \frac{\partial (L_F \sqrt{-g})}{\delta g^{\mu\nu}{}_{,\alpha}} \partial g^{\mu\nu}{}_{,\alpha} \right] d^4x \qquad (4.34)$$

The second term of the integrand in (4.34) may be written

$$\frac{\partial(L_F \sqrt{-g})}{\partial(g^{\mu\nu}{}_{,\alpha})} \delta g^{\mu\nu}{}_{,\alpha} = \left[\delta g^{\mu\nu} \frac{\partial}{\partial g^{\mu\nu}{}_{,\alpha}} (L_F \sqrt{-g})\right]_{,\alpha}$$
$$- \left[\frac{\partial}{\partial g^{\mu\nu}{}_{,\alpha}} (L_F \sqrt{-g})\right]_{,\alpha} \delta g^{\mu\nu} \tag{4.35}$$

The first term on the right of (4.35) can be transformed into a surface integral which again is zero because the variations vanish on the boundary. This gives

$$\delta I_F = \frac{1}{c} \int \left[\frac{\partial}{\partial g^{\mu\nu}} (L_F \sqrt{-g}) - \left(\frac{\partial}{\partial g^{\mu\nu}{}_{,\alpha}} (L_F \sqrt{-g})\right)_{,\alpha}\right] \delta g^{\mu\nu} d^4x \tag{4.36}$$

We set the bracket of the integrand of (4.36) equal to a second-rank tensor density $\frac{1}{2} T_{\mu\nu} \sqrt{-g}$. ($T_{\mu\nu}$ will in a moment be identified as the stress energy tensor.)

$$\frac{1}{\sqrt{-g}} \left[\left(\frac{\partial}{\partial g^{\mu\nu}{}_{,\alpha}} (L_F \sqrt{-g})\right)_{,\alpha} - \frac{\partial}{\partial g^{\mu\nu}} (L_F \sqrt{-g})\right] = (\tfrac{1}{2}) T_{\mu\nu} \tag{4.37}$$

(4.26), (4.33), (4.36), and (4.37) then lead to

$$R_{\mu\nu} - \tfrac{1}{2} g_{\mu\nu} R = \frac{8\pi G}{c^4} T_{\mu\nu} \tag{4.38}$$

The left side of (4.38) satisfies the Bianchi identities, so $T_{\mu\nu}$ defined by (4.37) satisfies

$$T_{\mu}{}^{\nu}{}_{;\nu} = 0 \tag{4.39}$$

and may therefore be identified as the stress energy tensor, subject to the usual issues of uniqueness. The prescription (4.37) for calculating $T_{\mu\nu}$ is in some respects superior to (4.10) since a symmetric quantity always results.

4.3 Maxwell's Equations

The Lagrangian density for electrodynamics is

$$L_M = -\frac{F_{\alpha\beta} F^{\alpha\beta}}{16\pi} + \frac{j^\alpha A_\alpha}{c} + L_P \qquad (4.40)$$

L_P is the Lagrangian density of the charged particles. j^α is the four-current density. Consider first a Lorentz metric. The field tensors $F_{\mu\nu}$ are obtained from a four potential A_μ, with

$$F_{\mu\nu} = A_{\nu,\mu} - A_{\mu,\nu} \qquad (4.41)$$

The components of the four potential are considered to be the field variables in (4.40). The Maxwell equations are given in terms of the field tensors and the four-current density as

$$F^{\mu\nu}{}_{,\nu} = \frac{4\pi}{c} j^\mu \qquad (4.42)$$

$$\frac{\partial F_{\alpha\beta}}{\partial x^\gamma} + \frac{\partial F_{\gamma\alpha}}{\partial x^\beta} + \frac{\partial F_{\beta\gamma}}{\partial x^\alpha} = 0 \qquad (4.43)$$

Substitution of (4.41) into (4.43) shows that (4.43) becomes an identity satisfied by any $F_{\mu\nu}$ obtained according to (4.41). For a field tensor obtained from a four potential, (4.42) is therefore the entire content of Maxwell's equations.

If we adopt the Lorentz gauge, given by

$$A^\nu{}_{,\nu} = 0 \qquad (4.44)$$

then substitution of (4.41) into (4.42) gives

$$A^\mu{}_{,\alpha}{}^{,\alpha} = -\frac{4\pi j^\mu}{c} \qquad (4.45)$$

as the four-potential formulation of electrodynamics.

We wish now to generalize these results for arbitrary systems of coordinates. (4.40) is still valid and (4.42) becomes

$$F^{\mu\nu}{}_{;\nu} = (4\pi/c) j^\mu \qquad (4.46)$$

(4.41) becomes $A_{\nu;\,\mu} - A_{\mu;\,\nu}$, which by (3.35) and the symmetry of $\Gamma^\kappa_{\;\mu\sigma}$ in its lower indices again reduces to (4.41). Since $F^{\mu\nu}$ is an antisymmetric tensor we may use (3.78) to write

$$\frac{1}{\sqrt{-g}}\,(F^{\mu\nu}\sqrt{-g})_{,\,\nu} = (4\pi/c)j^\mu \qquad (4.47)$$

The appropriate generalization of (4.43) is

$$(\varepsilon^{\alpha\beta\gamma\delta}(-g)^{-\frac{1}{2}}F_{\alpha\beta})_{;\,\delta} = 0 \qquad (4.48)$$

However, the quantity in the brackets is a second-rank tensor antisymmetric in the indices γ and δ, so it follows, again from (3.78), that (4.48) reduces to (4.43) in arbitrary systems of coordinates.

The expression (4.44) becomes

$$A^\nu_{\;;\,\nu} = 0 \qquad (4.49)$$

A calculation, which is most easily performed in geodesic coordinates (noting that the Christoffel symbols, but not their derivatives, vanish), leads to the following result for changing the order of covariant differentiation of a vector:

$$A^\nu_{\;;\,\rho;\,\sigma} - A^\nu_{\;;\,\sigma;\,\rho} = R^\nu_{\;\alpha\sigma\rho}A^\alpha$$

We apply this now to (4.46), which is first written in terms of A^μ.

$$A^{\nu;\,\mu}_{\quad;\,\nu} - A^{\mu;\,\nu}_{\quad;\,\nu} = (4\pi/c)j^\mu$$

Lowering the index μ, writing $A^\nu_{\;;\,\mu;\,\nu}$ in terms of $A^\nu_{\;;\,\nu;\,\mu}$, and using (4.49) gives

$$A_{\mu;\,\nu}^{\;\;\;;\nu} - R_{\mu\alpha}A^\alpha = (-4\pi/c)j_\mu \qquad (4.50)$$

as the generalization of (4.45).

4.4 Motion of a Charged Particle

The action function for a charged particle with charge e is given by

$$I = -mc \int ds + (e/c) \int A_\mu\, dx^\mu \qquad (4.51)$$

The equations of motion result from setting the variation of I equal to zero. For the first term of (4.51) we obtain from (3.62) through (3.68)

$$-mc\delta \int ds = -mc \int \left(\frac{d^2 x^\mu}{ds^2} + \Gamma^\mu_{\alpha\beta} \frac{dx^\alpha}{ds} \frac{dx^\beta}{ds} \right) g_{\mu\gamma} \delta x^\gamma\, ds \quad (4.52)$$

For the second term of (4.51),

$$(e/c)\delta \int A_\mu \, dx^\mu = (e/c) \int \delta A_\mu \, dx^\mu + (e/c) \int A_\mu \, d\delta x^\mu$$

$$= (e/c) \int [d(A_\mu \delta x^\mu) - \delta x^\mu \, dA_\mu + \delta A_\mu \, dx^\mu] \quad (4.53)$$

The first term in the integrand on the far right vanishes when integrated because the variations are zero at the end points of the path. For the remaining terms we note that

$$dA_\mu = \frac{\partial A_\mu}{dx^\rho} \, dx^\rho$$

while

$$\delta A_\mu = \frac{\partial A_\mu}{\partial x^\nu} \, \delta x^\nu$$

Making use of (4.41), combining (4.52) and (4.53), setting the result equal to zero, and raising one index on $F_{\alpha\beta}$ then yields

$$\frac{d^2 x^\mu}{ds^2} + \Gamma^\mu_{\alpha\beta} \frac{dx^\alpha}{ds} \frac{dx^\beta}{ds} = F^\mu_\alpha \frac{dx^\alpha}{ds} (e/mc^2) \quad (4.54)$$

References

1. F. Belinfante, *Physica* 6, 887 (1939).
2. L. Rosenfeld, *Mem. acad. roy. Belgique* 28, 6 (1940).
3. E. Mach, *Die Geschichte und die Wurzel des Satzes von der Erhaltung der Arbeit*, Prague, 1877, and Mechanik, Leipzig, 1883.
4. D. Hilbert, Grundlagen der Physik, I, *Nachr. Ges. Wiss. Göttingen* 1915, 395.
5. A. Einstein, *The Meaning of Relativity*, Princeton University Press, 1950, 3rd ed., p. 111.
6. A. Palatini, *Rend. circ. mat. Palermo* 43, 203 (1919).
7. A. Einstein, *Ann. Physik* 49, 769 (1916).

CHAPTER 5

Experimental Tests of General Relativity

5.1 The Schwarzschild Solution

Up to the present time, experimental tests of general relativity have consisted of the Eötvos experiment, the gravitational red shift, the advance of the perihelion of planetary orbits, and the deflection of light by the sum. The last three of these effects are based on the solution of the field equations for a spherically symmetric field. We now obtain this solution, following K. Schwarzschild (1).

The starting point is the spherically symmetric squared-line element of flat space-time:

$$-ds^2 = -c^2 dt^2 + dr'^2 + r'^2(d\theta^2 + \sin^2\theta \, d\varphi^2) \quad (5.1)$$

Now we introduce at the origin a mass with spherical symmetry. (5.1) must be modified but in a way that retains spherical symmetry and symmetry with respect to time reversal. This leads to

$$\begin{aligned}-ds^2 = &-f_0(r', t)c^2 dt^2 + f_1(r', t)dr'^2 \\ &+ f_2(r', t)r'^2(d\theta^2 + \sin^2\theta \, d\varphi^2)\end{aligned} \quad (5.2)$$

We choose a new coordinate r such that $f_2(r', t)r'^2 = r^2$. We set $f_0 = e^\nu, f_1 = e^\lambda$, to obtain $g_{00} = -e^\nu$, $g_{11} = e^\lambda$, $g_{22} = r^2$, $g_{33} = r^2 \sin^2\theta$; then

$$-ds^2 = -e^\nu c^2 dt^2 + e^\lambda dr^2 + r^2(d\theta^2 + \sin^2\theta \, d\varphi^2) \quad (5.3)$$

For the empty space surrounding the body, $T_{\mu\nu} = 0$, and the field equations become

$$R_{\mu\nu} - \tfrac{1}{2}g_{\mu\nu}R = 0$$

Multiplying this by $g^{\mu\nu}$ and contracting gives $R = 0$. The gravitational field equations for vacuum become

$$R_{\mu\nu} = 0 \qquad (5.4)$$

To facilitate calculations we give the nonvanishing components of $\Gamma^{\delta}{}_{\mu\nu}$ as

$$\Gamma^1{}_{11} = \tfrac{1}{2}\frac{\partial\lambda}{\partial r} \qquad\qquad \Gamma^2{}_{33} = -\sin\theta\cos\theta$$

$$\Gamma^1{}_{10} = \tfrac{1}{2}\frac{\partial\lambda}{c\partial t} \qquad\qquad \Gamma^1{}_{00} = \tfrac{1}{2}\frac{\partial\nu}{\partial r}e^{\nu-\lambda}$$

$$\Gamma^2{}_{12} = \Gamma^3{}_{13} = \frac{1}{r} \qquad\qquad \Gamma^0{}_{00} = \tfrac{1}{2}\frac{\partial\nu}{c\partial t} \qquad (5.5)$$

$$\Gamma^0{}_{11} = \tfrac{1}{2}\frac{\partial\lambda}{c\partial t}e^{\lambda-\nu} \qquad\qquad \Gamma^3{}_{23} = \cot\theta$$

$$\Gamma^0{}_{10} = \tfrac{1}{2}\frac{\partial\nu}{\partial r} \qquad\qquad \Gamma^1{}_{33} = -r\sin^2\theta\,e^{-\lambda}$$

$$\Gamma^1{}_{22} = -re^{-\lambda}$$

For the vacuum case we use (5.4) or $G_{\mu\nu} = R_{\mu\nu} - \tfrac{1}{2}g_{\mu\nu}R$ set equal to zero. The expressions for $G_{\mu\nu}$ are somewhat more simple and may also be used when a problem other than the vacuum with only gravitational fields is considered. The nonvanishing components of $G_{\mu}{}^{\nu}$ are given by straightforward calculation as

$$G_0{}^0 = e^{-\lambda}\left(\frac{1}{r^2} - \frac{1}{r}\frac{\partial\lambda}{\partial r}\right) - \frac{1}{r^2}$$

$$G_0{}^1 = \frac{e^{-\lambda}}{rc}\frac{\partial\lambda}{\partial t}$$

$$G_2{}^2 = G_3{}^3 = \tfrac{1}{2}e^{-\lambda}\left(\frac{\partial^2\nu}{\partial r^2} + \tfrac{1}{2}\left(\frac{\partial\nu}{\partial r}\right)^2 + \frac{1}{r}\left(\frac{\partial\nu}{\partial r} - \frac{\partial\lambda}{\partial r}\right) - \tfrac{1}{2}\frac{\partial\nu}{\partial r}\frac{\partial\lambda}{\partial r}\right)$$

$$\qquad - \tfrac{1}{2}e^{-\nu}\left(\frac{\partial^2\lambda}{c^2\partial t^2} + \tfrac{1}{2}\left(\frac{\partial\lambda}{c\partial t}\right)^2 - \tfrac{1}{2}\left(\frac{\partial\lambda}{c\partial t}\right)\left(\frac{\partial\nu}{c\partial t}\right)\right) \quad (5.6)$$

$$G_1{}^1 = e^{-\lambda}\left(\frac{1}{r}\frac{\partial\nu}{\partial r} + \frac{1}{r^2}\right) - \frac{1}{r^2}$$

Setting (5.6) equal to zero leads to the independent equations

$$\frac{\partial \nu}{\partial r} + \frac{1}{r} - \frac{e^\lambda}{r} = 0 \tag{5.7}$$

$$\frac{\partial \lambda}{\partial r} - \frac{1}{r} + \frac{e^\lambda}{r} = 0 \tag{5.8}$$

$$\frac{\partial \lambda}{\partial t} = 0 \tag{5.9}$$

The sum of the equations (5.7) and (5.8) gives

$$\frac{\partial}{\partial r} (\lambda + \nu) = 0 \tag{5.10}$$

(5.9) requires λ to be independent of time, (5.10) then implies that any time dependence in ν must arise from a function independent of r. (5.3) indicates that such a time dependence can be eliminated everywhere by a coordinate transformation involving only the time. This is equivalent to the statement that the assumption of spherical symmetry guarantees the possibility of a time-independent description of the geometry of the space. All time derivatives in (5.5) and (5.6) can be taken to be zero. The solution of (5.7) and (5.8) is

$$e^{-\lambda} = e^\nu = 1 + \frac{K_0}{r} \tag{5.11}$$

The constant K_0 may be determined from the requirement that Newton's law of gravitation be approached, at large distances from the mass.

From the geodesic equation it follows that the acceleration of a small test body at rest relative to the central mass M is

$$-c^2 \Gamma^r{}_{00} = c^2 \left(\frac{K_0}{2r^2}\right) \left(1 + \frac{K_0}{r}\right) \to \frac{c^2 K_0}{2r^2}$$

Comparing this with the Newtonian value $-GM/r^2$ gives

$$K_0 = -\frac{2GM}{c^2} \tag{5.12}$$

The Schwarzschild metric (5.3) now takes the form

$$-ds^2 = -\left(c^2 - \frac{2GM}{r}\right) dt^2 + r^2 (\sin^2 \theta \, d\varphi^2 + d\theta^2) + \frac{dr^2}{\left(1 - \dfrac{2GM}{c^2 r}\right)}$$

(5.13)

(5.13) exhibits[‡] the "Schwarzschild singularity" at $r = 2GM/c^2$. This appears to limit the size of massive bodies to $r > 2GM/c^2$. For an electron this is 13.2×10^{-56} cm, which is much too small to be related to present elementary particle theories. For a charged particle at the origin, the arguments which led to (5.3) are still valid. However, the energy associated with the electric field of the particle is distributed throughout space. The trace $T_\alpha{}^\alpha$ of the Maxwell stress tensor (4.15) vanishes. If we raise one index and then contract the field equations (4.25) the result is that $R = 0$ for the combined Einstein-Maxwell field and we obtain

$$R_{\mu\nu} = \frac{8\pi G}{c^4} \, T_{\mu\nu} \qquad (5.14)$$

for the case of energy sources which consist entirely of the electromagnetic field. The use of the metric (5.3), expressions (5.6) and (4.15), and the Maxwell equations (4.47) for spherically symmetric [§] A_0 then give in place of (5.13) for a particle with electric charge e

$$-ds^2 = -\left(c^2 - \frac{2GM}{r} + \frac{Ge^2}{c^2 r^2}\right) dt^2$$
$$+ r^2(\sin^2 \theta \, d\varphi^2 + d\theta^2) + \frac{dr^2}{\left(1 - \dfrac{2GM}{c^2 r} + \dfrac{e^2 G}{c^4 r^2}\right)} \qquad (5.13a)$$

[‡] H. P. Robertson has shown that a test body takes a finite time to cross the Schwarzschild singularity. New coordinates remove the Schwarzschild singularity, but not the one at the origin, with singular Riemann tensor invariants.

Finklestein[8] has given an analytic extension of the Schwarzschild solution, with no singularities except at the origin. It does not possess time symmetry. He attributes this to the nonlinear character of general relativity.

[§] To evaluate the constant we may compare the invariant $F_{\mu\nu} F^{\mu\nu}$ at large distances with the flat-space value for a charged particle.

For a spherical uncharged body of finite extension the metric (5.13) is valid only outside the body. An interior solution for a fluid sphere can be written in the form

$$-ds^2 = -\left[A - B \sqrt{\left[1 - \frac{r^2}{R_s^2} \right]} \right]^2 c^2 dt^2$$
$$+ \frac{dr^2}{1 - \dfrac{r^2}{R_s^2}} + r^2 [\sin^2 \theta \, d\varphi^2 + d\theta^2] \tag{5.13b}$$

and by requiring this to properly join up with (5.13) at the boundary $r = r_1$ we can obtain in terms of the density ρ,

$$R_s^2 = (3c^2/8\pi\rho G); \qquad A = (3/2) \sqrt{\left[1 - \frac{r_1^2}{R_s^2} \right]}; \qquad B = \tfrac{1}{2}$$

5.2   The Gravitational Red Shift

We return now to the metric (5.13) to again deduce the gravitational red-shift formula. Suppose we have an oscillator at the surface of a star, with interval between vibrations given by the invariant Δs. Imagine that a pulse of light is emitted at the peak of each vibration and let the time coordinate at any point in the space be established by the receipt of these pulses. First we note that the interval of coordinate time Δt, between successive pulses at a fixed point, is equal everywhere in the space to the value at the surface of the star. Each pulse is propagated along a null geodesic in the radial direction and (5.13) gives, for $ds = 0$,

$$dt = -\frac{g_{11}(r)dr}{cg_{00}(r)} \tag{5.15}$$

Integrating (5.15) for the time of the arrival of the nth pulse at the radial distance r leads to

$$t(r, n) - t(r_0, n) = -\int_{r_0}^{r} \frac{g_{11}(r')dr'}{cg_{00}(r')} = F(r, r_0) \tag{5.16}$$

Similarly,

$$t(r, n+1) - t(r_0, n+1) = F(r, r_0) \tag{5.17}$$

Subtracting (5.16) from (5.17) gives

$$t(r, n+1) - t(r, n) = t(r_0, n+1) - t(r_0, n) = \Delta t \tag{5.18}$$

which is independent of r. Let the coordinate frequency be ν_c

$$\nu_c = \frac{1}{\Delta t} = \frac{c\sqrt{-g_{00}}(\text{distant oscillator})}{\Delta s} \qquad (5.19)$$

For the identical oscillator located at the position of an observer at radius r, the locally generated frequency ν_l is assumed to be given in terms of the invariant intervals Δs by

$$\nu_l = \frac{c}{\Delta s} \sqrt{-g_{00}} \; (\text{local oscillator}) \qquad (5.20)$$

Comparing (5.19) and (5.20) results in

$$\nu_c - \nu_l = \nu_l \left(\sqrt{\frac{g_{00} \; (\text{distant oscillator})}{g_{00} \; (\text{local oscillator})}} - 1 \right) \quad (5.21)$$

The frequency shift at radial coordinate r for a body which has its surface at radial coordinate r_0 is

$$\Delta \nu = \nu_c - \nu_l \approx - \frac{GM}{c^2} \left(\frac{1}{r_0} - \frac{1}{r} \right) \nu_l \qquad (5.21a)$$

(toward the red), in agreement with (1.15), since r and r_0 are very nearly equal to the corresponding distances. The difference between (5.21) and the equivalence-principle result (1.15) amounts to a fractional frequency shift of about $(GM/c^2 r_0)^2$, roughly one part in 10^{18} for a terrestrial measurement of the entire red-shift.

Measurements on the companion of Sirius give a red-shift equivalent to the Doppler shift associated with a velocity of 19 km/sec, while the calculated equivalent value is 20 km/sec. For the binary star 40 Eridani, measurements on the white dwarf give 21 ± 4 km/sec, which is to be compared with the calculated value 17 ± 3 km/sec. Line-shift measurements on the sun give different results at different points on the surface. This is not understood.

Experimental work is in progress to measure the red shift by other methods, involving the earth's field. One type of experiment compares precision frequency standards of the "atomic clock" (4) type on earth and at a different gravitational potential, using rocket-launched satellites (3). A different method makes use of the discovery of Mössbauer (5) that some of the gamma radiation (in the energy range $\sim 10^4$ ev) emitted by long-lived (greater than 10^{-8} sec) "isomeric" states of nuclei is recoil-free. The recoil momentum is taken up by the solid as a whole, and there is no significant Doppler[‡]

‡ The recoil momentum may excite the lattice vibrations or may be transferred as linear momentum to the entire crystal. In the former case there will be a Doppler breadth because the emitting atom recoils. The criterion that the lattice vibrations not be excited can be stated in the following terms. Let the gamma-ray recoil momentum be $p = \hbar\omega_\gamma/c$. Let the mass of the atom be m. Then we may expect no appreciable Doppler effect if $(p^2/m) \ll k\theta_D$ where θ_D is the Debye temperature and k is Boltzmann's constant. This result can be understood by consideration of the effect of the radiated momentum transfer. Suppose the lattice vibration wavefunction is ψ_j before emission of the gamma ray. ψ_j is an eigenfunction of the Hamiltonian operator. If the gamma-ray emission transfers momentum p in some way to the crystal, then the wavefunction immediately after emission is $e^{ip_s q^s/\hbar}\psi_j$. Here q^s is the harmonic oscillator coordinate and this wavefunction is the one which has an expectation value for momentum p units greater than the initial one. After emission we may write

$$a_r\psi_r = e^{ip_s q^s/\hbar}\psi_j$$
$$a_r = \langle E_r|e^{ip_s q^s/\hbar}|E_j\rangle \approx \delta_{rj} + ip_s|q^s|_{rj}/\hbar$$

The term $p_s|q^s|_{rj}$ gives rise to phonon emission or absorption while the term δ_{rj} does not. To obtain the relative probability of emission without phonon excitation we need to evaluate

$$\hbar^{-2} \sum_{\text{modes}} p^2(|q|_{rj})^2$$

$|q|_{rj}$ are the harmonic oscillator matrix elements.

$$(|q|_{rj})^2 = \frac{\hbar}{Nm\omega_l}(N_{\text{ph}}+1) \quad \text{or} \quad \frac{\hbar}{Nm\omega_l}N_{\text{ph}}$$

where N_{ph} is the number of phonons, N is the number of atoms, mN is the mass of the crystal, and ω_l is the lattice vibration frequency.

$$\sum_{\text{modes}} (|q|_{rj})^2 \approx \frac{\hbar}{m\omega_l}(N_{\text{ph}}+1) \quad \text{or} \quad \frac{\hbar}{m\omega_l}N_{\text{ph}}$$

Since energy is at least approximately conserved, ω will be a high lattice vibration frequency, of the order of the Debye frequency $\omega_D = k\theta_D/\hbar$, also $N_{\text{ph}} \sim 1$. Using these relations and requiring

$$(p^2/\hbar^2) \sum_{\text{modes}} (|q|_{rj})^2 \ll 1$$

then gives $(p^2/m) \ll k\theta_D$.

shift, or broadening. The long lifetime is a consequence of the fact that the angular momentum of the nuclear ground state is different from that of the excited state. The radiation is either magnetic dipole or of a higher multipole order. The ratio of the frequency to line width is unusually great. Suggestions that this radiation be employed for terrestrial redshift measurements were first published by Pound and Rebka (6), and independently put forth by Wilkinson, by Boyle, by Devons, and by Cranshaw (7).

The properties of the 14,700-ev radiation of the 10^{-7}-sec Fe^{57}, obtained from the radioactive decay of 270-day Co^{57} have been reported. Pound and Rebka observed the radiation with a scintillation spectrometer and arranged to move the source toward and away from the spectrometer by cementing it to a moving coil transducer. In this way they observed that the radiation has a half width $\Delta\nu \sim 2 \times 10^6$ cycles/sec. Since the red shift is proportional to frequency, a shift of roughly one part in 10^{14} would be expected for a change in height of $\sim$50 m in the earth's gravitational field. For the Fe^{57} radiation this amounts to about 3×10^4 cycles/sec, or roughly 1 percent of the line width already achieved. This is, therefore, a feasible experiment.‡ Pound and Rebka

---

‡ Results of such an experiment were recently reported by Cranshaw, Schiffer, and Whitehead (*Phys. Rev. Letters* 4, 163 (1960)). They employed Fe^{57} and a total height difference of 12.5 m. A red shift 0.96 ± 0.45 times the predicted value was observed. A more precise result was achieved later by Pound and Rebka, *Phys. Rev. Letters* 4, 337, (1960). They obtained a red shift 1.05 ± 0.10 times the predicted value. Anomalous frequency shifts associated with particular sources and absorbers, and a temperature dependent frequency shift had to be taken into account. The latter effect is a time dilation associated with the temperature dependent velocity. The angular frequency shift is

$$\Delta\omega = \omega_\gamma \left(1 - \frac{\langle v^2 \rangle}{c^2}\right)^{\frac{1}{2}} - \omega_\gamma \approx -\frac{3\omega_\gamma kT}{2mc^2}$$

Here T is the absolute temperature, and the approximation on the far right is valid at high temperatures (where equipartition occurs).

This effect was minimized by controlling source and absorber temperatures. The other anomaly was corrected for by exchanging positions of source and absorber.

note that with a source of limited strength, statistical fluctuations decrease the precision, owing to decreased counting rates, as the distance between source and absorber is increased. This just about compensates the increased red shift as the height separation between source and observer is changed. Larger vertical distances do not therefore give much increase in precision, unless some means is provided to concentrate the radiation.

5.3   Effects on Planetary Orbits

(5.5) may be employed to write the geodesic equations[‡] for either a massive particle or a light ray. The differential equation for the θ coordinate is

$$\frac{d^2\theta}{ds^2} + \frac{2}{r}\frac{dr}{ds}\frac{d\theta}{ds} - \cos\theta\sin\theta\left(\frac{d\varphi}{ds}\right)^2 = 0 \qquad (5.22)$$

For the particle with nonvanishing rest mass, s is the interval along the geodesic. The problem is simplified if the plane containing the initial velocity and the central mass is taken as $\theta = \pi/2$. $d\theta/ds = 0$ initially, and from (5.22) $d^2\theta/ds^2 = 0$. The entire orbit will then lie in the equatorial plane. The remaining geodesic equations are

$$\frac{d^2r}{ds^2} + \tfrac{1}{2}\frac{d\lambda}{dr}\left(\frac{dr}{ds}\right)^2 - re^{-\lambda}\left(\frac{d\varphi}{ds}\right)^2 + \tfrac{1}{2}e^{\nu-\lambda}\frac{d\nu}{dr}\left(c\frac{dt}{ds}\right)^2 = 0 \quad (5.23)$$

$$\frac{d^2\varphi}{ds^2} + \frac{2}{r}\frac{dr}{ds}\frac{d\varphi}{ds} = 0 \qquad (5.24)$$

$$\frac{d^2t}{ds^2} + \frac{d\nu}{dr}\frac{dr}{ds}\frac{dt}{ds} = 0 \qquad (5.25)$$

Equations (5.24) and (5.25) are readily integrated and give

$$r^2\frac{d\varphi}{ds} = K_1 \qquad (5.26)$$

$$\frac{dt}{ds} = K_2\,e^{-\nu} \qquad (5.27)$$

For these calculations the assumption is made that the coordinate system has axes fixed with reference to the stars.

K_1 and K_2 are constants of the orbit. Instead of integrating (5.23) directly we obtain a first integral of it by writing the Schwarzschild metric (5.13), for $\theta = \pi/2$, in the form

$$e^{-\nu} \left(\frac{dr}{ds}\right)^2 + r^2 \left(\frac{d\varphi}{ds}\right)^2 - e^{\nu} \left(c\frac{dt}{ds}\right)^2 = -1 \qquad (5.28)$$

(5.28) is the relation between any set of quantities dr/ds, $d\varphi/ds$, and dt/ds in the space. If, however, we restrict $d\varphi/ds$ and dt/ds to the values given by (5.26) and (5.27), we can eliminate ds and dt and thus obtain an ordinary differential equation in terms of the variables r and φ for the orbit given by

$$(K_1)^2 \frac{e^{-\nu}}{r^4} \left(\frac{dr}{d\varphi}\right)^2 + \frac{K_1{}^2}{r^2} - e^{-\nu} c^2 (K_2)^2 = -1 \qquad (5.29)$$

We substitute $W = 1/r$ and differentiate (5.29) with respect to φ, obtaining with the help of (5.11)

$$\frac{d^2 W}{d\varphi^2} + W = \frac{GM}{(K_1)^2 c^2} + \frac{3GM}{c^2} W^2 \qquad (5.30)$$

(5.30) can be solved in successive orders by an approximation procedure. Let $\rho = 2GM/c^2$ be the Schwarzschild radius and let

$$\rho W = \rho W^{(1)} + \rho W^{(2)} + \dots \qquad (5.31)$$

where $\rho W^{(1)}$ is a first-order and $\rho W^{(2)}$ is a second-order quantity. Substitution of (5.31) into (5.30) and setting terms of corresponding order equal to zero separately yields the equations

$$\frac{d^2 W^{(1)}}{d\varphi^2} + W^{(1)} = \frac{GM}{(K_1)^2 c^2} \qquad (5.32)$$

$$\frac{d^2 W^{(2)}}{d\varphi^2} + W^{(2)} = \frac{3GM}{c^2} (W^{(1)})^2 \qquad (5.33)$$

The solution of (5.32) is

$$W^{(1)} = \frac{GM}{(K_1)^2 c^2} \left(1 + \varepsilon \sin (\varphi - \varphi_0)\right) \qquad (5.34)$$

Here ε is the eccentricity of an elliptical orbit described by (5.34). We orient the coordinate system so that $\varphi_0 = 0$. Let

$2a$ be the length of the major axis of the ellipse (Fig. 4.1):

$$2a = \left(\frac{1}{W^{(1)}}\right)_{\varphi=\pi/2} + \left(\frac{1}{W^{(2)}}\right)_{\varphi=3\pi/2} \tag{5.35}$$

An expression for the constant $(K_1)^2$ can be written, using (5.35), in terms of the eccentricity and semimajor axis, as

$$(K_1)^2 = \frac{aGM}{c^2}(1 - \varepsilon^2) \tag{5.36}$$

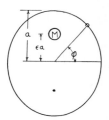

Fig. 4.1

Employing (5.36) and (5.34) enables us to write the solution of (5.33), and the entire solution (to second order) of (5.30) is found to be

$$W = \frac{1}{a(1-\varepsilon^2)}\left[1 + \varepsilon\sin\varphi - \frac{3GM\varepsilon}{c^2 a(1-\varepsilon^2)}\varphi\cos\varphi \right.$$
$$\left. + \frac{GM\varepsilon^2}{c^2 a(1-\varepsilon^2)}\cos^2\varphi + \frac{GM}{c^2 a(1-\varepsilon^2)}(3+\varepsilon^2)\right] \tag{5.37}$$

In (5.37) the term

$$-\frac{3GM\,\varepsilon\varphi\cos\varphi}{c^2 a^2(1-\varepsilon^2)^2}$$

will cause an advance of the perihelion. The second and third terms can be expressed in the form

$$\frac{\varepsilon}{a(1-\varepsilon^2)}\left[\sin\varphi - \frac{3GM\,\varphi\cos\varphi}{c^2 a(1-\varepsilon^2)}\right] \tag{5.38}$$
$$= \frac{\varepsilon}{a(1-\varepsilon^2)}\left[1 + \frac{9G^2 M^2 \varphi^2}{c^4 a^2(1-\varepsilon^2)^2}\right]^{\frac{1}{2}}\sin\left(\varphi + \tan^{-1} - \frac{3GM\varphi}{c^2 a(1-\varepsilon^2)}\right)$$

(5.38) implies that for each revolution the perihelion will advance an amount Δ given by

$$\Delta = \frac{6\pi GM}{c^2 a(1 - \varepsilon^2)} \qquad (5.39)$$

The dependence of the perihelion advance on the eccentricity ε and semimajor axis a is evident. The quantity c in (5.39) is the velocity of propagation of gravitational interactions. Thus the agreement of (5.39) with observed values for the planet Mercury (astronomical observations give 42.6 ± 0.9 sec per century and expression (5.39) predicts 43.0 sec per century) indicates that general relativity provides a good description of gravitation and that gravitational interactions propagate with the speed of light.

It is also of interest to note that the failure of a planetary orbit to be exactly periodic provides an especially sensitive test of the departures from an inverse-square law, for slow-moving bodies ($v \ll c$). The force on a body at rest is not the Newtonian value but rather

$$c^2 \Gamma^r{}_{00} = \frac{GM}{r^2} \left[1 - \frac{GM}{c^2 r} \right] \qquad (5.40)$$

with r given in terms of the distance l from the surface of the central body as

$$l = \int_{r_0}^{r} g_{11}^{\frac{1}{2}} \, dr$$

5.4 Deflection of Light

To discuss the deflection of light in a gravitational field we must again solve the geodesic equations given by (5.22), (5.23), (5.24), and (5.25). The integrals (5.26) and (5.27) are still valid. Instead of (5.28) we obtain a corresponding relation for null intervals. First we set the Schwarzschild squared-line element equal to zero, then we divide by ds^2:

$$e^{-\nu} \left(\frac{dr}{ds} \right)^2 + r^2 \left(\frac{d\varphi}{ds} \right)^2 - e^{\nu} c^2 \left(\frac{dt}{ds} \right)^2 = 0 \qquad (5.41)$$

S is now a parameter other than interval. Employing (5.26) and (5.27) in (5.41) and letting $W = 1/r$ leads to the equation

$$\left(\frac{dW}{d\varphi}\right)^2 = \left(\frac{cK_2}{K_1}\right)^2 - W^2\left(1 - \frac{2GM}{c^2}\,W\right) \qquad (5.42)$$

It is easier to deal with the equation obtained by differentiating (5.42), which is

$$\frac{d^2W}{d\varphi^2} + W = \frac{3W^2GM}{c^2} \qquad (5.43)$$

(5.43) can be solved, to second order, using the method employed for (5.30); the result is

$$W = \frac{1}{r} = \frac{\cos\varphi}{r_0} + \frac{GM}{c^2\,r_0^{\,2}}\,(1 + \sin^2\varphi) \qquad (5.44)$$

In (5.44) the integration constant r_0 is the distance of closest approach for the unperturbed light path (see Fig. 4.2).

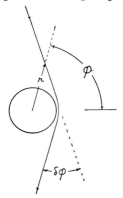

Fig. 4.2

For $r \to \infty$ we obtain two values of φ which are solutions of

$$\cos\varphi = -\frac{GM}{c^2\,r_0}\,(1 + \sin^2\varphi) \qquad (5.45)$$

Let the values be

$$\varphi_1 = \frac{\pi}{2} + \frac{\delta\varphi}{2}$$

$$\varphi_2 = -\frac{\pi}{2} - \frac{\delta\varphi}{2} \qquad (5.46)$$

Solving (5.45) gives for the total deflection

$$\delta\varphi = 4GM/c^2 r_0 \qquad (5.47)$$

For light from a star just grazing the sun's edge, (5.47) gives $\varphi = 1.75$ sec.

A summary of the astronomical data on the red shift and deflection of light has been given by Trumpler (2). For the deflection as observed during eclipses, the individual measured values have a probable error of roughly 10 percent and are usually within 10 percent of the value given by (5.47). The average for eleven eclipses agrees with (5.47) to roughly one part in 500.

5.5 Concluding Remarks

The four experiments discussed thus far constitute the entire experimental verification of general relativity. This is in marked contrast with the abundance of experimental data which support the quantum theory. It has been a great challenge to conceive other experiments which are feasible. The problem is to some extent a technological one. Techniques are usually not available to observe the very small effects which the very weak interactions of the theory predict. In later chapters additional experiments which were recently proposed will be discussed.

References

1. K. Schwarzschild, *Sitzber. preuss. Akad. Wiss.* **1916**, 424.
2. R. J. Trumpler, *Jubilee of Relativity Theory* (Helv. Acta Phys., Supplement IV), Mercier and Kervaire, p. 408.
3. S. F. Singer, *Phys. Rev.* **104**, 11 (1956). See also Exercise 18 at the end of the book.
4. H. Lyons, *Ann. N. Y. Acad. Sci.* **55**, 831 (19aa).
5. R. J. Mössbauer, *Z. Physik* **151**, 124 (1958); *Naturwissenschaften* **45**, 538 (1958); *Z. Naturforsch.* **14a**, 211 (1959).
6. R. V. Pound and G. A. Rebka, Jr., *Phys. Rev. Letters* **3**, 439 (1959).
7. J. P. Schiffer and W. Marshall, *Phys. Rev. Letters* **3**, 556 (1959).
8. D. Finklestein, *Phys. Rev.* **110**, 965 (1958).

CHAPTER 6

The Conservation Laws

6.1 The Canonical Stress Energy Pseudotensor

In special relativity the relation $T_{\mu}{}^{\nu}{}_{,\nu} = 0$, which is satisfied by the stress energy tensor, is integrated over the three space coordinates to get the conservation laws for energy and momentum. For $T_0{}^{\nu}{}_{,\nu}$ we have

$$\frac{\partial}{\partial x^0} \int T_0{}^0 \, dx^1 dx^2 dx^3$$
$$= -\int \left(\frac{\partial T_0{}^1}{\partial x^1} + \frac{\partial T_0{}^2}{\partial x^2} + \frac{\partial T_0{}^3}{\partial x^3} \right) dx^1 dx^2 dx^3 = -\int T_0{}^i \, dS_i \tag{6.1}$$

On the far right the volume integral has been transformed to a surface integral with dS_i a vector element of area of the boundary. This result relates the change of energy in a given volume to the flow of energy momentum into it.

The situation is different if a Lorentz metric is not employed. The stress energy tensor now satisfies $T_{\mu\nu;\nu} = 0$. Since $T_{\mu\nu}$ is symmetric we may use (3.79) to write

$$T_{\mu}{}^{\nu}{}_{;\nu} = (-g)^{-\frac{1}{2}}(T_{\mu}{}^{\nu}\sqrt{-g})_{,\nu} - \tfrac{1}{2}g_{\alpha\beta,\mu} T^{\alpha\beta} \tag{6.2}$$

If the metric is time-dependent then for $\mu = 0$, the second term of (6.2) represents a time-dependent exchange of energy and momentum between the gravitational field in each volume element, and the other fields. In order to be able always to carry out the operations which led to the integration of (6.1), we search for a quantity $t_{\mu}{}^{\nu}$ such that

$$(-g)^{-\frac{1}{2}}(t_{\mu}{}^{\nu}\sqrt{-g})_{,\nu} = -\tfrac{1}{2}g_{\alpha\beta,\mu} T^{\alpha\beta} \tag{6.3}$$

Then (6.2) becomes

$$[(T_\mu{}^\nu + t_\mu{}^\nu)\sqrt{-g}]_{,\nu} = 0 \qquad (6.4)$$

With (6.4), an integration similar to (6.1) may now in general be carried out which would be expected to yield conservation laws (1–5) including the gravitational field. Expression (6.3) does not uniquely define $t_\mu{}^\nu$. Also it follows from the right side of (6.3) that $t_\mu{}^\nu$ is not a tensor. We shall see that $t_\mu{}^\nu$ behaves like a tensor under certain restricted groups of transformations. It is called the stress energy pseudotensor. One way of obtaining an expression for $t_\mu{}^\nu$ is to follow essentially the procedure which led to (4.10). The problem is different from that ordinarily encountered in field theory because the gravitational action function

$$I_G = (c^3/16\pi G) \int R\sqrt{-g}\, d^4x \qquad (6.5)$$

contains second space and time derivatives of the field variables $g^{\mu\nu}$. However, the part containing second derivatives may be written as a surface integral. We have, in fact,

$$R\sqrt{-g} = g^{\mu\nu}R_{\mu\nu}\sqrt{-g} = [g^{\mu\nu}\Gamma^\alpha{}_{\mu\nu,\alpha} - g^{\mu\nu}\Gamma^\alpha{}_{\mu\alpha,\nu}$$
$$+ g^{\mu\nu}\Gamma^\alpha{}_{\mu\nu}\Gamma^\beta{}_{\alpha\beta} - g^{\mu\nu}\Gamma^\alpha{}_{\mu\beta}\Gamma^\beta{}_{\nu\alpha}]\sqrt{-g} \qquad (6.6)$$

The terms involving second derivatives are the first two on the right of (6.6). These may be rearranged in the following way:

$$(g^{\mu\nu}\Gamma^\alpha{}_{\mu\nu,\alpha} - g^{\mu\nu}\Gamma^\alpha{}_{\mu\alpha,\nu})\sqrt{-g} = (g^{\mu\nu}\Gamma^\alpha{}_{\mu\nu}\sqrt{-g})_{,\alpha}$$
$$-(g^{\mu\nu}\Gamma^\alpha{}_{\mu\alpha}\sqrt{-g})_{,\nu} - \Gamma^\alpha{}_{\mu\nu}(g^{\mu\nu}\sqrt{-g})_{,\alpha} + \Gamma^\alpha{}_{\mu\alpha}(g^{\mu\nu}\sqrt{-g})_{,\nu} \qquad (6.7)$$

If we now use (3.73)

$$\frac{\partial g}{\partial x^\alpha} = gg^{\iota\kappa}g_{\iota\kappa,\alpha}; \quad g^{\mu\nu}{}_{;\alpha} = 0; \quad g^{\mu\nu}{}_{,\alpha} = -\Gamma^\mu{}_{\gamma\alpha}g^{\gamma\nu} - \Gamma^\nu{}_{\gamma\alpha}g^{\mu\gamma};$$
$$\Gamma^\beta{}_{\mu\beta} = \tfrac{1}{2}g^{\iota\kappa}g_{\iota\kappa,\mu}$$

The last two terms of (6.7) may be written

$$-\Gamma^\alpha{}_{\mu\nu}(g^{\mu\nu}\sqrt{-g})_{,\alpha} + \Gamma^\alpha{}_{\mu\alpha}(g^{\mu\nu}\sqrt{-g})_{,\nu}$$
$$= 2g^{\mu\nu}[\Gamma^\alpha{}_{\mu\beta}\Gamma^\beta{}_{\nu\alpha} - \Gamma^\alpha{}_{\mu\nu}\Gamma^\beta{}_{\alpha\beta}]\sqrt{-g} \qquad (6.8)$$

Using (6.6), (6.7), and (6.8), we may express (6.5) in the form

$$\int R\sqrt{-g}\,d^4x = \int g^{\mu\nu}(\Gamma^\alpha{}_{\mu\beta}\Gamma^\beta{}_{\nu\alpha} - \Gamma^\alpha{}_{\mu\nu}\Gamma^\beta{}_{\alpha\beta})\sqrt{-g}\,d^4x$$
$$+ \int [\sqrt{-g}(g^{\alpha\beta}\Gamma^\delta{}_{\alpha\beta} - g^{\alpha\delta}\Gamma^\beta{}_{\alpha\beta})]_{,\delta}\,d^4x \qquad (6.9)$$

Thus we see that in (6.9) the first integral on the right is only a function of $g^{\mu\nu}$ and its first derivatives; the second integral can readily be converted into a surface integral using Gauss's theorem. For variations of the action function which vanish on the boundary, only the first integral on the right side of (6.9) will be needed. We may now define

$$\mathscr{L}_G = \left(\frac{c^4}{16\pi G}\right)g^{\mu\nu}(\Gamma^\alpha{}_{\mu\beta}\Gamma^\beta{}_{\nu\alpha} - \Gamma^\alpha{}_{\mu\nu}\Gamma^\beta{}_{\alpha\beta}) \qquad (6.10)$$

and a total Lagrangian density $\mathscr{L}$ by

$$\mathscr{L} = \mathscr{L}_G + L_F \qquad (6.11)$$

with L_F the Lagrangian density of fields other than the gravitational field. Since (6.10) contains only the part of the gravitational Lagrangian without second derivatives, and L_F also contains only the field variables and their first derivatives, we may apply the standard Lagrangian formalism of field theory (section 4.1) to the action integral

$$I = \frac{1}{c}\int \mathscr{L}\sqrt{-g}\,d^4x \qquad (6.12)$$

It therefore follows that the field equations are

$$\frac{\partial}{\partial x^\alpha}\frac{\partial(\mathscr{L}\sqrt{-g})}{\partial g^{\mu\nu}{}_{,\alpha}} - \frac{\partial(\mathscr{L}\sqrt{-g})}{\partial g^{\mu\nu}} = 0 \qquad (6.13)$$

Using (6.11) and (4.37) we may write

$$\frac{16\pi G}{c^4}\left[\frac{\partial(\mathscr{L}_G\sqrt{-g})}{\partial g^{\mu\nu}} - \frac{\partial}{\partial x^\alpha}\frac{\partial(\mathscr{L}_G\sqrt{-g})}{\partial g^{\mu\nu}{}_{,\alpha}}\right] =$$
$$(R_{\mu\nu} - \tfrac{1}{2}g_{\mu\nu}R)\sqrt{-g} = \left(\frac{8\pi G}{c^4}\right)T_{\mu\nu}\sqrt{-g} \qquad (6.14)$$

and using (4.10) we may define a total canonical stress energy pseudotensor $\tau_\mu{}^\nu$ by

$$\tau_\mu{}^\nu \sqrt{-g} = \left[\delta_\mu{}^\nu \mathscr{L} \sqrt{-g} - g^{\rho\beta}{}_{,\mu} \frac{\partial(\mathscr{L}\sqrt{-g})}{\partial g^{\rho\beta}{}_{,\nu}} \right] \qquad (6.15)$$

with a gravitational part

$$t_\mu{}^\nu \sqrt{-g} = \left[\delta_\mu{}^\nu \mathscr{L}_G \sqrt{-g} - g^{\rho\beta}{}_{,\mu} \frac{\partial(\mathscr{L}_G\sqrt{-g})}{\partial g^{\rho\beta}{}_{,\nu}} \right] \qquad (6.16)$$

with

$$(\tau_\mu{}^\nu \sqrt{-g})_{,\nu} = (t_\mu{}^\nu \sqrt{-g} + T_\mu{}^\nu \sqrt{-g})_{,\nu} = 0 \qquad (6.17)$$

The expressions (6.13) and (6.14) are especially interesting because they exhibit Einstein's field equations in the form of Lagrange's equations.

It is more instructive to derive (6.15) in a different way making use of invariance of $\mathscr{L}$ under certain coordinate transformations. We recall that the conservation laws of a theory are associated with certain invariance properties. For example, in mechanics energy conservation is related to invariance of the Hamiltonian under time translation, angular-momentum conservation is related to invariance of the Hamiltonian under rotations.

Let us carry out the infinitesimal coordinate transformation‡

$$x'^\mu = x^\mu + \delta x^\mu \qquad (6.18)$$

making use of the transformation law for $g^{\kappa\nu}$ gives for the change corresponding to (6.18),

$$\delta g^{\kappa\mu} = g^{\kappa\alpha} \frac{\partial}{\partial x^\alpha} (\delta x^\mu) + g^{\mu\alpha} \frac{\partial}{\partial x^\alpha} (\delta x^\kappa) = g'^{\kappa\mu}(x') - g^{\kappa\mu}(x) \quad (6.19)$$

‡ In this chapter the δ symbol always means what is expressed by (6.18) and (6.19). Some authors employ the symbol $\bar{\delta}$ for the different operation

$$\bar{\delta} g^{\kappa\mu} = g'^{\kappa\mu}(x) - g^{\kappa\mu}(x) = \delta x^\kappa{}_{;\mu} + \delta x^\mu{}_{;\kappa}$$

$$\delta g^{\kappa\mu}{}_{,\beta} = \frac{\partial g'^{\kappa\mu}(x')}{\partial x'^{\beta}} - \frac{\partial g^{\kappa\mu}(x)}{\partial x^{\beta}} = \frac{\partial}{\partial x^{\beta}}(\delta g^{\kappa\mu}) - g^{\kappa\mu}{}_{,\gamma}\frac{\partial}{\partial x^{\beta}}(\delta x^{\gamma}) \quad (6.20)$$

$$\delta\mathscr{L} = \frac{\partial\mathscr{L}}{\partial g^{\kappa\mu}}\delta g^{\kappa\mu} + \frac{\partial\mathscr{L}}{\partial g^{\kappa\mu}{}_{,\alpha}}\delta g^{\kappa\mu}{}_{,\alpha} \quad (6.21)$$

This follows because L_F is a scalar, so $\delta L_F = 0$.
Making use of (6.19) and (6.20) leads to

$$\delta\mathscr{L} = \left[2\frac{\partial\mathscr{L}}{\partial g^{\kappa\mu}}g^{\kappa\nu} + 2\frac{\partial\mathscr{L}}{\partial g^{\kappa\mu}{}_{,\alpha}}g^{\kappa\nu}{}_{,\alpha} - \frac{\partial\mathscr{L}}{\partial g^{\kappa\beta}{}_{,\nu}}g^{\kappa\beta}{}_{,\mu}\right](\delta x^{\mu}){}_{,\nu}$$
$$+ 2\frac{\partial\mathscr{L}}{\partial g^{\kappa\mu}{}_{,\alpha}}g^{\kappa\nu}(\delta x^{\mu}){}_{,\nu,\alpha} \quad (6.22)$$

We may write

$$\frac{\partial\mathscr{L}}{\partial g^{\kappa\mu}} = \frac{\partial}{\partial g^{\kappa\mu}}[(\mathscr{L}\sqrt{-g})(-g)^{-\frac{1}{2}}] = \frac{1}{\sqrt{-g}}\frac{\partial(\mathscr{L}\sqrt{-g})}{\partial g^{\kappa\mu}} + \tfrac{1}{2}g_{\kappa\mu}\mathscr{L} \quad (6.23)$$

Here we again made use of $dg = -gg_{\mu\nu}dg^{\mu\nu}$. We note that $\sqrt{-g}$ does not contain $g^{\kappa\mu}{}_{,\beta}$. Employing (6.23) in (6.22) gives

$$(\delta\mathscr{L})\sqrt{-g} = \left[2\frac{\partial(\mathscr{L}\sqrt{-g})}{\partial g^{\kappa\mu}}g^{\kappa\nu} + \mathscr{L}\sqrt{-g}\,\delta_{\mu}{}^{\nu} + 2\frac{\partial(\mathscr{L}\sqrt{-g})}{\partial g^{\kappa\mu}{}_{,\beta}}g^{\kappa\nu}{}_{,\beta}\right.$$
$$\left. - \frac{\partial(\mathscr{L}\sqrt{-g})}{\partial g^{\kappa\beta}{}_{,\nu}}g^{\kappa\beta}{}_{,\mu}\right](\delta x^{\mu}){}_{,\nu} + 2\frac{\partial(\mathscr{L}\sqrt{-g})}{\partial g^{\kappa\mu}{}_{,\alpha}}g^{\kappa\nu}(\delta x^{\mu}){}_{,\nu,\alpha} \quad (6.24)$$

$\mathscr{L}$ is invariant under linear coordinate transformations; for these, the last term on the right of (6.24) is zero, and $\delta\mathscr{L}$ must vanish. The remaining terms vanish, giving

$$2\frac{\partial(\mathscr{L}\sqrt{-g})}{\partial g^{\kappa\mu}}g^{\kappa\nu} + \mathscr{L}\sqrt{-g}\,\delta_{\mu}{}^{\nu} + 2\frac{\partial(\mathscr{L}\sqrt{-g})}{\partial g^{\kappa\mu}{}_{,\beta}}g^{\kappa\nu}{}_{,\beta}$$
$$- \frac{\partial(\mathscr{L}\sqrt{-g})}{\partial g^{\kappa\beta}{}_{,\nu}}g^{\kappa\beta}{}_{,\mu} = 0 \quad (6.25)$$

(6.25) does not contain δx^{μ}; it is an identity. It then follows that for a general coordinate transformation, (6.24) leads to

$$(\delta\mathscr{L})\sqrt{-g} = 2\frac{\partial(\sqrt{-g}\mathscr{L})}{\partial g^{\kappa\mu}{}_{,\alpha}}g^{\kappa\nu}(\delta x^\mu){}_{,\nu,\alpha} \qquad (6.26)$$

For any coordinate transformation which changes nothing on the boundary of the region of integration, the surface terms are zero and we write

$$\delta\int\left[\left(\frac{c^3}{16\pi G}\right)R + L_F\right]\sqrt{-g}\,d^4x = \delta\int\mathscr{L}\sqrt{-g}\,d^4x \qquad (6.27)$$

The left side of (6.27) vanishes because the integral is a scalar, so for the right side

$$\delta\int\mathscr{L}\sqrt{-g}\,d^4x = \int\delta\mathscr{L}\sqrt{-g}\,d^4x + \int\mathscr{L}\delta(\sqrt{-g}\,d^4x) = 0 \qquad (6.28)$$

The second integral on the right of (6.28) is zero because $\sqrt{-g}\,d^4x$ is a scalar. The vanishing of the first integral on the right together with (6.26) leads to

$$\int\frac{\partial\mathscr{L}\sqrt{-g}}{\partial g^{\kappa\mu}{}_{,\alpha}}g^{\kappa\nu}(\delta x^\mu){}_{,\nu,\alpha}\,d^4x = 0 \qquad (6.29)$$

We may write (6.29) in the form

$$\int\left(\left[(\delta x^\mu){}_{,\alpha}\frac{\partial\mathscr{L}\sqrt{-g}}{\partial g^{\kappa\mu}{}_{,\alpha}}g^{\kappa\nu}\right]_{,\nu} - (\delta x^\mu){}_{,\alpha}\left[\frac{\partial\mathscr{L}\sqrt{-g}}{\partial g^{\kappa\mu}{}_{,\alpha}}g^{\kappa\nu}\right]_{,\nu}\right)d^4x = 0 \qquad (6.30)$$

The first term in (6.30) can be converted into a surface integral which again vanishes for δx^μ with derivatives which approach zero sufficiently fast on the boundary. The remaining integral in (6.30) may again be transformed into a part containing a surface integral which vanishes and a remaining integral which for arbitrary δx^μ gives

$$\left[\frac{\partial\mathscr{L}\sqrt{-g}}{\partial g^{\kappa\mu}{}_{,\alpha}}g^{\kappa\nu}\right]_{,\nu,\alpha} = 0 \qquad (6.31)$$

(6.31) gives us the conserved quantity

$$\tau_\mu{}^\nu\sqrt{-g} = (T_\mu{}^\nu + t_\mu{}^\nu)\sqrt{-g} = -2\left(\frac{\partial\mathscr{L}\sqrt{-g}}{\partial g^{\kappa\mu}{}_{,\alpha}}g^{\kappa\nu}\right)_{,\alpha} \qquad (6.32)$$

written as an ordinary divergence. (6.32) is very useful for calculations.

We may now again obtain the forms (6.15) and (6.16) by multiplying the field equations (6.13) by $g^{\kappa\nu}$ and writing the first term as the difference of two terms to obtain

$$\left[g^{\kappa\nu} \frac{\partial \mathscr{L} \sqrt{-g}}{\partial g^{\kappa\mu}{}_{,\alpha}} \right]_{,\alpha} - \frac{\partial \mathscr{L} \sqrt{-g}}{\partial g^{\kappa\mu}{}_{,\alpha}} g^{\kappa\nu}{}_{,\alpha} - g^{\kappa\nu} \frac{\partial \mathscr{L} \sqrt{-g}}{\partial g^{\kappa\mu}} = 0 \quad (6.33)$$

Employing (6.25), differentiating with respect to x^ν, and making use of (6.31) leads directly to the expressions (6.15), and (6.16) for $t_\mu{}^\nu$.

For convenience in carrying out calculations we give expressions for

$$\frac{\partial \mathscr{L}_G \sqrt{-g}}{\partial g^{\alpha\beta}{}_{,\gamma}} \quad \text{and} \quad \frac{\partial \mathscr{L}_G \sqrt{-g}}{\partial g^{\mu\nu}}$$

First we evaluate

$$\frac{\partial (g^{\mu\nu} \Gamma^\alpha{}_{\mu\nu} \Gamma^\beta{}_{\alpha\beta})}{\partial g^{\rho\sigma}{}_{,\gamma}} = g^{\mu\nu} \Gamma^\alpha{}_{\mu\nu} \frac{\partial \Gamma^\beta{}_{\alpha\beta}}{\partial g^{\rho\sigma}{}_{,\gamma}} + \Gamma^\beta{}_{\alpha\beta} \frac{\partial (g^{\mu\nu} \Gamma^\alpha{}_{\mu\nu})}{\partial g^{\rho\sigma}{}_{,\gamma}} \quad (6.34)$$

The use of (3.73) and (3.74) gives

$$\frac{\partial \Gamma^\beta{}_{\alpha\beta}}{\partial g^{\rho\sigma}{}_{,\gamma}} = -\tfrac{1}{2} g_{\rho\sigma} \delta_\alpha{}^\gamma \quad (6.35)$$

Noting that $g^{\alpha\beta}{}_{;\mu} = 0 = g^{\alpha\beta}{}_{,\mu} + \Gamma^\alpha{}_{\mu\nu} g^{\beta\nu} + \Gamma^\beta{}_{\mu\nu} g^{\alpha\nu}$, setting $\beta = \mu$, and employing (3.74) leads to

$$\frac{\partial (g^{\mu\nu} \Gamma^\alpha{}_{\mu\nu})}{\partial g^{\rho\sigma}{}_{,\gamma}} = -\tfrac{1}{2} (\delta_\rho{}^\alpha \delta_\sigma{}^\gamma + \delta_\sigma{}^\alpha \delta_\rho{}^\gamma) + \tfrac{1}{2} g^{\alpha\gamma} g_{\rho\sigma} \quad (6.36)$$

With the use of these relations it follows that

$$\frac{\partial (g^{\mu\nu} \Gamma^\alpha{}_{\mu\nu} \Gamma^\beta{}_{\alpha\beta})}{\partial g^{\rho\sigma}{}_{,\gamma}} = -\tfrac{1}{2} g^{\mu\nu} \Gamma^\gamma{}_{\mu\nu} g_{\rho\sigma}$$
$$+ \Gamma^\nu{}_{\mu\nu} [-\tfrac{1}{2} (\delta_\rho{}^\mu \delta_\sigma{}^\gamma + \delta_\sigma{}^\mu \delta_\rho{}^\gamma) + \tfrac{1}{2} g^{\mu\gamma} g_{\rho\sigma}] \quad (6.37)$$

Also, the method used to obtain (6.36) gives

$$\frac{\partial(g^{\mu\nu}\Gamma^\beta_{\ \mu\alpha}\Gamma^\alpha_{\ \nu\beta}\sqrt{-g})}{\partial g^{\rho\sigma},_\gamma} = -\Gamma^\gamma_{\ \rho\sigma}\sqrt{-g} \qquad (6.38)$$

From (6.10), (6.37), and (6.38) it follows that

$$\frac{\partial(\mathscr{L}_G\sqrt{-g})}{\partial g^{\rho\sigma},_\gamma} = \{-\Gamma^\gamma_{\ \rho\sigma} + \tfrac{1}{2}(g^{\mu\nu}\Gamma^\gamma_{\ \mu\nu} - g^{\alpha\gamma}\Gamma^\beta_{\ \alpha\beta})g_{\rho\sigma}$$
$$+ \tfrac{1}{2}(\delta_\rho^{\ \gamma}\Gamma^\alpha_{\ \sigma\alpha} + \delta_\sigma^{\ \gamma}\Gamma^\alpha_{\ \rho\alpha})\}\left(\frac{c^4}{16\pi G}\sqrt{-g}\right) \qquad (6.39)$$

The use of the field equation (6.14) allows us to write

$$\frac{\partial\mathscr{L}_G\sqrt{-g}}{\partial g^{\rho\sigma}} = (R_{\rho\sigma} - \tfrac{1}{2}g_{\rho\sigma}R)\left(\frac{c^4}{16\pi G}\sqrt{-g}\right) + \left[\frac{\partial\mathscr{L}_G\sqrt{-g}}{\partial g^{\rho\sigma},_\gamma}\right]_{,\gamma}$$
$$(6.40)$$

Evaluation of (6.40) is facilitated[‡] by the fact that the result cannot contain derivatives such as $\Gamma^\alpha_{\ \mu\nu,\beta}$ since $\mathscr{L}\sqrt{-g}$ does not contain such derivatives, so these terms will cancel each other on the right of (6.40). We obtain

$$\left(\frac{16\pi G}{c^4}\right)\frac{\partial\mathscr{L}_G\sqrt{-g}}{\partial g^{\rho\sigma}} = \{-\Gamma^\alpha_{\ \rho\beta}\Gamma^\beta_{\ \sigma\alpha}$$
$$+ \tfrac{1}{2}(g^{\mu\nu}\Gamma^\alpha_{\ \mu\nu} - g^{\mu\alpha}\Gamma^\beta_{\ \mu\beta})(g_{\sigma\iota}\Gamma^\iota_{\ \rho\alpha} + g_{\rho\iota}\Gamma^\iota_{\ \sigma\alpha}) \qquad (6.41)$$
$$- \frac{8\pi G}{c^4}g_{\rho\sigma}\mathscr{L}_G + \Gamma^\mu_{\ \rho\mu}\Gamma^\nu_{\ \sigma\nu}\}\sqrt{-g}$$

We return to a consideration of the properties of the canonical stress energy pseudotensor $\tau_\mu^{\ \nu}$ of (6.15). Following (6.1) we write

$$\frac{\partial}{\partial x^0}\int\tau_\mu^{\ 0}\sqrt{-g}\,d^3x = -\int\tau_\mu^{\ i}\sqrt{-g}\,dS_i \qquad (6.42)$$

For an isolated system, for which the $g_{\mu\nu}$ approach the Lorentz metric sufficiently fast, and for which $T_\mu^{\ \nu}$ is localized, the surface integral on the right of (6.42) vanishes and

---

[‡] This follows Møller; it is more simple than direct calculation. The variables are $g^{\mu\nu}$ and $g^{\mu\nu},_\alpha$. $g_{\mu\nu}$ may be expressed in terms of $g^{\alpha\beta}$, but $g_{\mu\nu,\alpha}$ can only be expressed in terms of $g^{\iota\kappa}$ and $g^{\iota\kappa},_\nu$.

the integrals

$$P_\mu = \frac{1}{c} \int \tau_\mu{}^0 \sqrt{-g}\, d^3x \tag{6.43}$$

are independent of time. (τ is regular everywhere.) It follows from (6.32) that systems in which

$$g^{\kappa\nu} \frac{\partial(\mathscr{L}\sqrt{-g})}{\partial g^{\kappa\mu}{}_{,\,\alpha}}$$

has the same value over a closed surface will have the same P_μ. Under Lorentz transformations $\tau_\mu{}^0$ transforms as a four-tensor. P_μ will transform like the energy-momentum four vector of special relativity (13).

We now calculate $-P_0$ for a Schwarzschild particle and show that it is Mc. To do this we first carry out the coordinate transformation

$$r = r'\left(1 + \frac{GM}{2c^2r'}\right)^2; \quad r' = \frac{1}{2}\left[\left(r^2 - \frac{2GMr}{c^2}\right)^{\frac{1}{2}} + r - \frac{GM}{c^2}\right] \tag{6.44}$$

The coordinates r', θ, φ, and t are called isotropic coordinates. The Schwarzschild metric (5.13) becomes

$$-ds^2 = \left(1 + \frac{GM}{2c^2r'}\right)^4 (dr'^2 + r'^2 d\theta^2 + r'^2 \sin^2\theta\, d\varphi^2)$$
$$- \frac{\left(1 - \dfrac{GM}{2c^2r'}\right)^2}{\left(1 + \dfrac{GM}{2c^2r'}\right)^2} c^2 dt^2 \tag{6.45}$$

If we now introduce

$$x^2 + y^2 + z^2 = r'^2$$
$$x = r'\cos\varphi\sin\theta$$
$$y = r'\sin\varphi\sin\theta$$
$$z = r'\cos\theta$$

and assume that r' is very great, (6.45) may be written

$$-ds^2 \to \left(1 + \frac{2GM}{c^2r'}\right)(dx^2 + dy^2 + dz^2) - \left(1 - \frac{2GM}{c^2r'}\right)c^2 dt^2 \tag{6.46}$$

We note that all quantities are regular everywhere since a Schwarzschild interior solution is valid inside the body producing the field.

The use of (6.46), (6.39), (6.43), and (6.32) then leads to

$$-P_0 = Mc = \frac{E_0}{c}, \qquad (P_1 = P_2 = P_3 = 0)$$

$$E_0 = Mc^2$$

(6.47)

On the other hand, if we had used the Schwarzschild metric (5.13) directly we would have obtained

$$E_0 = -\infty$$

(6.48)

Also if a flat-space metric

$$-ds^2 = dr^2 + r^2(d\theta^2 + \sin^2\theta \, d\varphi^2) - c^2 dt^2$$

(6.49)

is employed an infinite result is again obtained for the energy. These results are not surprising because $\tau_\mu{}^\nu$ is not a tensor.

The conservation laws (6.15) and (6.16) are seen to give energy-momentum four vectors under quite restricted conditions. The Lorentz metric must be approached sufficiently rapidly at spatial infinity and the special metric (6.46) has to be used. No consistent interpretation of $t_0{}^0$ as an energy density is possible since only the volume integral is meaningful. Coordinate transformations affecting the interior of a region will change the values of $t_0{}^0$ within it, but not the volume integral as calculated in a coordinate system for which (6.46) is appropriate. The energy is simply the coefficient of $2G/r'c^4$ in (6.46), so all systems which have the same constants appearing in (6.46) will have the same energy regardless of the interior description.

6.2   Other Conservation Laws

A conservation law such as (6.17) states that something is conserved; in a given system of coordinates the conserved quantity may not be related to the energy density in a simple way. The expression (6.16) is only one of a class of pseudo-tensor densities which satisfy conservation laws. Addition of any quantity with a vanishing ordinary divergence to $t_\mu{}^\nu \sqrt{-g}$ will not affect (6.17). This arbitrariness in the specification of $t_\mu{}^\nu$ has been employed by Landau and Lifshitz (6) to obtain a conserved symmetric pseudotensor $K^{\mu\nu}$, and by Møller (8) to obtain a quantity whose zero-zero component transforms like a scalar under coordinate transformations not involving the time. In order to obtain these results it is convenient to introduce (7) a quantity $U_\mu{}^{\nu\sigma}$, which is antisymmetric in σ and ν. The circumflex symbol is often used to indicate this property. The canonical stress energy pseudotensor may be written in terms of $U_\mu{}^{\nu\sigma}$ as (6.50).

$$\tau_\mu{}^\nu \sqrt{-g} = U_\mu{}^{\nu\sigma}{}_{,\sigma} \qquad (6.50)$$

satisfies the conservation law $(\tau_\mu{}^\nu \sqrt{-g})_{,\nu} = 0$ in consequence of the antisymmetry of $U_\mu{}^{\nu\sigma}$. We may search for an expression[‡] for $U_\mu{}^{\nu\sigma}$ by studying (6.32) and noting that it must differ from

$$- 2 \frac{\partial(\mathscr{L}\sqrt{-g})}{\partial g^{\alpha\mu}{}_{,\sigma}} g^{\alpha\nu}$$

by some quantity whose ordinary divergence vanishes. If the quantity is written $a_\mu{}^{\nu\sigma\beta}{}_{,\beta}$ the vanishing of its divergence is guaranteed. We therefore write

$$- 2 \frac{\partial(\mathscr{L}\sqrt{-g})}{\partial g^{\alpha\mu}{}_{,\sigma}} g^{\alpha\nu} = U_\mu{}^{\nu\sigma} + a_\mu{}^{\nu\sigma\beta}{}_{,\beta} \qquad (6.51)$$

(6.39) enables us to evaluate

$$\frac{\partial(\mathscr{L}\sqrt{-g})}{\partial g^{\alpha\mu}{}_{,\sigma}} g^{\alpha\nu} = \{ -\Gamma^\sigma{}_{\mu\alpha} g^{\nu\alpha} + \tfrac{1}{2}(\delta_\mu{}^\sigma \Gamma^\beta{}_{\alpha\beta} + \delta_\alpha{}^\sigma \Gamma^\beta{}_{\mu\beta}) g^{\nu\alpha}$$

$$+ \frac{g_{\mu\alpha}}{2} (g^{\rho\gamma} \Gamma^\sigma{}_{\rho\gamma} - g^{\sigma\beta} \Gamma^\kappa{}_{\beta\kappa}) g^{\alpha\nu}\} \frac{c^4}{16\pi G} \sqrt{-g} \quad (6.52)$$

---

‡ The $U_\mu{}^{\nu\sigma}$ are sometimes called the superpotentials.

Remembering that

$$\Gamma^{\alpha}_{\beta\alpha} = g_{,\beta}/2g, \quad d(g_{\nu\kappa}g^{\nu\mu}) = 0 \quad \text{and} \quad g_{\nu\kappa,\alpha}g^{\nu\mu} = -g_{\nu\kappa}g^{\nu\mu}{}_{,\alpha}$$

rearranging terms then allows us to write (6.52) in the form

$$\frac{\partial(\mathscr{L}\sqrt{-g})}{\partial g^{\alpha\mu}{}_{,\sigma}} g^{\alpha\nu} = \left[\frac{1}{2\sqrt{-g}} g_{\mu\alpha}[g(g^{\nu\alpha}g^{\sigma\beta} - g^{\sigma\alpha}g^{\nu\beta})]_{,\beta}\right. \tag{6.53}$$
$$\left. - \tfrac{1}{2}(\sqrt{-g}\delta_{\mu}{}^{\sigma}g^{\beta\nu} - \sqrt{-g}\,\delta_{\mu}{}^{\beta}g^{\nu\sigma})_{,\beta}\right]\frac{c^4}{16\pi G}$$

Comparing (6.53) and (6.51) we see that

$$U_{\mu}^{\nu\sigma} = \frac{c^4}{16\pi G\sqrt{-g}} g_{\mu\alpha}[(-g)(g^{\nu\alpha}g^{\sigma\beta} - g^{\sigma\alpha}g^{\nu\beta})]_{,\beta} \tag{6.54}$$

$$a_{\mu}^{\nu\sigma\beta}{}_{,\beta} = \frac{c^4}{16\pi G}(\sqrt{-g}[\delta_{\mu}{}^{\sigma}g^{\nu\beta} - \delta_{\mu}{}^{\beta}g^{\sigma\nu}])_{,\beta} \tag{6.55}$$

These quantities transform like tensor densities under linear (affine) transformations, and are called affine tensor densities.

For formulation of angular-momentum conservation laws it is convenient (but not necessary) (4) to have a quantity corresponding to $\tau_{\alpha\beta}$, which is symmetric in the indices α and β. Such a quantity can be obtained from the $U_{\mu}^{\nu\sigma}$ in the following way. Consider $U^{\mu\nu\kappa}{}_{,\kappa}$:

$$U^{\mu\nu\kappa}{}_{,\kappa} = (g^{\mu\beta}U_{\beta}^{\nu\kappa})_{,\kappa} = \left[[-g(g^{\mu\nu}g^{\kappa\rho} - g^{\kappa\mu}g^{\nu\rho})]_{,\rho}[(-g)^{-\frac{1}{2}}]_{,\kappa}\right.$$
$$\left. + (-g)^{-\frac{1}{2}}[-g(g^{\nu\mu}g^{\kappa\rho} - g^{\kappa\mu}g^{\nu\rho})]_{,\rho,\kappa}\right]\frac{c^4}{16\pi G} \tag{6.56}$$

The last term in (6.56) is symmetric in μ and ν, but the first is not. If the factor $(-g)^{-\frac{1}{2}}$ in front of (6.54) is removed, the modified quantity

$$h^{\mu\nu\sigma} = [-g(g^{\nu\mu}g^{\sigma\rho} - g^{\sigma\mu}g^{\nu\rho})]_{,\rho}\left(\frac{c^4}{16\pi G}\right) \tag{6.57}$$

will have a divergence symmetric in ν and μ. We use $l^{\mu\nu}$ to indicate the Landau-Lifshitz gravitational pseudotensor and $K^{\mu\nu}$ for their combined pseudotensor density. Landau and

Lifshitz employ (6.57) to write

$$K^{\mu\nu} = (T^{\mu\nu} + t^{\mu\nu})(-g) = h^{\mu\nu\rho}_{,\rho} \qquad (6.58)$$

$K^{\mu\nu}$ then satisfies a conservation law in consequence of the antisymmetry of $h^{\mu\nu\rho}$ in ν and ρ. Integration yields a quantity $\mathscr{P}^\mu$ given by

$$\mathscr{P}^\mu = \frac{1}{c} \int (-g)\,[T^{\mu 0} + t^{\mu 0}]\,dx^1 dx^2 dx^3 \qquad (6.59)$$

Under linear transformations $\mathscr{P}^\mu$ transforms as a four-vector density rather than as a four vector. Making use of the field equations and the definition of $h^{\mu\nu\rho}$, Landau and Lifshitz give the following formula for $t^{\mu\nu}$:

$$
\begin{aligned}
t^{\mu\nu} = \frac{c^4}{16\pi G} \Big\{ &(2\Gamma^\alpha_{\beta\gamma}\Gamma^\rho_{\alpha\rho} - \Gamma^\alpha_{\beta\rho}\Gamma^\rho_{\gamma\alpha} - \Gamma^\alpha_{\beta\alpha}\Gamma^\rho_{\gamma\rho})(g^{\mu\beta}g^{\nu\gamma} - g^{\mu\nu}g^{\beta\gamma}) \\
&+ g^{\mu\beta}g^{\gamma\alpha}(\Gamma^\nu_{\beta\rho}\Gamma^\rho_{\gamma\alpha} + \Gamma^\nu_{\gamma\alpha}\Gamma^\rho_{\beta\rho} - \Gamma^\nu_{\alpha\rho}\Gamma^\rho_{\beta\gamma} - \Gamma^\nu_{\beta\gamma}\Gamma^\rho_{\alpha\rho}) \\
&+ g^{\nu\beta}g^{\gamma\alpha}(\Gamma^\mu_{\beta\rho}\Gamma^\rho_{\gamma\alpha} + \Gamma^\mu_{\gamma\alpha}\Gamma^\rho_{\beta\rho} - \Gamma^\mu_{\alpha\rho}\Gamma^\rho_{\beta\gamma} - \Gamma^\mu_{\beta\gamma}\Gamma^\rho_{\alpha\rho}) \\
&+ g^{\beta\gamma}g^{\alpha\rho}(\Gamma^\mu_{\beta\alpha}\Gamma^\nu_{\gamma\rho} - \Gamma^\mu_{\beta\gamma}\Gamma^\nu_{\alpha\rho}) \Big\}
\end{aligned}
\qquad (6.60)
$$

Again $K^{\mu\nu}$ has the undesirable properties that to obtain the required result a special coordinate system is required in which the isotropic metric is approached at large distances. Again no consistent interpretation of K^{00} as localized energy density is possible.

To remedy these defects, Møller noted that we may add another third-rank affine tensor density $V_\mu{}^{\nu\sigma}$ to the right side of (6.51) without affecting the validity of the conservation laws, as long as $V_\mu{}^{\nu\sigma}$ is antisymmetric in ν and σ. Møller suggested that we define a function $\chi_\mu{}^{\nu\sigma}$ by

$$\chi_\mu{}^{\nu\sigma} = U_\mu{}^{\nu\sigma} + V_\mu{}^{\nu\sigma} \qquad (6.61)$$

Then a stress energy pseudotensor $\Lambda_\mu{}^\nu$ is given by

$$\Lambda_\mu{}^\nu \sqrt{-g} = [(T_\mu{}^\nu + t_\mu{}^\nu)\sqrt{-g}] = \chi_\mu{}^{\nu\sigma}{}_{,\sigma} \qquad (6.62)$$

Here $t_\mu{}^\nu$ is the gravitational pseudotensor corresponding to $\Lambda_\mu{}^\nu$. The additional affine tensor density $V_\mu{}^{\nu\sigma}$ is now sought which will give $\Lambda_\mu{}^\nu$ the following properties. For physical systems for which it is possible to use the "Lorentz" metric (6.46) at large distances

$$\int \Lambda_\mu{}^0 \sqrt{-g}\, d^3x = \int \tau_\mu{}^0 \sqrt{-g}\, d^3x \qquad (6.63)$$

$\Lambda_0{}^\sigma$ should behave like a four vector under all coordinate transformations which do not involve the time coordinate. This results in $\Lambda_0{}^0$ being a scalar and $\Lambda_0{}^i$ being a three vector under arbitrary spatial transformations. In order to find a $V_\mu{}^{\nu\sigma}$ satisfying these requirements Møller investigated the transformation properties of $\tau_0{}^0\sqrt{-g}$ under arbitrary infinitesimal transformations which do not involve the time coordinate. This indicates in what way $\tau_0{}^0\sqrt{-g}$ fails to satisfy the requirements of a scalar density under spatial coordinate transformations. Combinations of $g_{\mu\nu}$ and their first derivatives, which for (6.46) lead to $V_0{}^{0\sigma}$, which fall off faster than

$$\frac{1}{r^2}, \qquad \text{for } r \to \infty$$

must be considered. In this manner Møller was led to propose the function

$$V_\mu{}^{\nu\sigma} = U_\mu{}^{\nu\sigma} - \delta_\mu{}^\nu U_\alpha{}^{\alpha\sigma} + \delta_\mu{}^\sigma U_\alpha{}^{\alpha\nu} \qquad (6.64)$$

Using (6.54), expressions for the functions $V_\nu{}^{\sigma\mu}$ and $\chi_\mu{}^{\nu\sigma}$ may be calculated.

$$\chi_\mu{}^{\nu\sigma} = \frac{\sqrt{-g}\, c^4}{8\pi G} (g_{\mu\beta,\alpha} - g_{\mu\alpha,\beta}) g^{\nu\alpha} g^{\sigma\beta} \qquad (6.65)$$

In order to calculate $\Lambda_0{}^\nu$ we will need

$$\chi_0{}^{\nu\sigma} = \frac{\sqrt{-g}\, c^4}{8\pi G} (g_{0\beta,\alpha} - g_{0\alpha,\beta}) g^{\nu\alpha} g^{\sigma\beta} \qquad (6.66)$$

We study now the behavior of (6.66) and $\Lambda_0{}^\nu$ under the group of coordinate transformations which do not involve anywhere the time coordinate, but are otherwise arbitrary. $g_{0\alpha}$ transforms like a four vector; recalling that for any vector B_μ, $B_{\mu; \nu} - B_{\nu; \mu} = B_{\mu, \nu} - B_{\nu, \mu}$ then tells us that the bracket in (6.66) transforms like a tensor. It follows then from (3.78) that $\chi_0{}^{0\mu}{}_{, \mu} = \Lambda_0{}^0 \sqrt{-g}$ transforms like a scalar density. $\chi_0{}^{\iota\mu}$ transforms like an antisymmetric tensor density, so it follows that $\Lambda_0{}^i$ transforms like a three vector. Thus we see that Møller's tensor, (6.62) and (6.65), does have the transformation properties which were sought.

Now we shall consider briefly the association of conserved quantities with infinitesimal coordinate transformations, following Peter G. Bergmann (9). Consider an infinitesimal coordinate transformation

$$x'^\mu = x^\mu + \delta x^\mu \tag{6.67}$$

The quantity M^ρ defined by

$$M^\rho = (\delta x^\alpha U_\alpha{}^{\rho\eta})_{,\eta} \tag{6.68}$$

satisfies $M^\rho{}_{,\rho} = 0$. Since δx^α is arbitrary, it is clear that (6.68) represents an infinite number of such laws. If we choose δx^α to be a set of constants, the Einstein formulation is obtained. If we choose $\delta x^\alpha = g^{\alpha\beta} k_\beta \sqrt{-g}$, where k_β is a set of constants, the Landau-Lifshitz expressions result. Angular-momentum conservation laws may be obtained by selecting

$$\delta x^\alpha = (g^{\alpha\beta} x^\gamma - g^{\alpha\gamma} x^\beta) J_{\beta\gamma} \sqrt{-g} \tag{6.69}$$

with $J_{\beta\gamma}$ again a set of constants. It is evident that any vector field may be employed in (6.68).

Komar (10) has shown how to construct a set of conservation laws in tensor form. Starting with Møller's result he writes

$$D^\rho \sqrt{-g} = (\delta x^\alpha U_\alpha{}^{\rho\beta} + \delta x^\alpha V_\alpha{}^{\rho\beta})_{,\beta}$$

$$= \left[\frac{c^4}{8\pi G} \delta x^\beta g^{\rho\alpha} g^{\delta\iota} (g_{\beta\iota, \alpha} - g_{\beta\alpha, \iota}) \sqrt{-g} \right]_{,\delta} \tag{6.70}$$

Addition of the curl field

$$W^\rho \sqrt{-g} = \left\{ \frac{c^4}{8\pi G} g^{\rho\iota} g^{\alpha\beta} [(\delta x^\eta)_{,\iota} g_{\eta\beta} - (\delta x^\eta)_{,\beta} g_{\eta\iota}] \sqrt{-g} \right\}_{,\alpha} \tag{6.71}$$

to (6.70) then gives

$$Q^\iota = \frac{c^4}{8\pi G} (\delta x^{\iota;\beta} - \delta x^{\beta;\iota})_{;\beta} \qquad (6.72)$$

(6.72) is conserved from (3.75), and it is in tensor form. A study of (6.70) and (6.71) shows that for $\delta x^\iota = \delta_0^\iota$, (6.72) gives the result of Møller.

6.3 Further Remarks on the Conservation Laws

It is clear from the foregoing that in situations where the matter-energy is sufficiently localized that a "Lorentz" metric (6.46) may be employed at large distances, the total energy is well defined and calculable using several of the expressions given here. The pseudotensor proposed by Møller does not require the metric (6.46), and the zero-zero component is the same in all coordinate systems which have the same time coordinates. The Landau-Lifshitz result is a symmetric quantity.

Many other stress energy pseudotensors may be constructed, and Dirac has noted the greater possible utility of particular ones in solving the equations of motion. Other expressions suggested by radiation problems are given later in this tract. In the chapter on radiation we shall note some other difficulties which lead to the conclusion that the problem of energy in general relativity has not been solved in a completely satisfactory way.

Peter G. Bergmann makes a distinction between conservation laws which are identities and those which are valid if the field equations are satisfied. The identities such as the Bianchi identities, or $U_\nu{}^{\sigma\mu}{}_{,\sigma\mu} = 0$ are called "strong" laws. Relations which are valid only if the field equations are satisfied are called "weak" laws.

It is interesting that a fourth-rank tensor, a completely symmetric quantity, has been discovered by Bel (11). To construct this we need first the concept of a dual tensor. If a given tensor is $A^{\mu\nu}$ its dual may be constructed by writing

$$*A_{\mu\nu} = \varepsilon_{\alpha\beta\mu\nu}A^{\alpha\beta} \sqrt{-g}/2 \qquad (6.73)$$

here $\varepsilon_{\alpha\beta\mu\nu}$ is again the Levi Civita tensor density. The dual of the Riemann tensor is

$$*R_{\alpha\beta\gamma\delta} = \varepsilon_{\alpha\beta\mu\nu} R^{\mu\nu}{}_{\gamma\delta} \sqrt{-g}/2 \tag{6.74}$$

Bel's tensor is

$$T_{\alpha\beta\gamma\delta} = R_{\alpha\mu\nu\delta} R_\beta{}^{\mu\nu}{}_\gamma + *R_{\alpha\mu\nu\delta} *R_\beta{}^{\mu\nu}{}_\gamma \tag{6.75}$$

and satisfies the relations

$$T^{\alpha\beta\gamma\delta}{}_{;\delta} = 0 \tag{6.76}$$

$$T^{\alpha\beta}{}_{\alpha\delta} = 0 \tag{6.77}$$

provided $R_{\mu\nu}$ satisfies the field equations. These properties were established by I. Robinson in as yet unpublished work.

In addition $T_{\alpha\beta\gamma\delta}$ is symmetric in all indices. The "conservation" law (6.76) does not lend itself to construction of the three-dimensional integrals used earlier. Bel's tensor is being studied in order to utilize its properties in the problems of gravitational radiation.

References

1. A. Einstein, *Berlin Ber.* **42**, 1111 (1916).
2. P. G. Bergmann, *Phys. Rev.* **75**, 680 (1949).
3. P. G. Bergmann and R. Schiller, *Phys. Rev.* **89**, 4 (1953).
4. P. G. Bergmann and R. Thomson, *Phys. Rev.* **89**, 400 (1953).
5. J. N. Goldberg, *Phys. Rev.* **111**, 315 (1958).
6. L. Landau and E. Lifshitz, *The Classical Theory of Fields*, Addison-Wesley, Reading, Mass., 1951, p. 316.
7. P. von Freud, *Ann. Math.* **40**, 417 (1939).
8. C. Møller, *Ann. phys.* **4**, 347 (1958).
9. P. G. Bergmann, *Phys. Rev.* **112**, 287 (1958).
10. A. Komar, *Phys. Rev.* **113**, 934 (1959).
11. L. Bel, *Compt. rend.* **248**, 1297 (1959).
12. J. G. Fletcher, *Rev. Mod. Phys.* **32**, 65, (1960).
13. W. Heitler, *The Quantum Theory of Radiation*, Oxford University Press, New York, 1954, 3rd ed., p. 17.

CHAPTER 7

Gravitational Waves

7.1 Weak-Field Solutions

One of the central issues in the general theory of relativity has always been the question of gravitational radiation. Gravitational waves have thus far not been observed. Until recently (18) no solutions of the exact gravitational field equations were known which represent spherical gravitational waves. For these reasons a great deal of theoretical work has appeared on this subject during the past four decades. We shall see later that some experimental work now appears feasible. Some theoretical issues have been resolved in recent years, and it has been possible for a number of physicists to conclude that general relativity really does predict the existence of gravitational waves.

In 1916 Einstein (1) studied the weak-field solutions of the field equations

$$R_{\mu\nu} - \tfrac{1}{2} g_{\mu\nu} R = \frac{8\pi G}{c^4} T_{\mu\nu} \qquad (7.1)$$

obtained by assuming

$$g_{\mu\nu} = \delta_{\mu\nu} + h_{\mu\nu} \qquad (7.2)$$

$\delta_{\mu\nu}$ is the Lorentz metric and $h_{\mu\nu}$ is a first-order quantity. $h_\mu{}^\lambda$ and h are defined by

$$h_\mu{}^\lambda = \delta^{\lambda\alpha} h_{\mu\alpha} \qquad (7.3)$$

$$h = h_\alpha{}^\alpha = \delta^{\sigma\lambda} h_{\sigma\lambda} \qquad (7.4)$$

The Ricci tensor is given in terms of the Christoffel

symbols as

$$R_{\mu\nu} = \Gamma^{\beta}{}_{\mu\nu,\beta} - \Gamma^{\beta}{}_{\mu\beta,\nu} + \Gamma^{\beta}{}_{\mu\nu}\Gamma^{\alpha}{}_{\beta\alpha} - \Gamma^{\alpha}{}_{\mu\beta}\Gamma^{\beta}{}_{\nu\alpha} \quad (7.5)$$

The use of (7.2), (7.3), and (7.4) enables us to write $R_{\mu\nu}$ to first order as

$$R_{\mu\nu} = -\tfrac{1}{2}\delta^{\sigma\lambda}h_{\mu\nu,\sigma\lambda} - \tfrac{1}{2}(h_{,\mu\nu} - h_{\mu}{}^{\beta}{}_{,\nu\beta} - h^{\beta}{}_{\nu,\mu\beta}) \quad (7.6)$$

The last three terms of (7.6) can be arranged in the form

$$h_{,\mu\nu} - h_{\mu}{}^{\beta}{}_{,\nu\beta} - h^{\beta}{}_{\nu,\mu\beta} = (\tfrac{1}{2}\delta_{\mu}{}^{\beta}h - h_{\mu}{}^{\beta})_{,\beta\nu} + (\tfrac{1}{2}\delta_{\nu}{}^{\beta}h - h_{\nu}{}^{\beta})_{,\beta\mu} \quad (7.7)$$

(7.7) can be made to vanish by choosing the coordinate conditions such that

$$(h_{\mu}{}^{\beta} - \tfrac{1}{2}\delta_{\mu}{}^{\beta})_{,\beta} = 0 \quad (7.8)$$

$R_{\mu\nu}$ will now consist only of the first term of (7.6), and the field equations may be written as

$$-\tfrac{1}{2}\delta^{\sigma\lambda}h_{\mu\nu,\sigma\lambda} + g_{\mu\nu}[\tfrac{1}{4}\delta^{\sigma\lambda}h_{,\sigma\lambda}] = \frac{8\pi G}{c^4}T_{\mu\nu} \quad (7.9)$$

Care must be exercised in the use of (7.9), since all components on the right will not ordinarily be of the same order. We now define

$$\varphi_{\mu}{}^{\nu} = h_{\mu}{}^{\nu} - \tfrac{1}{2}\delta_{\mu}{}^{\nu}h \quad (7.10)$$

The coordinate conditions (7.8) are written as

$$\varphi_{\mu}{}^{\nu}{}_{,\nu} = 0 \quad (7.11)$$

Raising the index ν in (7.9) and employing (7.10) gives

$$\Box\,\varphi_{\mu}{}^{\nu} = -\frac{16\pi G}{c^4}T_{\mu}{}^{\nu} \quad (7.12)$$

The solutions of (7.12) are well known from electrodynamics, as

$$\varphi_{\mu}{}^{\nu}(r,t) = \frac{4G}{c^4}\int \frac{(T_{\mu}{}^{\nu})_{\text{retarded}}\,d^3x'}{|\mathbf{r} - \mathbf{r}'|} \quad (7.13)$$

Here $|\mathbf{r} - \mathbf{r}'|$ is the distance from source point to field point. As we noted earlier, the relations (7.12) can be obtained directly from Newton's law of gravitation, in which ∇^2 is replaced by $\Box$; the conservation law $T_{\mu}{}^{\nu}{}_{,\nu} \approx 0$ then yields (7.11).

Some years ago Pauli and Fierz (3) considered the question, what relativistic wave equations would be appropriate for particles of zero rest mass and spin two. Now in a relativistic theory for spin S, $2(2S + 1)$ components are needed, so a second-rank tensor is required. They were led to propose the equations

$$\Box \psi_{\mu}{}^{\nu} = 0 \qquad (7.14)$$

with supplementary conditions

$$\psi_{\mu}{}^{\nu}{}_{,\nu} = 0 \qquad (7.15)$$

Since these equations are the same as (7.11) and (7.12) for vacuum it is expected that gravitons will have spin two. Since the only available direction is the direction of motion, it follows that the spin angular momentum must be oriented in the direction of motion. Since the gravitational forces have infinite range, it follows that the rest mass of the gravitons must be zero.[‡]

We consider now the conditions under which the expression (7.11) may be satisfied. Suppose we carry out an infinitesimal coordinate transformation

$$x'^{\alpha} = x^{\alpha} + \xi^{\alpha}(x) \qquad (7.16)$$

To a first approximation this can be written

$$x^{\alpha} = x'^{\alpha} - \xi^{\alpha}(x') \qquad (7.17)$$

The transformed metric tensor is then given by

$$g'_{\mu\nu} = g_{\mu\nu} - g_{\alpha\nu}\xi^{\alpha}{}_{,\mu} - g_{\beta\mu}\xi^{\beta}{}_{,\nu} \qquad (7.18)$$

Similarly

$$h'_{\mu\nu} = h_{\mu\nu} - \delta_{\alpha\nu}\xi^{\alpha}{}_{,\mu} - \delta_{\beta\mu}\xi^{\beta}{}_{,\nu} \qquad (7.19)$$

[‡] If the forces are transmitted by particles with rest mass m, a Yukawa potential $\varphi \sim (e^{-mcr/\hbar}/r)$ is appropriate. This has infinite range only if $m \to 0$.

$$\varphi'_{\mu}{}^{\alpha} = \delta^{\alpha\nu}[\varphi_{\mu\nu} - \delta_{\beta\nu}\xi^{\beta},_{\mu} - \delta_{\beta\mu}\xi^{\beta},_{\nu} + \delta_{\mu\nu}\xi^{\gamma},_{\gamma}] \quad (7.20)$$

$$\varphi'_{\mu}{}^{\alpha},_{\alpha} = \varphi_{\mu}{}^{\alpha},_{\alpha} - \delta^{\rho\sigma}\xi_{\mu},_{\rho\sigma} \quad (7.21)$$

If the coordinate conditions (7.11) are not satisfied, we have

$$\varphi_{\mu}{}^{\alpha},_{\alpha} \neq 0 \quad (7.22)$$

(7.21) states that an infinitesimal coordinate transformation may be carried out to make

$$\varphi'_{\mu}{}^{\alpha},_{\alpha} = 0 \quad (7.23)$$

provided

$$\Box\,\xi_{\mu} = \varphi_{\mu}{}^{\alpha},_{\alpha} \quad (7.24)$$

On the other hand, if $\varphi_{\mu}{}^{\alpha},_{\alpha} = 0$, then we may carry out arbitrary coordinate transformations which maintain this condition, provided that the ξ_{μ} functions satisfy the wave equation, according to (7.24).

We return to consideration of (7.12). In free space these equations represent waves with $\varphi_{\mu}{}^{\nu}$ given by

$$\Box\,\varphi_{\mu}{}^{\nu} = 0 \quad (7.25)$$

It is of interest to inquire how many independent components of $h_{\mu\nu}$ or $\varphi_{\mu\nu}$ are needed to describe a plane-wave solution of (7.25). We will find it convenient to discuss first the case of a locally plane disturbance of arbitrary strength, then to apply the result to the weak-field case.

7.2   Riemann Tensor for a Wave of Arbitrary Strength Which Is Locally Plane

Suppose we have a gravitational wave which has vanishing space derivatives in directions normal to the direction of propagation. Such a wave is therefore locally plane. In this case we shall show that at any given point all components of the Riemann tensor may be written in terms of the derivatives of the three components of $g_{\mu\nu}$, which describe intervals in the plane transverse to the direction of propagation. Introduce a geodesic coordinate system so that the Christoffel symbols vanish at the given space-time point and the metric has the Lorentz values there; the Riemann tensor becomes

$$R_{\alpha\beta\gamma\delta} = \tfrac{1}{2}(g_{\alpha\delta,\beta\gamma} + g_{\beta\gamma,\alpha\delta} - g_{\alpha\gamma,\beta\delta} - g_{\beta\delta,\alpha\gamma}) \quad (7.26)$$

Let the x^1 direction be the direction of propagation; then the partial derivatives of $g_{\mu\nu}$ and $g_{\mu\nu,\alpha}$ with respect to x^2 and x^3 vanish. A study of (7.26) indicates that we may write the components of $R_{\alpha\beta\gamma\delta}$ in the three groups

$$
\begin{aligned}
R_{2020} &= -\tfrac{1}{2}g_{22,00} & R_{1220} &= \tfrac{1}{2}g_{22,10} & R_{1212} &= -\tfrac{1}{2}g_{22,11} \\
R_{2030} &= -\tfrac{1}{2}g_{23,00} & R_{1230} &= \tfrac{1}{2}g_{23,10} & R_{1213} &= -\tfrac{1}{2}g_{23,11} \\
R_{3030} &= -\tfrac{1}{2}g_{33,00} & R_{1320} &= \tfrac{1}{2}g_{23,10} & R_{1313} &= -\tfrac{1}{2}g_{33,11} \\
& & R_{1330} &= \tfrac{1}{2}g_{33,10} & &
\end{aligned} \quad (7.27)
$$

$$
\begin{aligned}
R_{1223} &= 0 & R_{2323} &= 0 \\
R_{1323} &= 0 & R_{2320} &= 0 \\
R_{1023} &= 0 & R_{2330} &= 0
\end{aligned} \quad (7.28)
$$

$$
\begin{aligned}
R_{1030} &= -\tfrac{1}{2}g_{13,00} + \tfrac{1}{2}g_{30,10} & R_{1020} &= -\tfrac{1}{2}g_{12,00} + \tfrac{1}{2}g_{20,10} \\
R_{1310} &= -\tfrac{1}{2}g_{30,11} + \tfrac{1}{2}g_{13,10} & R_{1210} &= -\tfrac{1}{2}g_{20,11} + \tfrac{1}{2}g_{12,10} \\
\multicolumn{4}{c}{R_{1010} = -\tfrac{1}{2}g_{11,00} + g_{10,10} - \tfrac{1}{2}g_{00,11}}
\end{aligned} \quad (7.29)
$$

In vacuum $R_{\mu\nu} = 0$; at the given point the use of the Lorentz metric in conjunction with (7.27), (7.28), and (7.29) gives

$$
\begin{aligned}
R_{12} &= R_{1020} = 0 & R_{13} &= R_{1030} = 0 \\
R_{20} &= R_{1210} = 0 & R_{30} &= R_{1310} = 0 \\
R_{11} &= R_{1010} - R_{1313} - R_{1212} = 0 & R_{10} &= R_{1220} + R_{1330} = 0 \quad (7.30) \\
R_{22} &= R_{2020} - R_{1212} = 0 & R_{23} &= R_{2030} - R_{1213} = 0 \\
R_{33} &= R_{3030} - R_{1313} = 0 & R_{00} &= R_{3030} + R_{2020} + R_{1010} = 0
\end{aligned}
$$

The above equations for the vanishing of R_{12}, R_{20}, R_{13}, and R_{30} imply the vanishing of the first four values of $R_{\alpha\beta\gamma\delta}$ given in (7.29). The equations for the vanishing of R_{11}, R_{22}, R_{33}, and R_{00} can be combined to solve for the last expression, R_{1010}, in (7.29), which turns out to be zero. It follows therefore that the only nonvanishing components of the Riemann tensor are the ten components (7.27), and these are given entirely in terms of g_{22}, g_{23}, and g_{33}. The expressions (7.30) for R_{11}, R_{22}, R_{33}, and R_{00} also lead to

$$g_{22,00} + g_{33,00} = 0 \qquad (7.31)$$

(7.31) states that the required second derivatives of the two components g_{22}, and g_{33} are not independent. In the weak-field approximation, (7.26) is valid everywhere. At all points the Riemann tensor can therefore be written in terms of h_{22}, h_{33}, and h_{23}, subject to (7.31). It follows then that coordinate transformations may be carried out to "transform away" all components of $h_{\mu\nu}$ except the "transverse" ones, everywhere. This can be done in a relatively straightforward way, using infinitesimal coordinate transformations satisfying (7.24). In the next chapter we shall show that relative displacements of closely spaced free particles in the path of the wave occur only in directions transverse to the direction of propagation of the wave.

7.3   Approximate Evaluation of Source Volume Integrals

We return to a consideration of the weak-field solution integral expressions (7.13). These components may all be written in terms of T_{00} in a certain level of approximation. The stress energy tensor satisfies, to a first approximation, the conservation laws

$$T_{0k,k} - T_{00,0} = 0 \qquad (7.32)$$

$$T_{jk,k} - T_{j0,0} = 0 \qquad (7.33)$$

(7.33) can be multiplied by x^i and integrated (by parts) over all space, neglecting surface terms which vanish at infinity. This is written in the symmetrized form

$$\int T_{ij} \, d^3x = -\tfrac{1}{2} \left[\int (T_{i0} x^j + T_{j0} x^i) \, d^3x \right]_{,0} \qquad (7.34)$$

(7.32) can be multiplied by $x^i x^j$, integrated over all space, again neglecting surface terms which vanish at infinity; the result is

$$\left[\int T_{00} x^i x^j d^3x \right]_{,0} = - \int [T_{i0} x^j + T_{j0} x^i] \, d^3x \qquad (7.35)$$

Expressions (7.34) and (7.35) enable us to write

$$\int T_{ij} \, d^3x = \tfrac{1}{2} \left[\int T_{00} x^i x^j \, d^3x \right]_{,00} \qquad (7.36)$$

The use of (7.36) facilitates certain calculations in which the distribution of mass and energy is more readily dealt with than the distribution of stress. The relation (7.36) has neglected retardation effects and is not valid where a source large compared to a wavelength is involved.

For a source in a region which is small compared to a wavelength, (7.36) may be used to calculate all the space index components of $\varphi_\mu{}^\nu$, in the lowest nonvanishing approximation. The use of the coordinate conditions then allows determination of the remaining components. In some cases this is a simpler procedure than direct use of (7.13).

For a particle it is necessary to evaluate the integrals in the limit as the volume tends to zero, taking account of the fact that retardation effects imply that different volume elements are taken at different times. It is more direct to start with the result for a particle at rest, then to generalize it for a moving particle, as in electrodynamics. A particle of mass m which is at rest has

$$\varphi_{00}(\mathbf{r}) = \frac{4Gm}{c^2|\mathbf{r} - \mathbf{r}'|}$$

In the linear approximation we may infer that the generalization for a moving particle must be

$$\varphi_{\mu\nu}(\mathbf{r}, t) = \frac{4Gm U'_{\mu} U'_{\nu}}{c^2 U'_{\alpha}(r'^{\alpha} - r^{\alpha})} \qquad (7.13a)$$

where now U'_{μ} is the four velocity of the particle, m is the rest mass, and

$$r'^{\alpha} - r^{\alpha} = (r'^i - r^i),\ c(t' - t); \qquad t' = t - |\mathbf{r} - \mathbf{r}'|/c$$

(7.13a) may be written in the form

$$\varphi_{ij}(\mathbf{r}, t) = \frac{4Gm v'_i v'_j}{c^4 |\mathbf{r} - \mathbf{r}'| \sqrt{1 - v'^2/c^2}\left(1 - \dfrac{v_i'(r^i - r'^i)}{c\,|\mathbf{r} - \mathbf{r}'|}\right)}$$

$$\varphi_{0i}(\mathbf{r}, t) = \frac{- 4Gm v_i'}{c^3 |\mathbf{r} - \mathbf{r}'| \sqrt{1 - v'^2/c^2}\left(1 - \dfrac{v'_i(r^i - r'^i)}{c\,|\mathbf{r} - \mathbf{r}'|}\right)} \qquad (7.13b)$$

$$\varphi_{00}(\mathbf{r}, t) = \frac{4Gm}{c^2 |\mathbf{r} - \mathbf{r}'| \sqrt{1 - v'^2/c^2}\left(1 - \dfrac{v_i'(r^i - r'^i)}{c\,|\mathbf{r} - \mathbf{r}'|}\right)}$$

Here v_i' is the ordinary velocity of the particle.

7.4 Weak-Field Approximations for Energy Flux and Energy Density

The covariant divergence of the stress energy tensor vanishes, in consequence of the field equations and the Bianchi identities. This may be expressed using (3.79), in the form

$$T_{\mu}{}^{\nu}{}_{;\nu} = \frac{1}{\sqrt{-g}}\ (T_{\mu}{}^{\nu} \sqrt{-g})_{,\nu} - \tfrac{1}{2} g_{\alpha\beta,\mu} T^{\alpha\beta} = 0 \qquad (7.37)$$

The stress energy pseudotensor density $t_{\mu}{}^{\nu}\sqrt{-g}$ is related to the stress energy tensor density by

$$(T_{\mu}{}^{\nu} \sqrt{-g})_{,\nu} + (t_{\mu}{}^{\nu} \sqrt{-g})_{,\nu} = 0 \qquad (7.38)$$

$t_\mu{}^\nu$ may be calculated using the results of Chapter 6, but for weak fields it is more direct to compare (7.37) and (7.38) and write

$$(t_\mu{}^\nu \sqrt{-g})_{,\,\nu} = -\tfrac{1}{2}g_{\alpha\beta,\,\mu}T^{\alpha\beta}\sqrt{-g} \approx -\tfrac{1}{2}h_{\alpha\beta,\,\mu}T^{\alpha\beta} \quad (7.39)$$

The form of (7.39) suggests that we multiply (7.12) by $h^{\alpha\beta}{}_{,\,\mu}$ to obtain

$$h^{\alpha\beta}{}_{,\,\mu}\,\square\,\varphi_{\alpha\beta} = -\frac{16\pi G}{c^4}\,h^{\alpha\beta}{}_{,\,\mu}T_{\alpha\beta} \quad (7.40)$$

Utilizing (7.10) and (7.39) then leads to

$$h^{\alpha\beta}{}_{,\,\mu}[h_{\alpha\beta,\,\nu}{}^{,\,\nu}-\tfrac{1}{2}\delta_{\alpha\beta}h_{,\,\nu}{}^{,\,\nu}] = \frac{32\pi G}{c^4}(t_\mu{}^\nu\sqrt{-g})_{,\,\nu} \quad (7.41)$$

We may write

$$h^{\alpha\beta}{}_{,\,\mu}[h_{\alpha\beta,\,\nu}{}^{,\,\nu}-\tfrac{1}{2}\delta_{\alpha\beta}h_{,\,\nu}{}^{,\,\nu}]$$
$$= [h^{\alpha\beta}{}_{,\,\mu}h_{\alpha\beta}{}^{,\,\nu}-\tfrac{1}{2}\delta_\mu{}^\nu h_{\alpha\beta,\,\rho}h^{\alpha\beta,\,\rho}-\tfrac{1}{2}h_{,\,\mu}h^{,\,\nu}+\tfrac{1}{4}h_{,\,\rho}h^{,\,\rho}\delta_\mu{}^\nu]_{,\,\nu} \quad (7.42)$$

Comparing (7.42) and (7.41) gives

$$t_\mu{}^\nu\sqrt{-g} = \frac{c^4}{64\pi G}[2h^{\alpha\beta}{}_{,\,\mu}h_{\alpha\beta}{}^{,\,\nu}-h_{,\,\mu}h^{,\,\nu}+\delta_\mu{}^\nu(\tfrac{1}{2}h_{,\,\rho}h^{,\,\rho}-h_{\alpha\beta,\,\rho}h^{\alpha\beta,\,\rho})] \quad (7.43)$$

Contraction of (7.10) results in

$$\varphi_\alpha{}^\alpha = -h_\alpha{}^\alpha \quad (7.44)$$

Using (7.44) and 7.10 gives us the alternate form

$$t_\mu{}^\nu\sqrt{-g} = \frac{c^4}{64\pi G}[2\varphi^{\alpha\beta}{}_{,\,\mu}\varphi_{\alpha\beta}{}^{,\,\nu}-\varphi_{,\,\mu}\varphi^{,\,\nu}+\delta_\mu{}^\nu(\tfrac{1}{2}\varphi_{,\,\rho}\varphi^{,\,\rho}-\varphi_{\alpha\beta,\,\rho}\varphi^{\alpha\beta,\,\rho})] \quad (7.45)$$

7.5   Linear Mass Quadrupole Oscillator

Consider now a linear mass quadrupole oscillator at the origin of a rectangular system of coordinates. The motion of the masses is along the x^3 axis. Let I be the peak value of the

time-dependent part of the moment of inertia. We can use
(7.36) to write the solutions of (7.12) in the form

$$\varphi_{33} = \frac{2\omega^2 GI}{c^4 r} \cos \frac{\omega}{c} [x^0 - r] \qquad (7.46)$$

Oscillations in the x^3 direction can only give rise to
the components φ_{33}, φ_{30}, and φ_{00}. The coordinate conditions
$\varphi_\mu{}^\nu{}_{,\nu} = 0$ can be employed to calculate φ_{30} and φ_{00} if we know
that the coordinate conditions have been met. If the energy
density in the vicinity of the sources is not so great that the
space is appreciable curved, the Lorentz metric conservation
law $T_\mu{}^\nu{}_{,\nu} = 0$ will be valid, to a good approximation. If the
sources are in a small region so that retardation effects are
unimportant, it then follows from (7.12) that the coordinate
conditions are in fact being met. We may then write

$$\varphi_3{}^3{}_{,3} + \varphi_3{}^0{}_{,0} = 0 \qquad (7.47)$$

$$\varphi_0{}^3{}_{,3} + \varphi_0{}^0{}_{,0} = 0 \qquad (7.48)$$

Let the observer be situated along a radial line making
an angle θ with the x^3 axis. (7.46), (7.48) and (7.47) give

$$\varphi_{00} = \cos^2 \theta \; \varphi_{33}; \qquad \varphi_{03} = -\cos \theta \; \varphi_{33} \qquad (7.49)$$

We could have calculated φ_{00} and φ_{03} directly from (7.12)
or (7.13a); this would have required more careful considera-
tion of retardation effects, and the energy in parts of the
oscillator which furnish restoring forces.

The radiated power can be calculated in the following
way. We need

$$\frac{c\partial}{\partial x^0} \int T_0{}^0 \sqrt{-g} \, d^3x \qquad (7.50)$$

By use of the conservation laws, (7.50) may be written

$$-\frac{c\partial}{\partial x^0} \int \sqrt{-g} \; T_0{}^0 d^3x - c \int \sqrt{-g} \; T_0{}^i dS_i$$
$$= \frac{c\partial}{\partial x^0} \int \sqrt{-g} \; t_0{}^0 d^3x + c \int \sqrt{-g} \; t_0{}^i dS_i \qquad (7.51)$$

The second and fourth integrals are over a closed (two-dimensional) surface. The source is assumed to be in the vicinity of the origin, and if our bounding surface is far from the source, the second integral in (7.51) will vanish because $T_0{}^i$ is zero outside the source. The third integral will be periodic in time while the last integral will give the steady decrease of energy of the source. Making use of (7.46), (7.45), and (7.49) leads (15, 17) to the formula for the time-averaged radiated power P:

$$P = \frac{GI^2\omega^6}{15c^5} \qquad (7.52)$$

7.6 Radiation from a Spinning Rod

Historically the first gravitational radiation problem to be considered was the radiation from a spinning rod (1, 2). This will now be calculated. Assume the rod has a mass per unit length σ and spins in the xy plane with the angular velocity ω. At $t = 0$ the rod lies along the x axis. Then again using (7.36) and (7.13), we obtain

$$\varphi_{11} = \frac{2G}{c^2 r} \frac{\partial^2}{\partial x^{0^2}} \int_{\text{retarded}} \sigma r^2 \cos^2 \frac{\omega x^0}{c} dr = -\frac{4GI_m\omega^2}{c^4 r} \cos \frac{2\omega}{c}(x^0 - r) \quad (7.53)$$

$$\varphi_{22} = \frac{2G}{c^2 r} \frac{\partial^2}{\partial x^{0^2}} \int_{\text{retarded}} \sigma r^2 \sin^2 \frac{\omega x^0}{c} dr = \frac{4GI_m\omega^2}{c^4 r} \cos \frac{2\omega}{c}(x^0 - r) \quad (7.54)$$

$$\varphi_{12} = \frac{2G}{c^2 r} \frac{\partial^2}{\partial x^{0^2}} \int_{\text{retarded}} \sigma r^2 \sin\left(\frac{\omega x^0}{c}\right) \cos\left(\frac{\omega x^0}{c}\right) dr = -\frac{4GI_m}{c^4 r}\omega^2 \sin \frac{2\omega}{c}(x^0 - r)$$

$$\qquad (7.55)$$

In (7.53), (7.54), and (7.55) I_m is the moment of inertia of the rod. The coordinate conditions (7.11) are again employed to calculate φ_{00}, φ_{01}, and φ_{02}, and the radiated power is calculated using (7.45); the result is

$$P = \frac{32GI_m{}^2\omega^6}{5c^5} \qquad (7.56)$$

7.7   Further Remarks on the Weak-Field Solutions

It is of interest to note that (7.56) and (7.52) can be obtained if we assume only that gravitational effects are propagated with the speed of light and follow the kind of heuristic argument[‡] which has been used to calculate the radiation from an accelerated charge.

Expression (7.36) states that the lowest-order multipole radiation is quadrupole radiation. This follows also from the fact that for an isolated oscillating system the dipole moment vanishes in consequence of conservation of linear momentum. For example, suppose we have a small mass which is coupled to a large mass by a spring (Fig. 7.1) and the system is

Figure 7.1

oscillating. If x_m and x_M are the displacements of the small mass and the large mass, respectively, we have from momentum conservation

$$m\dot{x}_m + M\dot{x}_M = 0 \qquad (7.57)$$

and

$$m\ddot{x}_m + M\ddot{x}_M = 0 \qquad (7.58)$$

The left side of (7.58) would be expected to give the dipole contribution to the (accelerated mass) radiation, but it vanishes in consequence of (7.57).

Bonnor (17) has calculated the loss of mass energy of a quadrupole oscillator in the second approximation and found it equal to the radiated energy given by (7.52) in the first approximation.

[‡] See, for example, Richtmyer and Kennard, *Introduction to Modern Physics*, McGraw-Hill, New York, Fourth Edition, 1947, p. 62.

7.8   Exact Cylindrical Wave Solutions

Einstein and Rosen (4, 5) obtained some exact cylindrical wave solutions of the equations of general relativity. Their metric is

$$-ds^2 = c^{2\gamma-2\psi}(d\rho^2 - c^2 dt^2) + \rho^2 e^{-2\psi} d\varphi^2 + e^{2\psi} dz^2 \quad (7.59)$$

The functions γ and ψ are dependent upon ρ and t alone. The metric defined by (7.59) can be employed in the free-space equations

$$R_{\mu\nu} = 0 \quad (7.60)$$

to give the following (exact) equations which have to be satisfied by ψ and γ:

$$\psi_{,\rho,\rho} + \frac{1}{\rho}\psi_{,\rho} - c^{-2}\psi_{,t,t} = 0 \quad (7.61)$$

$$\gamma_{,\rho} = \rho[(\psi_{,\rho})^2 + (1/c^2)(\psi_{,t})^2] \quad (7.62)$$

$$\gamma_{,t} = 2\rho\psi_{,\rho}\psi_{,t}/c \quad (7.63)$$

(7.61) is a linear equation, the cylindrical coordinate wave equation. A solution of (7.61) representing outward traveling waves is

$$\psi = A[J_0(\omega\rho/c)\cos\omega t + N_0(\omega\rho/c)\sin\omega t] \quad (7.64)$$

Making use of (7.62) and (7.63) then gives

$$\begin{aligned}
\gamma = &(A^2\omega\rho/2c)\{J_0(\omega\rho/c)J_0'(\omega\rho/c) + N_0(\omega\rho/c)N_0'(\omega\rho/c) \\
&+ (\omega\rho/c)[(J_0(\omega\rho/c))^2 + (J_0'(\omega\rho/c))^2 + (N_0(\omega\rho/c))^2 \\
&+ (N_0'(\omega\rho/c))^2] \\
&+ [J_0(\omega\rho/c)J_0'(\omega\rho/c) - N_0(\omega\rho/c)N_0'(\omega\rho/c)]\cos 2\omega t \\
&+ [J_0(\omega\rho/c)N_0'(\omega\rho/c) + N_0(\omega\rho/c)J_0'(\omega\rho/c)]\sin 2\omega t\} \\
&- (2/\pi)A^2\omega t
\end{aligned} \quad (7.65)$$

The prime means differentiation with respect to $(\omega\rho/c)$. The last term of (7.65) increases linearly with time and at first it was thought that this represented the cumulative effect on the metric of continuous radiation of energy. Rosen argued (7) against this interpretation on the grounds that if the energy is being radiated by a cylindrical system near the origin, then the loss of energy would make it impossible for the function ψ, given by (7.64), to remain periodic in time. The occurrence of the function N_0 makes (7.65) singular on the axis. Marder remarks that it is not possible to join the free-space solution (7.65) to the solution for a region near the origin containing mass in a physically acceptable way since the sign of the density will ultimately change. He considers the difficulties associated with (7.65) as due to the fact that the field has been turned on for an infinitely long time.

A more interesting case is that of a pulse of radiation. The linearity of (7.61) enables this to be treated, employing the Fourier integral. The following discussion is a summary of a paper by Weber and Wheeler (16). For the Fourier transform of ψ we choose

$$\psi(\omega) = 2Be^{-(a\omega/c)} J_0(\omega\rho/c)/c \qquad (7.66)$$

This has the virtue that the integrations required to construct $\psi(t)$ and $\gamma(t)$ can readily be carried out.

$$\psi = 2B \int_0^\infty e^{-(a\omega/c)} J_0(\omega\rho/c) \cos \omega t \, d\omega/c$$
$$= B\left[([a - ict]^2 + \rho^2)^{-\frac{1}{2}} + ([a + ict]^2 + \rho^2)^{-\frac{1}{2}}\right] \qquad (7.67)$$

Integration of (7.62) and (7.63) then gives

$$\gamma = \tfrac{1}{2}B^2\{a^{-2} - \rho^2[(a-ict)^2 + \rho^2]^{-2} - \rho^2[(a+ict)^2 + \rho^2]^{-2}$$
$$-a^{-2}(c^2t^2 + a^2 - \rho^2)[c^4t^4 + 2c^2t^2(a^2 - \rho^2) + (a^2 + \rho^2)^2]^{-\frac{1}{2}}\} \qquad (7.68)$$

A study of (7.67) shows that for negative values of t, the "pulse" is imploding, onto the axis. It explodes back out again for positive values of t. It is a "time symmetric" solution of Einstein's field equations.

In order to calculate the "energy density" we employ the expression (6.32):

$$\sqrt{-g}\,\tau_\mu{}^\nu = \left[-2g^{\nu\lambda} \frac{\partial(\mathscr{L}_G \sqrt{-g})}{\partial g^{\mu\lambda}{}_{,\rho}}\right]_{,\rho} \qquad (7.69)$$

Direct calculation using (7.59) and (6.39) leads to

$$\frac{\partial(\mathscr{L}_G \sqrt{-g})}{\partial g^{00}{}_{,0}} = 0;$$

$$\frac{\partial \mathscr{L}_G \sqrt{-g}}{\partial g^{00}{}_{,1}} = -\tfrac{1}{2} g^{11} g_{00} \left(g^{22} \frac{\partial g_{22}}{\partial x^1} + g^{33} \frac{\partial g_{33}}{\partial x^1} \right) \left(\frac{c^4}{16\pi G} \right) \sqrt{-g}$$

$$(7.70)$$

With these (7.69) becomes, for $\tau_0{}^0 \sqrt{-g}$,

$$\tau_0{}^0 \sqrt{-g} = \frac{c^4}{8\pi G} \frac{\partial}{\partial \rho} \left(-1 + 2\rho \frac{\partial \psi}{\partial \rho} - 2\rho \frac{\partial \psi}{\partial \rho} \right) = 0 \quad (7.71)$$

This calculation, (7.71), is valid for *any* metric of the form (7.59) whether matter is present or not. The everywhere-vanishing energy density, (7.17), is confirmed by use of the Landau-Lifshitz forms (8) (6.58) and (6.60) for $\tau_\mu{}^\nu$. The use of Møller's tensor, (6.62) and (6.65), gives a somewhat similar result. Direct calculation gives for the metric (7.59)

$$\Lambda_0{}^0 \sqrt{-g} = \frac{c^4}{4\pi G} \left\{ \rho \frac{\partial \psi}{\partial \rho} - \rho^2 \left[\left(\frac{\partial \psi}{\partial \rho} \right)^2 + \left(\frac{\partial \psi}{c \partial t} \right)^2 \right] \right\}_{,\rho} \quad (7.72)$$

While this expression does not vanish identically, the integrated value for the energy per unit length,

$$\int \Lambda_0{}^0 \sqrt{-g}\, d\rho\, d\varphi = \frac{c^4}{2G} \left. \rho \frac{\partial \psi}{\partial \rho} - \rho^2 \left[\left(\frac{\partial \psi}{\partial \rho} \right)^2 + \left(\frac{\partial \psi}{c \partial t} \right)^2 \right] \right|_0^\infty \quad (7.73)$$

does vanish for (7.67) and (7.68). (7.72) is positive at some places and negative at others for the pulse-wave solution. We note that the pulse, (7.67) and (7.68), represents at $t = 0$ a space which is asymptotically flat at large ρ but which is not "Euclidean," since according to (7.68), $\gamma \to B^2 a^{-2}$ at large distances. The metric is therefore "conical" at large ρ, for $t = 0$.

Rosen has recently (20) calculated $\tau_0{}^0$ and $\tau_0{}^1$ for the cylindrical solutions in a "cartesian" coordinate system and finds them to be finite and reasonable. His result is not in conflict with that given by Møller's value for the energy density since the passage from the cylindrical to Rosen's cartesian coordinate system presumably requires a transformation involving the time. The Møller value is only invariant under spatial coordinate transformations. In the cylindrical coordinate system there is no guarantee that the "energy" will always be positive definite. If negative values are allowed, then the vanishing of $\tau_0{}^0$ may mean only that absorption of energy from the wave makes the wave energy negative. A lower bound for the energy would guarantee stability.

7.9   Interaction of a Particle with Cylindrical Gravitational Waves

Calculation of the components of the Riemann tensor for the metric (7.59) shows that the components do not all vanish for the cylindrical waves, so the waves must be real. In this section we show that the cylindrical waves do carry energy, by analyzing the motion of a particle initially at rest which interacts with the cylindrical pulse. We write the geodesic equation for ρ, and integrate it in successive orders, regarding ψ as a first-order quantity and γ as a second-order one. Let

$$\rho = \rho_{(0)} + \rho_{(1)} + \rho_{(2)} + \ldots \qquad (7.74)$$

From the metric (7.59),

$$c\frac{dt}{ds} = 1 + \psi - \gamma + \psi^2/2 + \ldots \left(\frac{d\rho}{ds}\right)^2 \bigg/ 2 + \ldots \qquad (7.75)$$

These relations lead to the first-order equation

$$
\begin{aligned}
\frac{d^2\rho_{(1)}}{dt^2} &= c^2\frac{\partial\psi}{\partial\rho} \\
&= -Bc^2\rho_{(0)}\left\{[(a-ict)^2+\rho_{(0)}{}^2]^{-\frac{3}{2}} + [(a+ict)^2+\rho_{(0)}{}^2]^{-\frac{3}{2}}\right\}
\end{aligned}
\qquad (7.76)
$$

and the second-order equation

$$\frac{d^2\rho_{(2)}}{c^2 dt^2} = \frac{d\rho_{(1)}}{c^2 dt}\left(\frac{\partial\psi}{\partial t}\right)_{\rho_{(0)}} - \left(\frac{d\gamma}{d\rho}\right)_{\rho_{(0)}} + \rho_{(1)}\left(\frac{\partial^2\psi}{\partial\rho^2}\right)_{\rho_{(0)}} \qquad (7.77)$$

In obtaining these equations we have made use of

$$\frac{\partial \psi}{\partial \rho} = \left(\frac{\partial \psi}{\partial \rho}\right)_{\rho_{(0)}} + \rho_{(1)}\left(\frac{\partial^2 \psi}{\partial \rho^2}\right)_{\rho_{(0)}}$$

Integration of (7.76) gives, for the boundary condition $d\rho/dt = 0$ at $t = -\infty$,

$$\frac{d\rho_{(1)}}{dt} = -\frac{icB}{\rho_{(0)}}\left[\frac{a - ict}{[(a-ict)^2 + \rho_{(0)}{}^2]^{\frac{1}{2}}} - \frac{a + ict}{[(a+ict)^2 + \rho_{(0)}{}^2]^{\frac{1}{2}}}\right]$$

$$(7.78)$$

The change in ρ from $t = -\infty$ to $t = 0$ may be written

$$\Delta \rho = \int_{-\infty}^{0}\int_{-\infty}^{t'}\left(\frac{\partial \psi}{\partial \rho}\right)dt'dt = \frac{2B}{\rho_{(0)}}\left[(\rho_{(0)}{}^2 + a^2)^{\frac{1}{2}} - a\right] \to 2B \quad (7.79)$$

for large ρ. The distance from the axis, at $t = 0$, for large ρ, is

$$\int g_{11}^{\frac{1}{2}}\,d\rho = \int_0^{\rho_0 + \Delta\rho} e^{\gamma - \psi}\,d\rho \approx \rho_0 + 2B - 2B \ln(2\rho_{(0)}/a) \quad (7.80)$$

The results (7.78), (7.79), and (7.80) indicate that to first order, the particle, initially at rest, starts to move when the wave arrives; the change in the coordinate ρ at the instant of maximum implosion of the wave is $+2B$, but at that instant the change in distance is $2B - 2B \ln(2\rho_{(0)}/a)$. As the wave explodes back out again these steps are reversibly retraced in this approximation so that at $t = +\infty$ the particle ends up where it started and at rest. However, one could imagine the particle to be coupled to a second, distant particle by a mechanism giving irreversibility.[‡] The relative motion would then lead to absorption of energy from the wave even in the first approximation.

To consider the second approximation we need to integrate (7.77). Carrying out the indicated operations leads to

[‡] In the next chapter we show that energy may always be absorbed from a system for which the Fourier transform of $R_{i_0 j_0}$ does not vanish, in a local Lorentz frame propagated along a geodesic.

twenty-two integrals. We calculate only the velocity at $t \to +\infty$. Then all but three integrals can readily be shown to vanish, by contour integral arguments, and the result is

$$
\left(\frac{d\rho_{(2)}}{dt}\right)_{t\to+\infty}
$$

$$
= -\frac{4B^2}{\rho_{(0)}}(a^2+\rho_{(0)}{}^2)^2\int_{-\infty}^{\infty}\frac{c^2dt}{\{[(a+ict)^2+\rho_{(0)}{}^2][(a-ict)^2+\rho_{(0)}{}^2]\}^{\frac{3}{2}}}
$$

$$
+ \frac{12a^2B^2}{\rho_{(0)}}\int_{-\infty}^{\infty}\frac{c^4t^2dt}{\{[(a+ict)^2+\rho_{(0)}{}^2][(a-ict)^2+\rho_{(0)}{}^2]\}^{\frac{3}{2}}}
$$

$$
+ 6\rho_{(0)}B^2\int_{-\infty}^{\infty}\frac{c^2[(a-ict)^2+\rho_{(0)}{}^2]^{\frac{1}{2}}\,dt}{[(a+ict)^2+\rho_{(0)}{}^2]^{\frac{5}{2}}} \tag{7.81}
$$

These integrals may be written in terms of

$$
F = \int_0^{\pi/2}\frac{d\theta}{[1-z\sin^2\theta]^{\frac{1}{2}}}; \qquad z = \frac{\rho_{(0)}{}^2}{a^2+\rho_{(0)}{}^2} \tag{7.82}
$$

as

$$
\left(\frac{d\rho}{cdt}\right)_{t\to+\infty}
$$

$$
= B^2F\left[\frac{-4}{\rho_{(0)}(a^2+\rho_{(0)}{}^2)^{\frac{1}{2}}}+\frac{5\rho_{(0)}}{(a^2+\rho_{(0)}{}^2)^{\frac{3}{2}}}+\frac{3\rho_{(0)}(5a^2+\rho_{(0)}{}^2)}{(a^2+\rho_{(0)}{}^2)^{\frac{5}{2}}}\right]
$$

$$
+ B^2\frac{dF}{dz}\left[\frac{4(a^2-\rho_{(0)}{}^2)}{\rho_{(0)}(a^2+\rho_{(0)}{}^2)^{\frac{3}{2}}}+\frac{12a^2}{\rho_{(0)}(a^2+\rho_{(0)}{}^2)^{\frac{3}{2}}}-\frac{8(a^2-\rho_{(0)}{}^2)\rho_{(0)}}{(a^2+\rho_{(0)}{}^2)^{\frac{5}{2}}}\right.
$$

$$
- \frac{9\rho_{(0)}(5a^4+6a^2\rho_{(0)}{}^2+\rho_{(0)}{}^4)}{(a^2+\rho_{(0)}{}^2)^{\frac{7}{2}}}-\frac{12\rho_{(0)}(5a^2+\rho_{(0)}{}^2)(a^2-\rho^2{}_{(0)})}{(a^2+\rho_{(0)}{}^2)^{\frac{7}{2}}}
$$

$$
\left.- 3\rho_{(0)}(a^2+\rho_{(0)}{}^2)^{-\frac{3}{2}}\right] + B^2\frac{d^2F}{dz^2}\left[\frac{\rho_{(0)}(a^2+\rho_{(0)}{}^2)^3(a^2-\rho_{(0)}{}^2)^2}{(a^2+\rho_{(0)}{}^2)^{\frac{13}{2}}}\right.
$$

$$
+ \frac{3\rho_{(0)}(5a^4+6a^2\rho_{(0)}{}^2+\rho_{(0)}{}^4)(a^2-\rho_{(0)}{}^2)}{(a^2+\rho_{(0)}{}^2)^{\frac{9}{2}}}
$$

$$
\left.+ \frac{3\rho(5a^2+\rho_{(0)}{}^2)(a^2-\rho_{(0)}{}^2)^2}{(a^2+\rho_{(0)}{}^2)^{\frac{9}{2}}}+\frac{\rho_{(0)}(a^2-\rho_{(0)}{}^2)}{(a^2+\rho_{(0)}{}^2)^{\frac{5}{2}}}\right] \tag{7.83}
$$

This lengthy expression reduces, for the limits $\rho_{(0)}$ small and $\rho_{(0)}$ large $t \to \infty$ to:

$$\frac{d\rho_{(2)}}{dt} \to - \frac{2\pi B^2 c \rho_{(0)}}{a^3}, \qquad \left(\frac{\rho_0}{a} \ll 1\right) \qquad (7.84)$$

$$\frac{d\rho_{(2)}}{dt} \to - \frac{2 B^2 c}{a^2}, \qquad \left(\frac{a}{\rho_0} \ll 1\right) \qquad (7.85)$$

(7.84) and (7.85) indicate that the particle is left with a residual velocity[‡] relative to the axis after the wave has left and the interior space is again flat. The axis has a real significance in this problem because a test particle could be placed there; according to (7.79) it would not move at any time thereafter. Observing a particle at radial coordinate ρ therefore amounts to observing the relative motion of a pair of particles.

Conclusions similar to these have been reached independently by L. Marder (18). He extends the pulse solution to the interior of a mass cylinder which is the radiator. After emission of the pulse he finds that the mass of the cylinder has decreased.

7.10   Exact Plane-Wave Solutions[‡‡]

Plane gravitational waves have been considered by a number of authors. Taub (6) and McVittie (11) showed that

[‡] This velocity produces infinite displacement, over an infinite time. This does not affect the validity of our series expansion, which is in powers of B/a.

[‡‡] These waves are not plane, since for propagation in the x direction the departures from flatness depend on y and z. Bondi calls them plane because they have as much symmetry as plane electromagnetic waves. These metrics admit a group of motions with five parameters.

An illuminating discussion of these solutions has been given by Bonnor (24) and is summarized below. Consider the metric

$$-ds^2 = A d\xi^2 + B dy^2 + C dz^2 - 2b dy dz - D d\eta^2$$

Here A, B, C, b, and D are functions of $\xi - \eta$ alone.

(footnote cont'd)

there were no unpolarized plane waves. Robinson and, later, Bondi were able to show (13, 14) that the field equations permit "plane" wave zones of finite extent between two flat space-time regions. They start with a metric originally given by Rosen:

$$ds^2 = e^{2\Omega}(d\tau^2 - d\xi^2) - u^2\{e^{2\beta}d\eta^2 + e^{-2\beta}d\zeta^2\} \qquad (7.86)$$

with $u = \tau - \xi$. β and Ω are functions of u alone: $2\Omega_{,u} = u(\beta_{,u})^2$. This metric satisfies the vacuum field equations $R_{\mu\nu} = 0$. It represents, in general, a curved space. If the

---

Choose coordinates for which $A = D$; then let $\xi \to \tau - x$, $\eta \to \tau + x$, obtaining

$$-ds^2 = -dx d\tau + B dy^2 + C dz^2 - 2b dy dz$$

Here B, C, and b are functions of x alone.

For this metric the vacuum field equations are

$$R_{11} = \frac{\partial^2\chi}{\partial x^2} - \frac{1}{2\chi}\left(\frac{\partial\chi}{\partial x}\right)^2 + \left(\frac{\partial b}{\partial x}\right)^2 - \frac{\partial B}{\partial x}\frac{\partial C}{\partial x} = 0$$

and $\chi = BC - b^2$. The other vacuum field equations are satisfied without further restriction on B, C, and b. We have then three unknown functions with only one relation which they satisfy. Two of the three may be arbitrarily chosen. Take $b = 0$ and let $B = p^2$, $C = q^2$; then the field equation for R_{11} becomes

$$\frac{1}{p}\frac{\partial^2 p}{\partial x^2} + \frac{1}{q}\frac{\partial^2 q}{\partial x^2} = 0$$

Take as a particular solution of this equation $p = \sin nx$, $q = \sinh nx$, where n is a real constant. This solution appears singular on the hypersurfaces: $x = m\pi/n$, $x = \pm\infty$, where m is an integer.

These singularities may be removed by carrying out the following transformation

$$\left.\begin{aligned}
x^0 &= \tau + ny^2 \sin nx \cos nx + nz^2 \sinh nx \cosh nx \\
x^1 &= x \\
x^2 &= y \sin nx \\
x^3 &= z \sinh nx
\end{aligned}\right\}$$

and when this is carried out the metric becomes

$$-ds^2 = -dx^0 dx^1 + dx^{2^2} + dx^{3^2} - n^2 dx^{1^2}(x^{2^2} - x^{3^2})$$

The singularities at $x = m\pi/n$ have disappeared. The singularities at infinity may also be removed, by choosing a new origin.

relation

$$u\beta_{,u,u} + 2\beta_{,u} = u^2(\beta_{,u})^3 \qquad (7.87)$$

is satisfied, all components of $R_{\alpha\beta\gamma\delta}$ vanish and the space is flat. By carrying out the coordinate transformation

$$u = \tau - \xi = ct - x; \qquad e^{2\Omega}(\tau + \xi) = ct + x - u^{-1}(y^2 + z^2),$$

$$\eta u e^\beta = y, \qquad u\zeta e^{-\beta} = z$$

for $u > 0$, the metric (7.86) becomes

$$ds^2 = c^2 dt^2 - dx^2 - dy^2 - dz^2$$
$$+ 2\beta_{,u}[(ydy - zdz)(cdt - dx) - (y^2 - z^2)(cdt - dx)^2(ct - x)^{-1}]$$
$$- (\beta_{,u})^2(c^2 t^2 - x^2)(cdt - dx)^2 \qquad (7.88)$$

For $\beta_{,u} = 0$ except for a finite positive range of u, there is a curved region of space between two flat regions. The amplitude of the waves is determined by β, which is an arbitrary function of u.

A second wave type is described by the metric

$$ds^2 = e^{2\Omega}(d\tau^2 - d\xi^2) - (\tau - \xi)^2 [(\cosh 2\beta)(d\eta^2 + d\zeta^2)$$
$$+ \sinh 2\beta \cos 2\theta(d\eta^2 - d\zeta^2) - 2\sinh 2\beta \sin 2\theta \, d\eta d\zeta] \qquad (7.89)$$

here again Ω, β, and θ depend on $u = \tau - \xi$, with

$$2\Omega_{,u} = (\tau - \xi)[\beta_{,u}^2 + \theta_{,u}^2 \sinh^2(2\beta)] \qquad (7.90)$$

Bondi notes that at the boundaries the conditions of Lichnerowicz on the continuity of $g_{\mu\nu}$ and its first derivatives can be met. (These conditions are given later in this chapter.)

7.11 Initial-Value Formulation of the Radiation * Problem

A different approach to gravitational waves is to note that the field equations may be regarded as setting up requirements on the initial values** of the fields,* then predicting what the future evolution will be. A study of the acceptable

* Such investigations were first carried out by Lichnerowicz (10) and Foures-Bruhat (27).

** This section is a partial summary of the thesis of D. Brill, Princeton University, 1959.

initial values then gives information concerning possible wave solutions (22, 23).

The corresponding situation for the Maxwell equations is well known. For no charges or currents the equations

$$\nabla \cdot E = 0; \qquad \nabla \cdot H = 0 \qquad (7.91)$$

constitute conditions on E and H at say $t = 0$. The remaining equations

$$\nabla \times E = -\frac{1}{c}\frac{\partial H}{\partial t}; \qquad \nabla \times H = \frac{1}{c}\frac{\partial E}{\partial t} \qquad (7.92)$$

then give the time evolution, preserving (7.91) at all stages.

For the general relativity equations we may choose the spacelike surface $x^0 = 0$. The equations contain second-time derivatives, so the initial values will be the $g_{\mu\nu}$ and their first-time derivatives. By use of the contracted Bianchi identities, we write for the Einstein tensor

$$(G_\mu{}^0)_{;0} = -(G_\mu{}^i)_{;i} \qquad (7.93)$$

$$(G^{\mu 0})_{;0} = -(G^{\mu i})_{;i} \qquad (7.94)$$

No higher than second-time derivatives occur on the right side of (7.93) and (7.94), so it follows that $G^{\mu 0}$ and $G_\mu{}^0$ cannot contain higher than first-time derivatives of the $g_{\mu\nu}$. The stress energy tensor will not contain derivatives of $g_{\mu\nu}$. It follows, therefore, that the four equations

$$R^{\mu 0} - \tfrac{1}{2}g^{\mu 0}R = \frac{8\pi G}{c^4}\,T^{\mu 0} \qquad (7.95)$$

or

$$R_0{}^\mu - \tfrac{1}{2}\delta_0{}^\mu R = \frac{8\pi G}{c^4}\,T_0{}^\mu \qquad (7.96)$$

may be taken as initial value equations, and that the six equations

$$R^{ij} - \tfrac{1}{2}g^{ij}R = \frac{8\pi G}{c^4}\,T^{ij} \qquad (7.97)$$

or

$$R_{ij} - \tfrac{1}{2}g_{ij}R = \frac{8\pi G}{c^4}\,T_{ij} \qquad (7.98)$$

are the equations of time evolution.

We can now show that if the set (7.95) or (7.96) is satisfied at the initial time, then any solution generated by integration of (7.97) or (7.98) will continue to satisfy the initial value equations (7.95) or (7.96). Let

$$X^{\mu\nu} = R^{\mu\nu} - \tfrac{1}{2}g^{\mu\nu}R - \frac{8\pi G}{c^4}\,T^{\mu\nu} \qquad (7.99)$$

Since the covariant divergence of $T^{\mu\nu}$ vanishes, we may write, from (7.94),

$$X^{\mu 0}{}_{;0} = -X^{\mu i}{}_{;i} \qquad (7.100)$$

For $\mu = k$, (7.100) becomes

$$\begin{aligned}
X^{k0}{}_{;0} &= X^{k0}{}_{,0} + \Gamma^{k}{}_{\alpha 0}X^{\alpha 0} + \Gamma^{0}{}_{\alpha 0}X^{k\alpha}\\
&= -[X^{ki}{}_{,i} + \Gamma^{k}{}_{\alpha i}X^{\alpha i} + \Gamma^{i}{}_{\alpha i}X^{\alpha k}]
\end{aligned} \qquad (7.101)$$

and for $\mu = 0$ (7.100) gives

$$\begin{aligned}
X^{00}{}_{,0} &= X^{00}{}_{,0} + \Gamma^{0}{}_{\alpha 0}X^{\alpha 0} + \Gamma^{0}{}_{\alpha 0}X^{0\alpha}\\
&= -[X^{0i}{}_{,i} + \Gamma^{0}{}_{\alpha i}X^{\alpha i} + \Gamma^{i}{}_{\alpha i}X^{\alpha 0}]
\end{aligned} \qquad (7.102)$$

Consider first expression (7.101). At $t = 0$, $X^{\mu\nu}$ vanishes everywhere so the space derivatives $X^{ki}{}_{,i}$ also vanish. Therefore we may conclude that $X^{k0}{}_{,0}$ vanishes initially. Now consider (7.102); since $X^{\mu\nu}$ and X^{0i} vanish everywhere at $t = 0$, $X^{0i}{}_{,i}$ also vanishes; therefore $X^{00}{}_{,0}$ vanishes initially. Now differentiate (7.101) partially with respect to time. It can then be shown that initially $X^{k0}{}_{,00}$ vanishes. If we differentiate (7.102) partially with respect to time, then the vanishing of $X^{0i}{}_{,0}$ everywhere initially guarantees the vanishing of $X^{0i}{}_{,0i}$, which then guarantees the vanishing of $X^{00}{}_{,00}$ at the initial time. By continuing this process it then becomes clear that $X^{\mu 0}$ and all its time derivatives vanish initially. The Taylor expansion of $X^{\mu 0}$ therefore guarantees that $X^{\mu 0}$ vanishes for all time.

7.12   Time-Symmetric Solution with Positive Energy

A tensor T is called time-symmetric if

$$T_{\alpha\beta}^{\gamma\delta\cdots}(x^0, x^i) = (-1)^n T_{\alpha\beta}^{\gamma\delta\cdots}(-x^0, x^i) \qquad (7.103)$$

where n is the number of times that zero occurs amongst $\alpha\beta\gamma\delta \ldots$

We shall see that introduction of this element of symmetry substantially simplifies the problem of solving the set (7.95) and (7.96). A time-symmetric solution should give the same value for ds^2 for a pair of events with the same coordinate differentials, at $+x^0$ and $-x^0$, so $g_{i0} = 0$; also all tensors in the problem must have the same kind of symmetry. It follows, therefore, that the equations $R^{0i} - (\frac{1}{2})g^{0i}R = 8\pi G T^{0i}/c^4$ are automatically satisfied since R^{0i}, g^{0i}, and T^{0i} vanish. The initial-value relations reduce to the one equation

$$R_0^{\;0} - \tfrac{1}{2}R = \left(\frac{8\pi G}{c^4}\right) T_0^{\;0} \qquad (7.104)$$

(7.104) may be written in the forms

$$R_0^{\;0} - \tfrac{1}{2}(R_0^{\;0} + R_i^{\;i}) = \tfrac{1}{2}[R_{i0}^{\;\;i0} - (R_{i0}^{\;\;i0} + R_{ik}^{\;\;ik})]$$

$$= -\tfrac{1}{2}R_{ik}^{\;\;ik} = \left(\frac{8\pi G}{c^4}\right) T_0^{\;0} \qquad (7.105)$$

In a time-orthogonal system of coordinates $R_{ik}^{\;\;ik}$ reduces to $^{(3)}R$, the curvature scalar computed from the three-dimensional metric. This is because $R_{ik}^{\;\;ik} = R_{ik\alpha\beta}\, g^{i\alpha}\, g^{k\beta}$. Since i and k are space indices and $g^{i0} = 0$, it follows that only sums of space derivatives of the space index g_{ij} enter into $R_{ik}^{\;\;ik}$. The initial-value equations become

$$^{(3)}R + \left(\frac{16\pi G}{c^4}\right) T_0^{\;0} = 0 \qquad (7.106)$$

In vacuum, for "pure" gravitational waves, (7.106) is

$$^{(3)}R = 0 \qquad (7.107)$$

Consider the solutions of (7.107). These allowed initial values should show the essential characteristics of the complete solution. Brill obtains information about the solutions in the following way. Let the required metric be $g'_{\mu\nu}$, satisfying $^{(3)}R' = 0$. Let ds'^2 be obtained from another metric ds^2, according to

$$ds'^2 = e^{2P}ds^2 \qquad (7.108)$$

The unprimed $g_{\mu\nu}$ is called the base metric. P is a function of the coordinates. The transformation (7.108) is a new kind of operation, for unlike the coordinate transformations used thus far, intervals *do* change. At a particular point all differential intervals are changed by a factor e^P. It follows that the shape of a small triangle or any small figure will not change. Transformations (7.108) are therefore called conformal. It can be shown that the value of R' in terms of (the base metric) R may be written (25)

$$R' = e^{-2P}[R + (n-1)(2\nabla^2 P + (n-2)(\nabla P)^2)] \qquad (7.109)$$

In (7.109), n is the number of dimensions of the space

$$\nabla^2 P = g^{ij}P_{;i;j}; \qquad (\nabla P)^2 = g^{ij}P_{,i}P_{,j}$$

In our case we are concerned with R' for the three space, so $n = 3$. It is convenient to make the substitution

$$\Psi = e^{((n-2)/2)P} \qquad (7.110)$$

(7.109) and (7.108) become, for $R' = 0$,

$$ds'^2 = \Psi^4 ds^2; \qquad \nabla^2\Psi + \tfrac{1}{8}\,^{(3)}R\Psi = 0 \qquad (7.111)$$

A careful study of (7.111) by Brill has led him to the conclusion that solutions of (7.111) exist with Ψ well behaved and not vanishing anywhere,[‡] corresponding to a metric with the asymptotic behavior

$$ds'^2 \to \left(1 + \frac{2Gm}{c^2 r}\right)(dr^2 + r^2 d\Omega^2) + g_{00}c^2 dt^2 \qquad (7.112)$$

The function Ψ may be expanded asymptotically in a series $A + B_i r^{-i}$, where $i = 1, 2, 3, \ldots$ A study of (7.111)

[‡] The second equation of (7.111) has the form of the curved space Schroedinger equation, for which such solutions are known.

shows that the first nonvanishing term in the expansion of R goes as r^{-4}. (7.112) provides an unambiguous way to specify the mass energy of any wave for which the expansion in negative powers of r is appropriate, so that (7.112) applies. Brill finds that this "Schwarzschild" mass is a positive definite quantity for fields having axial symmetry [‡]. To show this, the second equation in (7.111) is divided by Ψ and integrated to obtain

$$\int \frac{\nabla^2 \psi}{\psi} \sqrt{^{(3)}g}\, d^3x = \int_{\text{surface}} \frac{\nabla \psi}{\psi} dS + \int_v \left(\frac{\nabla \psi}{\psi}\right)^2 \sqrt{^{(3)}g}\, d^3x$$

$$= -\tfrac{1}{8} \int {}^{(3)}R \sqrt{^{(3)}g}\, d^3x \tag{7.113}$$

Since

$$\psi^4 \to 1 + \frac{2Gm}{c^2 r} \qquad \text{and} \qquad \psi \to 1 + \frac{Gm}{2c^2 r}$$

$$\int \frac{\nabla \psi}{\psi} dS \to -2\pi Gm/c^2 \tag{7.114}$$

From (7.113) and (7.114) we have

$$\frac{2\pi Gm}{c^2} = \int \left(\frac{\nabla \psi}{\psi}\right)^2 \sqrt{^{(3)}g}\, d^3x + \tfrac{1}{8} \int {}^{(3)}R \sqrt{^{(3)}g}\, d^3x \tag{7.115}$$

For the axially symmetric case the metric may be written

$$ds'^2 = \psi^4 \left[e^{2q}(d\rho^2 + dz^2) + \rho^2 d\varphi^2\right] = \psi^4 ds^2 \tag{7.116}$$

Here q falls off asymptotically at least as fast as $1/r^2$; $r^2 = \rho^2 + z^2$. q, $\psi_{,\rho}$ and $q_{,\rho}$ vanish on the z axis.

For the base metric (within the bracket of (7.116)) the integral $\int {}^{(3)}R \sqrt{^{(3)}g}\, d^3x$ may be evaluated directly and approaches zero as the radius of a large sphere centered at the origin approaches infinity. It follows then that the mass (7.115) can be written

$$m = \frac{c^2}{2\pi G} \int \left(\frac{\nabla \psi}{\psi}\right)^2 \sqrt{^{(3)}g}\, d^3x \tag{7.117}$$

[‡] Araki (23) has shown that the energy is positive definite, in the weak field approximation, without the assumption of axial symmetry.

Since Ψ has no zeros anywhere, the "Schwarzschildian" mass given by (7.117) is well defined and is a positive definite quantity for a localized disturbance with axial symmetry which implodes for negative t and explodes for positive t. The conservation laws guarantee the invariance of m before and after the moment of time symmetry. Furthermore it is apparent from (7.117) and (7.112) that the mass is zero only if the space is flat.

7.13 Conditions on the Differentiability and Continuity of Manifolds

Until comparatively recently it was customary to require that the entire space-time continuum be covered by one nonsingular coordinate system. This has turned out to be unnecessarily restrictive. More than one coordinate system may be employed, provided that certain conditions can be met in the region where they overlap. A region in which a particular coordinate system is employed is sometimes called a coordinate patch.

Lichnerowicz (10) has carefully studied the conditions which have to be met in order to ensure that the gravitational field equations have unique solutions for the case $T_{\mu\nu} = 0$. He requires that at the intersection of two coordinate patches the local coordinates of a point in one of the coordinate systems be fourfold-differentiable with respect to the coordinates in the other system and have nonvanishing Jacobian. The first and second partial derivatives must be continuous; the third and fourth partial derivatives must be at least piecewise-continuous. The metric tensor must be continuous, and is required to have continuous first partial derivatives; the second and third partial derivatives must be at least piecewise-continuous. These conditions on the metric tensor are required everywhere.

7.14 Six-Dimensional Treatment of Gravitational Radiation

Pirani (12) has given an interesting discussion of gravitational radiation. This is based on the work of Petrov (9) and the generalization of ideas familiar in the treatment of electromagnetic radiation. For the vacuum case,

$$R_{\mu\nu} = 0 \qquad (7.118)$$

First consider a gravitational wave characterized by a discontinuity of the Riemann tensor across the wavefront. The Lichnerowicz continuity conditions on the metric tensor and its partial derivatives ensure uniqueness. Suppose we have a given point in a coordinate system such that $g_{\mu\nu}$ is a Lorentz metric at the point, the Christoffel symbols vanish, and the wavefront discontinuity there is moving in the x^1 direction. Let the new coordinates ξ and ζ be defined by

$$\xi = (x^0 - x^1)/\sqrt{2} \qquad (7.119)$$

$$\zeta = (x^0 + x^1)/\sqrt{2} \qquad (7.120)$$

The line element at the point becomes

$$ds^2 = 2d\xi\,d\zeta - dx^{2^2} - dx^{3^2} \qquad (7.121)$$

The surface of discontinuity is $d\xi = 0$. Then $g_{\mu\nu}$ and its first derivatives must be continuous, so it follows that $\partial^2 g_{\mu\nu}/\partial\xi\partial\zeta$ must also be continuous. However,

$$\frac{\partial^2 g_{\mu\nu}}{\partial\xi^2} \qquad (7.122)$$

will not necessarily be continuous. A study of the expression for the covariant Riemann tensor $R_{\alpha\beta\gamma\delta}$ in the manner of Section 7.2 shows that in this special coordinate system the discontinuity in the Riemann tensor can be written in terms of $\partial^2 g_{22}/\partial\xi^2$, $\partial^2 g_{33}/\partial\xi^2$, and $\partial^2 g_{23}/\partial\xi^2$ alone. Only two variables, σ and φ, with

$$\sigma = \frac{\partial^2 g_{33}}{\partial\xi^2} = -\frac{\partial^2 g_{22}}{\partial\xi^2}; \qquad \varphi = \frac{\partial^2 g_{23}}{\partial\xi^2} \qquad (7.123)$$

are needed to describe it. The terms in φ may be made to vanish by an appropriate choice of axes in the 23 plane.

A six-dimensional formalism proves convenient for the

classification of the discontinuities in the Riemann tensor and for other purposes. Coordinates are again chosen such that the six-dimensional space has a pseudo-Euclidean metric at the point, given by $\delta_{AB} = (1, 1, 1, -1, -1, -1)$. The physical components of a given tensor at a point are defined to be those measured by an observer in a locally Lorentz frame. If $H_{\alpha\beta}$ are the physical components of an antisymmetric tensor, the corresponding six vector is obtained by relabeling the suffixes in accordance with the rule

$$
\begin{array}{ccccccc}
\alpha\beta & 23 & 31 & 12 & 10 & 20 & 30 \\
A & 1 & 2 & 3 & 4 & 5 & 6
\end{array}
\tag{7.124}
$$

The physical components of the Riemann tensor $R_{\alpha\beta\gamma\delta}$ are related to the symmetric six tensor R_{AB}, also according to the above prescription, taking pairs $\alpha\beta$ and $\gamma\delta$. The discontinuity of the Riemann tensor may then be written

$$
\Delta R_{AB} =
\begin{vmatrix}
0 & 0 & 0 & 0 & 0 & 0 \\
0 & -\sigma & -\varphi & 0 & -\varphi & \sigma \\
0 & -\varphi & \sigma & 0 & \sigma & \varphi \\
0 & 0 & 0 & 0 & 0 & 0 \\
0 & -\varphi & \sigma & 0 & \sigma & \varphi \\
0 & \sigma & \varphi & 0 & \varphi & -\sigma
\end{vmatrix}
\tag{7.125}
$$

This result followed from the Lichnerowicz conditions. Comparison of (7.125) with Section 7.2 shows what was to be expected, namely, that if we have a wave which is a discontinuity over a plane propagating in the x^1 direction, the nonvanishing components of the discontinuity in $R_{\alpha\beta\gamma\delta}$ are just those of (7.27).

Some aspects of energy flow in electrodynamics are now reviewed for the purpose of generalizing them for the gravitational field. An observer at rest in a Lorentz frame has a Poynting vector T_{0i}, where $T_{\mu\nu}$ is the electromagnetic stress tensor. Let a Poynting-like vector be given by P_ρ. Then a covariant expression for P_ρ, valid for an observer with four velocity U_ρ may be written in the form

$$
P_\rho = (\delta_\rho{}^\mu - U_\rho U^\mu) T_{\mu\nu} U^\nu
\tag{7.126}
$$

Observers who move with the wave velocity observe no energy flux, so for them (7.126) vanishes. This leads to

$$T_{\rho\nu} U^\nu = (T_{\mu\nu} U^\mu U^\nu) U_\rho \qquad (7.127)$$

(7.127) states that an observer who measures no energy flux has velocity U^ν, which is an eigenvector of the electromagnetic stress tensor $T_{\rho\nu}$. If the electromagnetic field is a radiation field, the field tensor satisfies the relations $F_{\mu\nu} F^{\mu\nu} = 0$ and $\varepsilon_{\alpha\beta\gamma\delta} F^{\alpha\beta} F^{\gamma\delta} = 0$. Such a field is called a null field. A study of the electromagnetic stress tensor indicates that if the field is a null field, $T_{\mu\nu}$ has one null eigenvector ξ^ρ corresponding to the eigenvalue zero. A radiation field, in electrodynamics, is, therefore, a field whose corresponding stress energy tensor has a vanishing eigenvalue. Since all four velocity vectors are unit vectors, it follows that the Poynting vector cannot be transformed away.

To consider somewhat similar ideas for the gravitational case, the eigenbivectors $P_{\mu\nu}$ of the Riemann tensor are defined by

$$R_{\mu\nu\rho\sigma} P^{\rho\sigma} = \lambda P_{\mu\nu}$$
$$R_{AB} P^B = \lambda P_A \qquad (7.128)$$

$P_{\mu\nu}$ is antisymmetric and is written as $a_\mu b_\nu - a_\nu b_\mu$. The unit vectors a_μ and b_ν define a two dimensional space. A second two space which is completely orthogonal to the first is also defined by $P_{\mu\nu}$. The term completely orthogonal means that every vector in the first two space is orthogonal to every vector in the second two space. The pairs of two spaces associated with different eigenbivectors may intersect each other to define at each intersection point a four vector tangent to the intersection curve. These four vectors are called Riemann principal vectors. If the Riemann principal vector is a null vector, the gravitational field is said, by Pirani, to be a radiation field.

Petrov (9) has shown that by suitable orientation of the coordinate system in which the metric has the Lorentz form at a given point, the Riemann tensor may be reduced to a canonical form of one of the following kinds:

Type I:

$$
R_{AB} =
\begin{vmatrix}
\alpha_1 & 0 & 0 & \beta_1 & 0 & 0 \\
0 & \alpha_2 & 0 & 0 & \beta_2 & 0 \\
0 & 0 & \alpha_3 & 0 & 0 & \beta_3 \\
\beta_1 & 0 & 0 & -\alpha_1 & 0 & 0 \\
0 & \beta_2 & 0 & 0 & -\alpha_2 & 0 \\
0 & 0 & \beta_3 & 0 & 0 & -\alpha_3
\end{vmatrix}
;
\quad
\begin{aligned}
&\sum_{k=1}^{k=3}\alpha_k=0 \\[6pt]
&\sum_{k=1}^{k=3}\beta_k=0
\end{aligned}
\qquad (7.129)
$$

Type II:

$$
R_{AB} =
\begin{vmatrix}
-2\alpha & 0 & 0 & -2\beta & 0 & 0 \\
0 & \alpha-\sigma & 0 & 0 & \beta & \sigma \\
0 & 0 & \alpha+\sigma & 0 & \sigma & \beta \\
-2\beta & 0 & 0 & 2\alpha & 0 & 0 \\
0 & \beta & \sigma & 0 & \sigma-\alpha & 0 \\
0 & \sigma & \beta & 0 & 0 & -\alpha-\sigma
\end{vmatrix}
\qquad (7.130)
$$

Type III:

$$
R_{AB} =
\begin{vmatrix}
0 & -\sigma & 0 & 0 & 0 & \sigma \\
-\sigma & 0 & 0 & 0 & 0 & 0 \\
0 & 0 & 0 & \sigma & 0 & 0 \\
0 & 0 & \sigma & 0 & \sigma & 0 \\
0 & 0 & 0 & \sigma & 0 & 0 \\
\sigma & 0 & 0 & 0 & 0 & 0
\end{vmatrix}
\qquad (7.131)
$$

The α and β are scalar invariants of the Riemann tensor. The value of σ depends on the orientation of axes in the 10 plane. [‡]

A study of these types shows that type I has one time-like, and the three spacelike, principal vectors; type II has one null principal vector and two spacelike ones. Type III has only one principal vector and it is null. Pirani's criterion is, therefore, that gravitational radiation is present if the Riemann tensor is of type II (null) or III, but not if it is type I.

[‡] 3×3 matrices can also be used, in consequence of the obvious symmetry. If the upper left 3×3 is called M and the upper right 3×3 is called N, the matrices $M + iN$ give the essential features.

If at each point in a space in which the metric has the Schwarzschild value we introduce a Lorentz frame with axes parallel to the coordinate axes, the Riemann tensor turns out to be of type I above with

$$-\tfrac{1}{2}\alpha_1 = \alpha_2 = \alpha_3 = GM/c^2 r^3; \qquad \beta_k = 0$$

For the Einstein-Rosen metric a similar procedure leads to type II with

$$\sigma = [\psi_{,\rho,t} + 5\psi_{,\rho}\psi_{,t} + \psi_{,t}\gamma_{,\rho} - 3\psi_{,\rho}\gamma_{,t}]/c$$

It must be emphasized that the components of $R_{\alpha\beta\gamma\delta}$ must be calculated in a locally Lorentz frame at any given point, in order to make use of the classification scheme of Petrov.

A special coordinate system which has a Lorentz metric in the vicinity of one point, vanishing first derivatives of $g_{\mu\nu}$, and specified second derivatives of $g_{\mu\nu}$ is the "normal" coordinate system. At the pole the following conditions are met:

$$
\begin{aligned}
x^\mu &= 0 \\
g_{\mu\nu} &= \delta_{\mu\nu} \\
\Gamma^\rho{}_{\mu\nu} &= g_{\mu\nu,\rho} = 0 \\
g_{\mu\nu,\rho\sigma} &= \tfrac{1}{2}(R_{\rho\mu\nu\sigma} + R_{\rho\nu\mu\sigma})
\end{aligned}
\tag{7.132}
$$

Pirani has calculated the average value of the canonical stress energy pseudotensor density

$$t_\mu{}^\nu \sqrt{-g} = \delta_\mu{}^\nu \mathscr{L}_G \sqrt{-g} - g_{\rho\sigma,\mu}\frac{\partial(\mathscr{L}_G\sqrt{-g})}{\partial g_{\rho\sigma,\nu}}$$

about a point in a frame described by (7.132). The average is defined by

$$\langle \sqrt{-g}\, t_\mu{}^\nu \rangle = (4\pi r^4)^{-1} \int_{\lim\ r\to 0} t_\mu{}^\nu \sqrt{-g}\, d^2S \tag{7.133}$$

This is done to provide support for the definition of radiation given here. $t_\mu{}^\nu$ can be written in terms of $g_{\alpha\beta,\sigma}$, so it vanishes at the pole of any geodesic coordinate system. The average defined above will not vanish since the second derivatives of $g_{\mu\nu}$ can contribute. Unfortunately this average does not have the dimensions of energy density. It is an energy like object which gives (section 8.2) a measure of the energy which may be abstracted by an observer with four velocity U^ν, for whom (7.132) is appropriate. The average is calculated to be

$$\langle \sqrt{-g}\, t_\mu{}^\nu \rangle$$
$$= (\tfrac{1}{27})\, (\delta_\tau{}^\rho\, \delta_\mu{}^\nu - 2\delta_\mu{}^\rho\, \delta_\tau{}^\nu)(U^\kappa U^\lambda + g^{\kappa\lambda})(R^{\tau\alpha\beta}{}_\kappa + R^{\tau\beta\alpha}{}_\kappa) R_{\rho\alpha\beta\lambda} \left(\frac{-c^4}{16\pi G}\right)$$

$$(7.134)$$

For an observer at rest with type I Riemann tensor this gives (summations over $\varkappa$)

$$\langle \sqrt{-g}\, t_\mu{}^\nu \rangle = (\tfrac{1}{27})\, [2\{\sum_1^3 \alpha_\kappa{}^2(\delta_\mu{}^0\, \delta_0{}^\nu + 2\delta_\mu{}^\kappa\, \delta_\kappa{}^\nu$$
$$+ 3\delta_\mu{}^{\kappa+1}\delta_{\kappa+1}{}^\nu + 3\delta_\mu{}^{\kappa+2}\, \delta_{\kappa+2}{}^\nu)\} - 9\delta_\mu{}^\nu \sum_1^3 \alpha_\kappa{}^2] \left(\frac{-c^4}{16\pi G}\right)$$

$$(7.135)$$

and for type II,

$$\langle \sqrt{-g}\, t_\mu{}^\nu \rangle = (\tfrac{1}{27})\, [\alpha^2(-42\delta_\mu{}^\nu + 16\delta_\mu{}^1\, \delta_1{}^\nu + 22\delta_\mu{}^2\, \delta_2{}^\nu$$
$$+ 22\delta_\mu{}^3\, \delta_3{}^\nu) + 4\alpha\sigma(\delta_\mu{}^2\, \delta_2{}^\nu - \delta_\mu{}^3\, \delta_3{}^\nu)$$
$$+ 8\sigma^2(\delta_\mu{}^0 + \delta_\mu{}^1)(\delta_0{}^\nu - \delta_1{}^\nu)] \left(\frac{-c^4}{16\pi G}\right)$$

$$(7.136)$$

7.15   Other Petrov Class II Wave Solutions

The tetrad (sometimes called quadruped, tetrapod, vierbein, or four nuple) is a set of four unit vectors which may be introduced at any point to define a locally Lorentz frame.[‡] Three of the vectors are spacelike and normal to each other

‡ The transformation to a locally Lorentz frame with coordinates x'^α may be obtained by writing

for
$$dx'^\alpha = \lambda_{(\alpha)\mu}\, dx^\mu$$

$$g'^{\alpha\beta} = \frac{\partial x'^\alpha}{\partial x^\mu} \frac{\partial x'^\beta}{\partial x^\nu}\, g^{\mu\nu} = \lambda_{(\alpha)}{}^\nu\, \lambda_{(\beta)\nu} = \delta^{\alpha\beta}$$

and to the time direction which specifies the fourth one. The tetrad vectors are usually written $\lambda_{(\alpha)}{}^{\mu}$, where μ is the vector index and (α) labels a particular one. Peres has obtained another class of wave solutions of $R_{\mu\nu} = 0$, which have less symmetry than the plane and cylindrical waves. His metric is

$$-ds^2 = dx^2 + dy^2 + dz^2 + 2F(x, y, z+\tau)(dz + d\tau)^2 - d\tau^2 \quad (7.137)$$

The field equations become $R_{zz} = R_{z\tau} = R_{\tau\tau} = F_{,xx} + F_{,yy} = 0$ and are therefore satisfied if F is a harmonic function. A tetrad of orthonormal vectors is introduced by

$$
\begin{aligned}
\lambda_{(0)}{}^{\mu} &= (1 + F, 0, 0, -F) \\
\lambda_{(1)}{}^{\mu} &= (0, \cos a, \sin a, 0) \\
\lambda_{(2)}{}^{\mu} &= (0, -\sin a, \cos a, 0) \\
\lambda_{(3)}{}^{\mu} &= (F, 0, 0, 1 - F)
\end{aligned}
\quad (7.138)
$$

with $\tan 2a = F_{,xy}/F_{,xx}$. The components of $R_{\alpha\beta\gamma\delta}$ which do not vanish are (in a frame defined by the reference tetrad)

$$\sigma = R_{\mu 1 \nu 1} = -R_{\mu 2 \nu 2} = (F_{,xx}{}^2 + F_{,xy}{}^2)^{\frac{1}{2}} \quad (7.139)$$

for μ and ν equal to 3 and 0 only. This class of metrics therefore falls in Petrov's class II.

For

$$F = (x^2 - y^2)\sin(z + \tau); \qquad \sigma = 2\sin(z + \tau) \quad (7.140)$$

we have a plane wave. A wave packet solution is

$$
\begin{aligned}
F &= xy(x^2+y^2)^{-2}\, e^{[b^2-(z+\tau)^2]^{-2}}, \quad \text{for } |z + \tau| < b \\
F &= 0, \quad \text{for } |z + \tau| > b
\end{aligned}
\quad (7.141)
$$

We now show that all wave solutions of $R_{\mu\nu} = 0$ of physical interest approach type II. Any physically interesting wave solution is likely to be generated by localized distributions of matter, and will therefore be plane at large distances (not cosmologically large distances). It follows that our analysis of Section 7.2 describes it. We emphasize that our definition of a locally plane wave is one which has $g_{\mu\nu,\alpha i} =$

$g_{\mu\nu,\alpha j} = 0$, where i and j are the two tetrad directions normal to the direction of propagation of the wave. The ten components of expression (7.27) are arranged in the canonical form following the prescription (7.124) with the result

$$
R_{AB} =
\begin{vmatrix}
0 & 0 & 0 & 0 & 0 & 0 \\
0 & -\tfrac{1}{2}g_{33,11} & \tfrac{1}{2}g_{23,11} & 0 & -\tfrac{1}{2}g_{23,10} & -\tfrac{1}{2}g_{33,10} \\
0 & \tfrac{1}{2}g_{23,11} & -\tfrac{1}{2}g_{22,11} & 0 & \tfrac{1}{2}g_{22,10} & \tfrac{1}{2}g_{23,10} \\
0 & 0 & 0 & 0 & 0 & 0 \\
0 & -\tfrac{1}{2}g_{23,10} & \tfrac{1}{2}g_{22,10} & 0 & -\tfrac{1}{2}g_{22,00} & -\tfrac{1}{2}g_{23,00} \\
0 & -\tfrac{1}{2}g_{33,10} & \tfrac{1}{2}g_{23,10} & 0 & -\tfrac{1}{2}g_{23,00} & -\tfrac{1}{2}g_{33,00}
\end{vmatrix}
\quad (7.142)
$$

$g_{23,10}$ and $g_{23,00}$ may be eliminated by suitably orienting the reference tetrad. A study of (7.142) shows that it is of type II with $\alpha = \beta = 0$. It follows therefore that all physically interesting gravitational waves approach Petrov type II (null) with $\alpha = \beta = 0$, at large distances. Since (7.142) is valid without approximation, we have shown rigorously that the Riemann tensor is Petrov type II (null) at all points where a gravitational wave is locally plane (31).

Robinson and Trautman (30) have given some exact spherical solutions representing waves, with a Riemann tensor which again approaches Petrov type II (null) at large distances. Their metric is

$$
ds^2 = 2d\rho d\sigma + (K - 2H\rho - 2m/\rho)d\sigma^2
$$
$$
- \rho^2 p^{-2}\{[d\xi + q_{,\eta}d\sigma]^2 + [d\eta + q_{,\xi}d\sigma]^2\}
$$

Here m is a function of σ alone, p and q are functions of σ, ξ and η,

$$
H = p^{-1}p_{,\sigma} + p(p^{-1}q)_{,\xi\eta} - pq(p^{-1})_{,\xi\eta}
$$

K is the Gaussian curvature (chapter 3) of the surface $\rho = 1$, $\sigma = $ constant.

$$
K = p^2[(lnp)_{,\xi\xi} + (lnp)_{,\eta\eta}]
$$

For this metric, $R_{\mu\nu} = 0$ reduces to

$$
q_{,\xi\xi} + q_{,\eta\eta} = 0; \quad K_{,\xi\xi} + K_{,\eta\eta} = 4p^{-2}(m_{,\sigma} - 3Hm)
$$

The Riemann tensor may be written

$$R_{\mu\nu\alpha\beta} = \rho^{-3} D_{\mu\nu\alpha\beta} + \rho^{-2} III_{\mu\nu\alpha\beta} + \rho^{-1} N_{\mu\nu\alpha\beta}$$

D, III, N are tensors of type I (degenerate), type III, and type II (null), respectively. They are covariantly constant on any ray of constant σ, ξ, η

The solutions are degenerate type I if $m \neq 0$ and K is independent of ξ, η and are reducible to $m = 1$, $p = \cosh \mu\xi$, $q = 0$. μ is a real or purely imaginary constant. If μ is real and $\neq 0$, the Schwarzschild solution results.

If $(K_{,\xi})^2 + (K_{,\eta})^2 \neq 0$ and $R_{\mu\nu} = 0$, the solutions correspond to type II non null or type III, with type III resulting when $m = 0$. If $m = 0$ and K is independent of ξ, η the solutions are type II null or flat, with

$$\left(\frac{\partial}{\partial \xi} + i \frac{\partial}{\partial \eta} \right) \left[p^2 \left(\frac{\partial}{\partial \xi} + i \frac{\partial}{\partial \eta} \right) H \right] = 0$$

the condition for flatness.

Solutions periodic in σ can be constructed. For source velocity $< c$, there is at least one singularity on any wavefront where fields do not vanish.

References

1. A. Einstein, *Sitzber. Preuss. Akad. Wiss.* **1916**, 688; **1918**, 154.
2. A. S. Eddington, *Proc. Roy. Soc. (London)* **A102**, 268 (1923).
3. M. Fierz and W. Pauli, *Proc. Roy. Soc. (London)* **173**, 211 (1939).
4. A. Einstein and N. Rosen, *J. Franklin Inst.* **223**, 43 (1937).
5. N. Rosen, *Physik Z. Sowjetunion* **12**, 366 (1937).
6. A. H. Taub, *Ann. Math.* **53**, 472 (1951).
7. N. Rosen, *Bull. Research Council Israel* **3**, 328 (1953).
8. L. Landau and E. Lifshitz, *The Classical Theory of Fields*, Addison-Wesley, Reading Mass., 1951, Chap. 11.
9. A. Z. Petrov, *Sci. Notes Kazan State Univ.* **114**, 55 (1954).
10. A. Lichnerowicz, *Théories Relativistes de la Gravitation et de L'électro-magnétisme*, Masson, Paris, 1955.
11. G. C. McVittie, *J. Rational Mech. and Analysis* **4**, 201 (1955).
12. F. A. E. Pirani, *Phys. Rev.* **105**, 1089 (1957).
13. H. Bondi, F. A. E. Pirani, and I. Robinson, *Proc. Roy. Soc. (London)* **A251**, 519 (1959).
14. H. Bondi, *Nature* **179**, 1072 (1957).

15. H. Rosen and H. Shamir, *Revs. Modern Phys.* **29**, 429 (1957).
16. J. Weber and J. A. Wheeler, *Revs. Modern Phys.* **29**, 3, 509 (1957).
17. W. B. Bonnor, *Phil. Trans. Roy. Soc. (London)* Axxx, 994 (1954).
18. L. Marder, *Proc. Roy. Soc. (London)* A244, 524 (1958).
19. J. Boardman and P. G. Bergmann, *Phys. Rev.* **115**, 1318 (1959).
20. N. Rosen, *Phys. Rev.* **110**, 1, 291 (1958).
21. D. Brill, thesis, Princeton University, 1959.
22. D. Brill, *Ann. Physics* **7**, 466 (1959).
23. H. Araki, *Ann. Physics* **7**, 456 (1959).
24. W. B. Bonnor, *Ann. inst. Henri Poincaré* **15**, 146 (1957).
25. L. P. Eisenhart, *Riemannian Geometry*, Princeton University Press, 1926.
26. A. Peres, *Phys. Rev. Letters* **3**, 571 (1959).
27. Y. Foures-Bruhat, *J. Rat. Mech. Anal.* **5**, 951, (1956).
28. K. L. Stellmacher, Math. Annalen, **115**, 136, (1937)
29. K. L. Stellmacher, Math. Annalen, **115**, 740, (1938).
30. I. Robinson and A. Trautman, Phys. Rev. Letters, **4**, 431, (1960).
31. J. Weber and D. Zipoy, *Il Nuovo Cimento*, **18**, 191 (1960).

CHAPTER 8

Detection and Generation of Gravitational Waves[‡]

8.1 Detection

Suppose that we have a system of masses which may interact with each other. We start with the action principle

$$\delta I = 0 \qquad (8.1)$$

The action function I may be written

$$I = -mc \int ds + W \qquad (8.2)$$

Here m is the rest mass and W is the part of the action function associated with nongravitational forces arising from the motion of the mass relative to other masses with which it interacts. The principle of virtual work suggests that for δW we assume a function given by

$$\delta W = -\frac{1}{c} \int F_\mu \delta x^\mu ds \qquad (8.3)$$

(8.3) identifies F_μ as the four force. The Euler-Lagrange equations resulting from (8.1) are arranged using the method of Section 3.6 to obtain

$$\frac{d^2 x^\mu}{ds^2} + \Gamma^\mu{}_{\alpha\beta} \frac{dx^\alpha}{ds} \frac{dx^\beta}{ds} = \frac{F^\mu}{mc^2} \qquad (8.4)$$

‡ The results of this section appeared in the author's Gravity Research Foundation prize essays, April, 1958, and April, 1959. This chapter follows the paper *Phys. Rev.* **117**, 306, (1960). We thank the *Physical Review* for permitting its publication here.

(8.4) may be expressed in terms of the four velocity $U^\mu = dx^\mu/ds$ as

$$\frac{\delta}{\delta s}\left(\frac{dx^\mu}{ds}\right) = \frac{\delta U^\mu}{\delta s} = \frac{F^\mu}{mc^2} \qquad (8.5)$$

The symbol $\delta/\delta s$ means the covariant derivative with respect to s.

Following essentially the methods of Synge and Schild, we introduce a parameter v such that the world line of each mass element corresponds to a given value of v. Taking the covariant derivative of (8.5) with respect to v gives

$$\frac{\delta^2 U^\mu}{\delta v \delta s} = \frac{\delta F^\mu/m}{c^2 \delta v} \qquad (8.6)$$

Direct calculation leads to

$$\frac{\delta^2 U^\mu}{\delta s \delta v} = \frac{\delta^2 U^\mu}{\delta v \delta s} + R^\mu{}_{\alpha\beta\gamma} U^\alpha U^\beta \frac{\partial x^\gamma}{\partial v}$$

Employing this commutation law for covariant differentiation enables us to express (8.6) in the form

$$\frac{\delta^2 U^\mu}{\delta v \delta s} = \frac{\delta^2 U^\mu}{\delta s \delta v} - R^\mu{}_{\alpha\beta\gamma} U^\alpha U^\beta \frac{\partial x^\gamma}{\partial v} = \frac{\delta F^\mu/m}{c^2 \delta v} \qquad (8.7)$$

In (8.7) $\partial x^\gamma/\partial v$ is a unit vector normal to the world lines, and the four velocity U^μ is a unit vector tangent to the world lines. The vector n^γ, defined by

$$n^\gamma = \frac{\partial x^\gamma}{\partial v}\, dv \qquad (8.8)$$

is an infinitesimal vector joining points with the same value of s on neighboring world lines with values of v differing by dv. The covariant derivative of $\partial x^\gamma/\partial v$ with respect to s can be written in the forms

$$\frac{\delta}{\delta s}\left(\frac{\partial x^\gamma}{\partial v}\right) = \frac{\delta}{\delta v}\left(\frac{\partial x^\gamma}{\partial s}\right) = \frac{\delta U^\gamma}{\delta v} \qquad (8.9)$$

Employing (8.6), (8.7), (8.8), and (8.9) then gives

$$\frac{\delta^2 n^\mu}{\delta s^2} + R^\mu{}_{\alpha\beta\gamma} U^\alpha n^\beta U^\gamma = \frac{\delta F^\mu/m}{c^2 \delta v} \, dv \qquad (8.10)$$

If the particles do not interact, the right side of (8.10) is zero and

$$\frac{\delta^2 n^\mu}{\delta s^2} + R^\mu{}_{\alpha\beta\gamma} U^\alpha n^\beta U^\gamma = 0 \qquad (8.10a)$$

For (8.10a) the particles move along geodesics. (8.10a) is called the equation of geodesic deviation.

8.2   Mass Quadrupole Detector

In order to discuss the detector[‡] of Fig. 8.1, we imagine

Figure 8.1

the two world lines are those of the two masses. Let n^γ be given by

$$n^\gamma = r^\gamma + \xi^\gamma \qquad (8.11)$$

with r^γ defined by

$$\frac{\delta r^\gamma}{\delta s} = 0, \qquad \text{(for all } s) \qquad (8.12)$$

$$r^\gamma \to n^\gamma$$

in the limit of large internal damping and all components

‡ An arrangement somewhat similar to this was independently suggested by H. Bondi at the Royaumont conference in June, 1959.

of $R^\mu{}_{\alpha\beta\delta} = 0$. (8.10) becomes

$$\frac{\delta^2\xi^\mu}{\delta s^2} + R^\mu{}_{\alpha\beta\gamma}U^\alpha U^\gamma[r^\beta + \xi^\beta] = \frac{f^\mu}{mc^2} \qquad (8.13)$$

In (8.13) we have denoted by f^μ the differences in (nongravitational) forces at the two masses. For f^μ we assume a restoring force $-k^\mu{}_\alpha\xi^\alpha$ and a damping force $-cD^\mu{}_\alpha(\delta\xi^\alpha/\delta s)$. $k^\mu{}_\alpha$ and $D^\mu{}_\alpha$ are tensors associated with the spring. (8.13) then becomes

$$\frac{\delta^2\xi^\mu}{\delta s^2} + \frac{D^\mu{}_\alpha}{cm}\frac{\delta\xi^\alpha}{\delta s} + \frac{k^\mu{}_\alpha\xi^\alpha}{mc^2} = -R^\mu{}_{\alpha\beta\gamma}U^\alpha U^\gamma[r^\beta + \xi^\beta] \qquad (8.14)$$

We now let time run in the direction of the tangent to the world line of the center of mass. The oscillator is in free fall. We use coordinates in which the Christoffel symbols vanish and write (8.14) in the approximate form‡ (assuming $\xi \ll r$),

$$\frac{d^2\xi^\mu}{dt^2} + \frac{D^\mu{}_\alpha}{m}\frac{d\xi^\alpha}{dt} + \frac{k^\mu{}_\alpha\xi^\alpha}{m} = -c^2 R^\mu{}_{0\alpha 0}r^\alpha \qquad (8.15)$$

In (8.15) we see that the driving force for the harmonic oscillator is the Riemann tensor. Measurement of displacement amplitude or power absorbed enables one to calculate certain components of the Riemann tensor.‡‡

‡ If the particles are free, the second and third terms of (8.15) vanish. In Section 7.2 we showed that a locally plane gravitational wave traveling in the x^1 direction has $R_{\mu 010}$ equal to zero. It therefore follows from (8.15) that if the vector which joins two closely spaced free particles is in the direction of propagation of the wave, no relative displacements occur. For free particles the maximum relative displacements occur if the particles are in the transverse plane. This result has appeared in the work of Pirani.

‡‡ Measurement of the Riemann tensor by comparing accelerations of free test particles has been considered by F. A. E. Pirani.[2,3] The results of this chapter indicate that interacting particles must be used, in practice. The correspondence between voltage in a piezoelectric crystal and R_{i0j0}, which is discussed in Section 8.2, may provide a basis for consideration of measurement problems in quantized general relativity. A very small volume of crystal is needed in consequence of the fact that the wavelength of the acoustic resonance vibrations is five orders smaller than the wavelength of the gravitational waves.

From (8.15) we may conclude that energy may always be absorbed from any gravitational field for which the Fourier transform of R_{i0j0} does not vanish in a locally Lorentz frame which is propagated along a geodesic line. This geodesic is then the world line of the center of mass of our harmonic oscillator.

Suppose now that sinusoidal (weak-field-approximation) gravitational waves are incident. An orthogonal comoving coordinate system is employed, with the oscillator oriented in the direction of the x^1 axis. $k^\mu{}_\alpha$ and $D^\mu{}_\alpha$ are imagined to have one component only, $k^1{}_1 = k$ and $D^1{}_1 = D$. Taking the Fourier transform of (8.15) leads to

$$\xi^\mu(\omega) = \frac{mc^2 R^\mu{}_{0\alpha0}(\omega) r^\alpha}{(\omega^2 m - i\omega D\delta^\mu{}_1 - k\delta^\mu{}_1)} \tag{8.16}$$

(8.16) is a maximum at resonance, $-\omega^2 m + k = 0$. The total dissipation $D = D_{ex} + D_{in}$ where D_{ex} is the external dissipation and D_{in} is the internal dissipation associated with irreversible processes within the antenna. The power which can be delivered to auxiliary apparatus with D_{ex} is

$$\tfrac{1}{2}\omega^2 D_{ex} \xi^2 = \frac{m^2 c^4 (R^\mu{}_{0\alpha0} r^\alpha)^2 D_{ex}}{2(D_{ex} + D_{in})^2} \tag{8.17}$$

(8.17) is a maximum when $D_{ex} = D_{in}$, and the maximum power P_M is given by

$$P_M = \frac{m^2 c^4 (R^\mu{}_{0\alpha0} r^\alpha)^2}{8D_{in}} \tag{8.18}$$

The sinusoidal gravitational waves are now assumed to be radiated by a linear mass quadrupole oscillator. The transformation laws indicate that to a good approximation, $R^\mu{}_{0\alpha0}$, as seen in a frame fixed in the center of mass of the radiator, is the same as that seen in a frame fixed in the center of mass of the detector, for small velocities. Using the solution for the linear mass quadrupole oscillator of Section 7.5, the mean-squared value of $R^\mu{}_{0\alpha0} r^\alpha$ is calculated and averaged over all possible orientations of the receiver. Let t_{or} be the radiated power per unit area averaged over a sphere, for the linear mass quadrupole oscillator. The total radiated power P is given by

$$P = 4\pi r^2 t_{or} = \frac{GI_0{}^2 \omega^6}{15\pi c^5} \tag{8.19}$$

where I_0 is the amplitude of the quadrupole moment. (8.19) and the known expressions for the fields then give, for the mean-squared value of $R^\mu{}_{0\alpha 0} r^\alpha$ in a direction normal to the axis of the radiator

$$[(R^\mu{}_{0\alpha 0} r^\alpha)^2]_{av} = \frac{4\pi \beta^2 |r|^2 G}{c^5} t_{or} \tag{8.20}$$

In (8.20) β is the propagation vector of the gravitational wave. Employing (8.18) and (8.20) gives

$$P_M = \frac{\pi m^2 \beta^2 |r|^2 G}{2c D_{in}} t_{or} \tag{8.21}$$

The influence of the internal dissipation D_{in} will now be considered. First we assume that no irreversible processes take place within the antenna itself and that D_{in} is due entirely to radiation damping of the detector. The known solution for a linear mass quadrupole oscillator enables us to calculate the radiation resistance of the detector D_{in} as

$$D_{in} = \frac{2G\omega^4 m^2 |r|^2}{15 c^5} \tag{8.22}$$

(8.21) and (8.22) give

$$P_{M \text{ (radiation damping only)}} = \frac{15\lambda^2}{16\pi} t_{or} \tag{8.23}$$

The implication of (8.23) is that the average absorption cross section S_A for a detector which is damped only by its own reradiation is

$$S_A = \frac{15\lambda^2}{16\pi} \tag{8.24}$$

We see from (8.24) that under these conditions the average absorption cross section is roughly a wavelength squared, and is independent of the constant of gravitation. Unfortunately the condition that the internal damping be only due to radiation cannot be attained in practice because other irreversible phenomena within the antenna are many orders greater than the radiation damping. In order to make this clear, we calculate the quality factor, denoted by the symbol Q, which is defined by

$$Q = \frac{\omega \ (\text{maximum stored energy})}{\text{power dissipated}}$$

The Q associated with radiation damping, denoted by Q_R, is

$$Q_R = \frac{15c^5}{2G\omega^3 m |r|^2} \tag{8.25}$$

For an antenna at $\omega = 2\pi \times 10^7$, a reasonable value of $mr^2 = 10$ g cm^2 and (25) gives $Q_R \sim 10^{34}$. A practical antenna might be expected to have a $Q \sim 10^6$.

We therefore must deal with systems limited by internal damping orders larger than gravitational radiation damping, and under these conditions the average absorbed power will not be independent of the kind of antenna. For an antenna orientation arranged for maximum response,

$$[(R^\mu{}_{0\alpha 0} r^\alpha)^2]_{\text{av}} = \frac{15\pi G \beta^2 |r|^2}{c^5} t_{\text{or}} \tag{8.26}$$

(8.26) and (8.18) lead to power absorbed P_A, given by

$$P_A = \frac{15\pi G m^2 \beta^2 |r|^2}{8c D_{\text{in}}} t_{\text{or}} = \frac{15\pi G m Q_{\text{in}} \beta^2 |r|^2}{8\omega c} t_{\text{or}} \tag{8.27}$$

In (8.27) Q_{in} is the Q associated with internal irreversible processes, $Q_{\text{in}} = \omega m / D_{\text{in}}$. The cross section S, implied by (8.27), is

$$S = \frac{15\pi G m Q_{\text{in}} \beta^2 |r|^2}{8\omega c} \tag{8.28}$$

For a continuous spectrum the absorbed power is

$$P_A = \frac{1}{t'} \int_{-t'/2}^{t'/2} \int_{-\infty}^{\infty} \frac{m^2 c^4 D_{\text{ex}} \, \omega\omega' R^\mu_{0\alpha0}(\omega) R^\mu_{0\beta0}(\omega') r^\alpha r^\beta e^{i(\omega-\omega')t}}{2(-\omega^2 m + i\omega D + k)(-\omega'^2 m - i\omega' D + k)} \, d\omega d\omega' dt$$

$$\approx \pi^2 Gmc^{-1} \beta^2 |r|^2 t_{\text{or}}(\omega_0) \qquad (8.29)$$

In (8.29) $t_{\text{or}}(\omega_0)$ is the power spectrum of t_{or} in the vicinity of the resonant frequency ω_0.

In order to further discuss these results we must consider the excitation of a continuous medium by a gravitational wave. This is necessary in order to be able to account for the interaction of the mass of the spring with the wave and to account for the effects of the finite velocity of propagation of the elastic forces of the spring.

8.3 Interaction of a Crystal with a Gravitational Wave

The starting point for our discussion is expression (8.10). The infinitesimal vector n^μ is from a reference point in the crystal to a neighboring point. The mass m is imagined to belong to an infinitesimal volume surrounding the neighboring point. On the right side of (8.10) we must now include both elastic forces and dissipative forces. We write n^μ as

$$n^\mu = r^\mu + \theta_\alpha{}^\mu r^\alpha \qquad (8.30)$$

r^μ is defined by the conditions

$$\frac{\delta r^\mu}{\delta s} = 0, \qquad \text{(for all } s\text{)}$$

$$r^\mu \to n^\mu \qquad (8.31)$$

in the limit of large internal damping and flat space. We may now express Eq. (8.10) in the form

$$r^\mu \frac{\delta^2 \theta_{\mu\nu}}{\delta s^2} + r^\mu B \frac{\delta \theta_{\mu\nu}}{\delta s} + r^\mu Y^{\alpha\beta} \frac{\delta^2 \theta_{\mu\nu}}{\delta x^\alpha \delta x^\beta} + R_{\nu\alpha\mu\beta}[r^\mu + \theta_\gamma{}^\mu r^\gamma] U^\alpha U^\beta = 0$$

$$(8.32)$$

Here we are assuming an isotropic crystal. The second

term accounts for internal damping and the third term accounts for the elastic forces. B and $Y^{\alpha\beta}$ are normalized to unit mass density. Again U^α is a unit vector tangent to the world lines. Since r^μ can be arbitrarily specified, it follows that

$$\frac{\delta^2\theta_{\mu\nu}}{\delta s^2} + B\,\frac{\delta\theta_{\mu\nu}}{\delta s} + Y^{\alpha\beta}\frac{\delta^2\theta_{\mu\nu}}{\delta x^\alpha\,\delta x^\beta} + R_{\nu\alpha\mu\beta}U^\alpha U^\beta + R_{\nu\alpha\gamma\beta}U^\alpha U^\beta\theta_\mu{}^\gamma = 0$$

$$(8.33)$$

In (8.33) the fourth term is clearly symmetric in the indices ν and μ. The last term in (8.33) may ordinarily be dropped because it is many orders smaller than the fourth one. For the strain tensor which is the symmetric part of $\theta_{\mu\nu}$ we may therefore write

$$\frac{\delta^2\theta_{\mu\nu\,(\text{sym})}}{\delta s^2} + B\,\frac{\delta\theta_{\mu\nu\,(\text{sym})}}{\delta s} + Y^{\alpha\beta}\frac{\delta^2\theta_{\mu\nu\,(\text{sym})}}{\delta x^\alpha\,\delta x^\beta} \approx -R_{\nu\alpha\mu\beta}U^\alpha U^\beta$$

$$(8.33a)$$

We now consider a special case of (8.33a), namely excitation of longitudinal acoustic waves. An approximate form, for waves in the direction x^1 of an orthogonal coordinate system (with the time direction tangent to the world line of the observer) is

$$y\,\frac{\partial^2\theta}{\partial(x^1)^2} - \rho_M\,\frac{\partial^2\theta}{\partial t^2} - b\,\frac{\partial\theta}{\partial t} = c^2\rho_M R^1{}_{010}\qquad(8.34)$$

In (8.34) ρ_M is the density, y is an appropriate modulus, and b is a damping constant. We assume that $R^1{}_{010}$ has its origin in incident sinusoidal gravitational waves so that

$$c^2 R^1{}_{010} = -fe^{i(\omega t - \beta_k x^k)}\qquad(8.35)$$

In (8.35) the index k runs from 1 to 3. Let v_s be the sound velocity $\sqrt{[y/\rho_M]}$, λ_s be the wavelength of sound, $k_s = 2\pi/\lambda_s$, $\alpha = b/2\rho_M v_s$, and $\gamma = \alpha + ik_s$. Then to a good approximation the solution of (8.34) is

$$\theta = [A\gamma\cosh\gamma x^1 - f\omega^{-2}e^{-i\beta_k x^k}]e^{i\omega t}\qquad(8.36)$$

The displacement of points relative to the center of mass of the crystal, which we denote by ξ, may be calculated by integration of (8.36) with respect to x^1 as

$$\xi = \left[A \sinh \gamma x^1 - \frac{f}{i\beta_1\omega^2} (1 - e^{-i\beta_1 x^1}) \right] e^{i\omega t} \qquad (8.36a)$$

Making use of the boundary condition that θ vanishes at the ends leads to

$$A \approx \frac{f \cos \beta_1 l}{\omega^2 \gamma (i\alpha l \sin k_s l + \cos k_s l)} \qquad (8.37)$$

In (8.37) l is half the length of the crystal. The first term of (8.36) gives the contribution of the acoustic waves[‡] and the second term gives the strains which would be set up if there were no internal forces at all. (8.37) must be modified if the crystal is piezoelectric.

(8.37) has maxima when $k_s l$ is an odd multiple of $\pi/2$; however it is clear from the denominator that the largest maximum is the first one for which the total length is half an acoustic wavelength. The system composed of the two masses and spring (Fig. 8.1) must be described by an equation such as (8.34), when the spacing of the masses approaches half an acoustic wavelength. It is clear that the largest value we can expect from (8.28) will occur when r is half an

---

[‡] A study of (8.36a) indicates that the apparatus located on the earth's surface will behave as though it were in free fall. For consider the effect of gravitational waves on the internal motions of the earth, applying (8.36a) to the normal modes of the earth itself. The first term on the right represents the acoustic waves, the remaining terms represent the motion if there were no interactions. The ratio of the terms is, using (8.37),

$$\frac{\beta_1 \omega^2 A}{f} \approx \frac{\lambda_s}{\lambda \alpha l} = \frac{v_s}{c(\alpha l)}$$

The ratio of the velocity of sound to the velocity of light is about 10^{-5}, much smaller than the product of length and absorption coefficient for sound α in the earth. This argument is only valid for gravitational wavelengths comparable with or shorter than the earth's radius.

acoustic wavelength in the spring. This is an important limitation because the velocity of acoustic waves is about five orders smaller than the velocity of light, so the cross sections implied by (8.28) are ten orders smaller than would be the case if the elastic forces of the spring were propagated with the velocity of light. Such a limitation could be overcome in a number of ways. One might employ restoring forces transmitted by electric and magnetic fields, with the velocity of light. The piezoelectric effect may be employed, in which case the polarization charges on the crystal faces may give rise to some stress components which do not change sign every half acoustic wavelength.

In a piezoelectric crystal a strain results in an electric polarization P_μ given by

$$P_\mu = \varepsilon_{\alpha\beta} \mathscr{E}^{\alpha\beta}{}_\mu$$

Here $\mathscr{E}^{\alpha\beta}{}_\mu$ is the piezoelectric stress tensor. The electric polarization gives rise to an electric field over the crystal. Its integrated value may give a terminal voltage large enough to be observed with a low-noise radio receiver. Measurement of this voltage measures components R_{i0j0} of the Riemann tensor if a crystal with suitable constants is employed.

The system of stresses in the crystal is modified in a significant way if it is piezoelectric. Additional terms involving the piezoelectric constants need to be added to Eq. (8.33). We consider a very simple example. Suppose a single longitudinal mode is excited, with sound velocity in the x^1 direction. Let the thickness in the x^2 direction be small and assume that the crystal faces normal to the x^2 direction are plated with a conductor. The piezoelectric relations (5) are

$$-T = \theta Y_0 + DH/4\pi; \qquad E = D/K + H\theta \qquad (8.38)$$

In (8.38) T is the stress, K is the dielectric constant, θ is the strain, Y_0 is the elastic modulus, E is the electric field intensity, and D is the electric displacement. Both D and E are assumed to have components in the x^2 direction only.

H is the piezoelectric constant relating open-circuit voltage to strain. A study of (8.38) and the equations of motion of mass elements of the crystal indicates that a wave equation similar to (8.34) results with

$$y = Y_0 - H^2K/4\pi$$

Since the crystal surface normal to the x^2 direction is plated with a conductor, $\partial E/\partial x^1 = 0$. At the free ends of the crystal $T = 0$. If the crystal is coupled to an external impedance Z we may write

$$-\int E\,dx^2 = (4\pi)^{-1}Z\frac{\partial}{\partial t}\int D\,dx^1\,dx^3$$

These boundary conditions and the wave equation (8.34) then lead to the result

$$\theta = [A_1\gamma \cosh \gamma x^1 - f\omega^{-2}e^{-i\beta_k x^k}]e^{i\omega t} \qquad (8.36a)$$

where γ, β, and f are as defined earlier. This has the same form as (8.36), but now the constant A_1 is given in terms of the length l_1 in the x^1 direction and lengths l_2 and l_3 in directions x^2 and x^3, and the "clamped" capacitance C as

$$A_1 = \left(\frac{f}{\beta_1\omega^2}\right)$$

$$\left[\frac{8\pi^2\beta_1 l_2(1+i\omega C Z)(Y_0-H^2K/4\pi)\cos\beta_1 l_1/2 + iH^2K^2 l_3\omega Z \sin \beta_1 l_1/2}{8\pi^2 l_2(Y_0-H^2K/4\pi)(\gamma\cosh\gamma l_1/2)(1+i\omega C Z)+i\omega Z H^2K^2 l_3\sinh\gamma l_1/2}\right]$$

$$(8.39)$$

and the voltage which appears at the crystal terminals when coupled to an impedance Z is

$$V = \left(\frac{1}{2\pi}\right)\left(\frac{i\omega ZHKl_3}{1+i\omega C Z}\right)[A_1\sinh\gamma l_1/2 - (f/\beta_1\omega^2)\sin\beta_1 l_1/2] \qquad (8.40)$$

The electrical network theorems now permit straightforward calculation of the power which can be delivered by the detector to a radio receiver. For a crystal with constants similar to ordinary crystalline quartz on which sinusoidal gravitational waves are incident, the power which can be transferred is roughly

$$P_A \approx 10^{-25} \omega^{-1} V Q_t t_{\text{or}} \text{ ergs/sec} \qquad (8.41)$$

In (8.41) ω is again the angular frequency and t_{or} is the incident gravitational power flow in ergs per square centimeter per second. Q_t is the Q of the crystal and associated electric circuit. A cubic meter of crystal at $\omega \sim 10^3$ gives a cross section for absorption $\sim 10^{-14}$ cm^2. This is for perfect crystals driving amplifiers without positive feedback. Imperfect crystals may have cross sections three orders smaller. For a continuous spectrum with a power spectrum function $t_{\text{or}}(\omega)$, the power absorbed is

$$P_A \approx 10^{-25} V t_{\text{or}}(\omega_0) \text{ ergs/sec} \qquad (8.42)$$

(8.41) and (8.42) provide a basis for discussion of sensitivity. In microwave spectroscopy it has been found that all spurious effects other than random fluctuations can be recognized. A similar assumption will be made here. The random fluctuations are partly thermal in origin, partly the result of spontaneous emission processes. For synchronous detection of sinusoidal waves, the power output of the detector must exceed the noise power (6) P_{N1} given by

$$P_{N1} = \frac{N\hbar\omega}{8\tau_A [e^{\hbar\omega/kT} - 1]}$$

k is Boltzmann's constant, T is the gravitational antenna temperature, N is the noise factor of the receiver (expected to be less than 25 and more than 1), and τ_A is the averaging time. A different expression is required if radiation with a continuous spectrum is being studied. In this case the power delivered by the detector must exceed

$$P_{N2} = \left(\frac{\pi^3 \omega}{64\tau_A Q_t} \right)^{\frac{1}{2}} \left[\frac{N\hbar\omega}{e^{\hbar\omega/kT} - 1} \right]$$

Experiments are being planned to search for interstellar[‡] gravitational radiation[‡‡] using methods described here. For the first method the earth itself is the block of material constituting the antenna. The normal modes of the earth (about 1 cycle per hour) are excited by incident gravitational

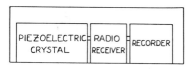

Figure 8.2

waves. This procedure is limited by the relatively low Q of the earth and the high noise background of its core. The apparatus of Fig. 8.2 is employed in the second method, in which the strains induced in the crysal are employed. Search

[‡] J. A. Wheeler has noted (onzième Conseil de l'Institut International de Physique Solvay, *La Structure et l'évolution de l'universe*, Editions Stoops, Brussels, 1958, p. 112) that the density of gravitational radiation could be as high as 10^{-29} to 10^{-28} g/cm^3 ($\sim 10^3$ ergs/cm^2 sec) and still be consistent with present information about the rate of expansion of the universe. He and M. Schwarzschild (private communication) have subsequently noted that if this radiation were set free by the same process which caused the inhomogeneous collection of matter into galaxies, it would be characterized at that time, and therefore also now by the same scale of lengths, of the order of 10^{24} cm today (10^6 years vibration period).

$$\left(\frac{\partial g_{\text{typical}}}{\partial x}\right)^2 \sim \frac{\rho_M G}{c^2} \sim 0.2 \times 10^{-56} \text{ cm}^{-2}$$

$$\delta g_{\text{typical}} \sim 0.5 \times 10^{-28} \text{ cm}^{-1} \times 10^{24} \text{ cm} \sim 10^{-4}$$

This would appear to be not too small, but too slow to measure, by these methods.

[‡‡] Experimental work along this line is now being carried out by David Zipoy and Robert L. Forward, in collaboration with the author. The piezoelectric effect gives enhanced sensitivity when a mass which is many acoustic wavelengths on a side is used. At low frequencies this is not important because a mass which is one-half acoustic wavelength long is already quite large and may not be obtainable as a single crystal. Excitation of resonant acoustic vibrations in a large block of metal, by the gravitational wave, is being considered, along with the arrangements of Figs. 8.2 and 8.3.

at frequencies $\sim 10^3$ cycles/sec is planned. The earth rotates the apparatus. If radiation is incident from some given direction it may be observed from the diurnal change in amplifier noise output. The arrangement of Fig. 8.3 should not require

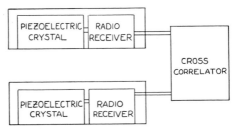

Figure 8.3

rotation. If radiation is incident it will cause correlated outputs. All sources of internal fluctuations will be uncorrelated. Low-noise amplifiers such as masers (7) may be employed.

The apparatus must not respond to earth vibrations. Dr. Zipoy has proposed ingenious acoustic filters with amplifiers to sense, then drive the mounts to cancel the effects.

8.4   Rotations Induced by Gravitational Radiation

Dirac (private communication) has suggested that astronomical anomalies might be correlated with effects of gravitational radiation. To discuss this and to consider detection by observing rotations we return to expression (8.5). Let a group of masses be situated near the space origin of a coordinate system and let the infinitesimal vector r^μ be the position vector of one of the masses. Let $\varepsilon_{\mu\alpha\beta\kappa}$ be the Levi Civita tensor density. Multiply (8.5) by $\varepsilon_{\mu\alpha\beta\kappa} r^\beta$ to obtain

$$\varepsilon_{\mu\alpha\beta\kappa} r^\beta \frac{\delta}{\delta s} \frac{dx^\alpha}{ds} = \frac{d}{ds} \varepsilon_{\mu\alpha\beta\kappa} r^\beta \frac{dx^\alpha}{ds} + \varepsilon_{\mu\alpha\beta\kappa} r^\beta \Gamma^\alpha{}_{\gamma\delta} U^\gamma U^\delta = \varepsilon_{\mu\alpha\beta\kappa} r^\beta F^\alpha / mc^2$$

$$(8.43)$$

Here again U^δ is a unit vector tangent to the world lines and in the second term of (8.43) we have used the identity $\varepsilon_{\mu\alpha\beta\kappa}U^\alpha U^\beta = 0$. Let the world line of the origin be a path for which the Christoffel symbols vanish. Then it follows that (8.43) can be written

$$\varepsilon_{\mu\alpha\beta\kappa}r^\beta \frac{\delta}{\delta s}\frac{dx^\alpha}{ds} = \frac{d}{ds}\varepsilon_{\mu\alpha\beta\kappa}r^\beta \frac{dx^\alpha}{ds} + \varepsilon_{\mu\alpha\beta\kappa}r^\beta \frac{\partial\Gamma^\alpha{}_{\gamma\delta}}{\partial x^\omega}U^\gamma U^\delta r^\omega \quad (8.44)$$

In these coordinates $R^\alpha{}_{\gamma\omega\delta} = \partial\Gamma^\alpha{}_{\gamma\delta}/\partial x^\omega$, so (8.44) becomes

$$\varepsilon_{\mu\alpha\beta\kappa}r^\beta \frac{\delta}{\delta s}\frac{dx^\alpha}{ds} = \frac{d}{ds}\varepsilon_{\mu\alpha\beta\kappa}r^\beta \frac{dx^\alpha}{ds} - \varepsilon_{\mu\alpha\beta\kappa}R^\beta{}_{\gamma\omega\delta}U^\gamma U^\delta r^\alpha r^\omega \quad (8.45)$$

If we now use (8.43) and (8.45) and sum over all masses we obtain

$$\begin{aligned}
\sum_{\text{masses}} \frac{d}{ds}\varepsilon_{\mu\alpha\beta\kappa}r^\beta \frac{dx^\alpha}{ds} \\
= \sum_{\text{masses}} \varepsilon_{\mu\alpha\beta\kappa}R^\beta{}_{\gamma\omega\delta}U^\gamma U^\delta r^\alpha r^\omega - \sum_{\text{masses}} \frac{\varepsilon_{\mu\alpha\beta\kappa}r^\alpha F^\beta}{mc^2}
\end{aligned} \quad (8.46)$$

(8.46) is a generalization of the relation between torque and change of angular momentum. If there are no nongravitational forces acting and if we take the time direction tangent to the world line of the center of mass, (8.46) becomes

$$\sum_{\text{masses}} \frac{d}{ds}\varepsilon_{\mu\alpha\beta\kappa}r^\beta \frac{dx^\alpha}{ds} = \sum_{\text{masses}} \varepsilon_{\mu\alpha\beta\kappa}R^\beta{}_{0\omega0}r^\alpha r^\omega \quad (8.47)$$

We may apply (8.47) to the calculation of the irregular fluctuations in the period of rotation of the earth caused by incident gravitational radiation with a continuous spectrum. Under these conditions a straightforward calculation leads to the result

$$\frac{(\Delta L)^2{}_{\text{ms}}}{L^2} \approx \frac{25\pi G}{\omega^2 c^3} t_{\text{or}} \quad (8.48)$$

Here $(\Delta L)^2{}_{\text{ms}}$ is the mean-square fluctuation in the earth's angular momentum, L is the angular momentum of rotation, and t_{or} is the total gravitational wave flux in ergs per square centimeter per second, assuming its Fourier transform is concentrated near zero frequency. If we arbitrarily assume that all the earth's rotational anomalies are due to incident gravitational waves, t_{or} is calculated to be 5×10^8 ergs/cm² sec. It is clear from this that the earth's rotation is not a useful detector unless the size of the anomaly can be reduced. The other astronomical anomalies lead to larger figures.

8.5   Generation of Gravitational Waves

It would be very desirable to be able to generate gravitational waves with sufficient energy to be detected in the laboratory. A number of important experiments could be done.

For a spinning rod, (7.56) gave the formula for the radiated power P_R as

$$P_R = 1.73 \times 10^{-59} I_m{}^2 \omega^6 \text{ ergs/sec} \tag{8.49}$$

For a given moment of inertia I_m, the angular frequency ω can be increased until the rod ultimately breaks. If we write the maximum value of ω in terms of the tensile strength and express the result in terms of the elastic modulus and strain, we obtain for the length l the formula

$$l = \lambda_s \sqrt{[2\delta]}/\pi \tag{8.50}$$

In (8.50) δ is the maximum allowed strain for the material and λ_s is the wavelength of sound in the rod at the angular frequency of rupture. The implication of (8.50) is that the wavelength of the gravitational waves which can be radiated by a rod is at least 1,000,000 times the length of the rod. Also the moment of inertia is limited to values less than about

$$\frac{10^{-3} \rho_M \lambda_s{}^5 \delta^{\frac{5}{2}}}{12\pi^5} \tag{8.51}$$

In (8.51) ρ_M is again the density, and we are considering a fairly slender rod, for which the length is an order larger than the lateral dimensions. Employing (8.51) in (8.49) leads to

$$P_R < 4 \times 10^{-63} \rho_M{}^2 v_s{}^{10} \delta^5 \omega^{-4} \qquad (8.52)$$

(8.52) shows that contrary to the appearance of (8.49) low-frequency operation with large rods gives more radiation than high-frequency spinning of small rods. About 10^{-30} ergs/sec can be radiated by such a 1-m rod.

A new method for generation of gravitational waves is suggested by the field equations. The source of the gravitational field is the stress energy tensor. Time-dependent stresses can be produced electrically in a piezoelectric crystal, and these give rise to radiation. The weak-field solutions are entirely adequate for this kind of discussion since the metric is expected to differ from the Lorentz metric by perhaps one part in 10^{30}. Recall the weak-field solutions

$$\varphi_\mu{}^\nu = h_\mu{}^\nu - \tfrac{1}{2}\delta_\mu{}^\nu h \approx \frac{4G}{c^4} \int \frac{(T_\mu{}'^\nu)_{\text{retarded}}\, d^3x'}{|\mathbf{r} - \mathbf{r}'|} \qquad (8.53)$$

In order to apply (8.53) to the problem of radiation by a crystal we first assume that acoustic resonance is employed and that one-dimensional compressional waves are set up. The components of $T_\mu{}^\nu$ are then given by

$$T_0{}^0 \approx -\rho_M c^2 \left[1 - \frac{V_p}{v_3} \cos \omega t \cos k_s x^3 \right] [1 - U(x^3 - l - A_0 \cos \omega t)$$
$$- U(-x^3 - l - A_0 \cos \omega t)] \qquad (8.54)$$

$$T_0{}^3 \approx \rho_M V_p c \sin \omega t \sin k_s x^3 [1 - U(x^3 - l - A_0 \cos \omega t)$$
$$- U(-x^3 - l - A_0 \cos \omega t)] \qquad (8.55)$$

$$T_3{}^3 \approx -\rho_M V_p v_s \cos \omega t \cos k_s x^3 [1 - U(x^3 - l - A_0 \cos \omega t)$$
$$- U(-x^3 - l - A_0 \cos \omega t)] \qquad (8.56)$$

In these expressions it is assumed that the waves travel in the direction x^3, V_p is the particle velocity, v_s is the sound velocity, and U is a step function defined by $U(x) = 0$ for

$x < 0$ and $U(x) = 1$ for $x > 0$. A_0 is the vibration amplitude of the free end. Making use of these expressions in (8.46) and employing the Einstein form of the stress energy pseudotensor enables the total radiated power to be calculated. The maximum value of A_0 is determined by the maximum strain which is allowed before rupture takes place.

For quartz the result for acoustic resonance is

$$P < \left[\tfrac{16}{15} G \rho_M{}^2 S^2 v_s \left(\frac{v_s}{c} \right)^5 \times 10^{-6} \right]_\omega$$
$$+ \left[\tfrac{\pi}{15} G \rho_M{}^2 S^2 n_\lambda{}^2 v_s \left(\frac{v_s}{c} \right)^5 \times 10^{-12} \right]_{2\omega} \tag{8.57}$$

In (8.57) S is the cross-sectional area, the term with subscript ω gives the radiated power at the fundamental frequency, and the second term gives the power radiated at twice the fundamental frequency. The resonator must be a multiple n_λ of a half acoustic wavelength long. The first term of (8.57) is seen to be independent of n_λ. This is because for $n_\lambda > 1$ the crystal is essentially an assemblage of electric quadrupoles with a given quadrupole driven out of phase with respect to its nearest neighbors. The resulting fundamental frequency radiation is approximately that of a single quadrupole. Each half wave section has an equivalent moment $M A_0 \lambda_s / 2\pi$, where M is the mass of a single half wave resonator; A_0 and λ_s are defined by (8.54), (8.55), and (8.56). If a large number of separate resonators are located within a region of linear dimensions less than a gravitational-wave half wavelength, the radiated power will be proportional to the square of the total number of crystals. In order to radiate 10^{-15} ergs/sec at the fundamental frequency, 10^6 crystals would be needed, each one half an acoustic wavelength thick and with a cross-sectional area of 50 cm². A complex phasing arrangement would be needed in order to properly drive the array.

It appears better to suppress the acoustic resonance vibrations and create, by the piezoelectric effect or by electrostriction, mechanical stress components which do not reverse sign every half acoustic wavelength. In order to see that this is possible it is only necessary to study the solution given (8) in the literature for the component T_{11} of the stress in a longitudinally vibrating crystal with x^3 as the thickness direction, with a conducting plating on the faces normal to x^3. The thickness is assumed small, for simplicity, and an externally applied electric field parallel to x^3 drives the crystal. The component T_{11} is then

$$T_{11} = d_{31}E_3 \left[\frac{\sin \dfrac{\omega(L-x)}{v_s} + \sin \dfrac{\omega x}{v_s} - \sin \dfrac{\omega L}{v_s}}{\sin \dfrac{\omega L}{v_s}} \right] \sin \omega t \quad (8.58)$$

In (8.58) d_{ij} is the tensor relating stress to electric field, E_3 is the electric field in the direction of x^3, and L is the total length. At resonance, $L\omega/v_s = \pi$, and losses would have to be taken into account in (8.58) by a hyperbolic function in the denominator. However, off resonance, for example at $L\omega/v_s = \pi/2$, (8.58) becomes

$$T_{11} = d_{31}E_3 \left[\cos \frac{\omega x}{v} + \sin \frac{\omega x}{v} - 1 \right] \sin \omega t \quad (8.59)$$

(8.59) is seen to have a component $-d_{31}E_3 \sin \omega t$, which does not reverse sign every half acoustic wavelength. A single large crystal, driven in this manner, will then give volume-integrated stress components which are large. The radiated power would be expected to be

$$P_R \approx \frac{G P^2_{\text{max}} \lambda^4 \pi^2}{120c^3} \quad (8.60)$$

In (8.60) P_{max} is the effective tensile strength in dynes per square centimeter and λ is again the gravitational-wave wavelength. The alternative method is to use electrostriction, either in a solid or a liquid. For a liquid a region comparable to a half gravitational wavelength on a side would have to be used. The space derivatives of the driving electric field would give rise to electrostriction stresses. A result similar to (8.60) gives the radiated power.

Waves 1 m long could be radiated by a crystal with dimensions 50 cm on a side. If it is driven just below the breaking point, each cyrstal would radiate 10^{-13} ergs/sec, assuming P_{max} is its static published value. This amounts to 100,000 gravitons/sec. Single crystal detectors of the type considered earlier may detect a power of about 10^{-3} ergs/sec at these wavelengths. A large gap therefore still exists between what can be generated and what can be detected in a small laboratory. Complex detection and generation arrays can narrow this gap. Large amounts of electrical power would have to be dissipated in crystals driven to the fracture point — perhaps 10^8 watts in a crystal 50 cm on a side. This might well be substantially reduced if low-temperature operation can be achieved. Also one might hope that low-temperature high-frequency operation might raise the effective tensile strengths. All these issues need careful experimental investigation. If the numbers employed earlier cannot be improved upon, it would require a crystal roughly 100 m on a side, and a large detection system, to generate and detect the gravitational radiation.

8.6   Other Radiation Experiments

The foregoing discussion was limited to very low energy gravitons. A large number of calculations were carried out by the author for the purpose of studying the feasibility of radiation experiments at higher energies. The results indicate that the situation is probably hopeless at intermediate energies corresponding to atomic, molecular, and nuclear transitions. As we have seen, the equations of general relativity have solutions in the weak field approximation which are very similar to those of electrodynamics. The lowest-order radiation processes in electrodynamics give radiation proportional to e^2, where e is the electronic charge. An electronic transition for which the selection rules permit graviton radiation would in lowest order be calculable by expressions similar to those of electrodynamics except that for e^2 we need to substitute Gm^2, where m is the mass of the electron. There are other, less important modifications. Another factor of the order of the square of the ratio of the Bohr radius to the wavelength would have to be included because quadrupole radiation is the lowest nonvanishing order. Now, $Gm^2/e^2 \approx 10^{-43}$, so it follows that graviton emission will be at least forty-three orders smaller than photon emission. At extremely high energies the situation will improve because the mass increases while the charge does not. For $Gm^2/e^2 \approx 1$, energies of the order of 10^{30} ev are needed. Since even 10^{20} ev is beyond the range of presently conceived machines the outlook for such experiments is not promising.

References

1. F. A. E. Pirani, *Proceedings of the Chapel Hill Conference on the Role of Gravitation in Physics*, 1957; ASTIA Document AD118180, p. 61.
2. F. A. E. Pirani, *Acta Phys. Polon.* 15, 6, 389 (1956).
3. J. Weber, Gravity Research Foundation prize essays, New Boston, New Hampshire, April, 1958, and April, 1959.
4. J. Weber, *Phys. Rev.* 117, 306 (1960).
5. W. P. Mason, *Electromechanical Transducers and Wave Filters*, Van Nostrand, New York, 1948, p. 202.
6. R. H. Dicke, *Rev. Sci. Instr.* 17, 268 (1946).
7. J. Weber, *Revs. Modern Phys.* 31, 681 (1959).
8. W. P. Mason, *Piezoelectric Crystals and Their Applications to Ultrasonics*, Van Nostrand, New York, 1950, p. 64.

CHAPTER 9

Selected Topics in General Relativity

There are reasons for thinking that the elementary formations which go to make up the atom are held together by gravitational forces.
A. Einstein

9.1 Unified Field Theories

In this concluding chapter we give a brief account of some important aspects of general relativity which are very significant, from a philosophical point of view, and may lead to developments in elementary particle theory.

The success in geometrization of the gravitational field led Einstein and others to search for a way to geometrize electromagnetism. The desirable elimination of forces by having particles move along geodesics ceases as soon as electrical forces are introduced. This is indicated by Eq. (4.54), which has the Lorentz force included in it.

When the general theory of relativity was formulated it was believed that the only forces in nature were those of gravity and electromagnetism, and that by geometrization of electromagnetism a unified treatment covering all of physics would result. The field equations relate a geometrical object on the left to a physical object on the right. Einstein felt that this was undesirable and that the use of the electromagnetic stress tensor in this way was at best a provisional solution. Also Einstein never accepted the postulates of the quantum mechanics. He hoped that a completely deterministic description of elementary particle and quantum phenomena would emerge from a search for the unified field (4, 5).

No complete geometrization of electrodynamics was

achieved. Indeed the search for a unified field theory would seem now to be a much more formidable task since nuclear forces and the phenomena of high-energy physics would have to be included. It is interesting that the 1916 general theory of relativity and classical electromagnetism can be expressed in terms of the geometrical quantity $R_{\mu\nu}$ alone, without ordinarily altering the physical content. This partial geometrization[†] was accomplished by Rainich (1) in 1927 and has recently been enlarged by Wheeler (2, 3) and Misner. Suppose we have only gravitation and electromagnetism, without charges. The Maxwell stress tensor (4.15) satisfies the relations[‡]

[†] No geometrical interpretation is given to the Maxwell tensor. It is eliminated from the equations by expressing the Maxwell stress tensor in terms of $R_{\mu\nu}$.

[‡] (9.1) and (9.2) follow directly from (4.15). To deduce (9.3) and for proof of other equations in this section, the following relations are very helpful. A generalized kronecker delta may be defined in terms of the Levi-Civita tensor density by writing

$$\varepsilon_{\alpha\beta\gamma\kappa}\,\varepsilon^{\mu\nu\rho\sigma} = \delta^{\mu\nu\rho\sigma}_{\alpha\beta\gamma\kappa} = \begin{vmatrix} \delta_\alpha{}^\mu & \delta_\beta{}^\mu & \delta_\gamma{}^\mu & \delta_\kappa{}^\mu \\ \delta_\alpha{}^\nu & \delta_\beta{}^\nu & \delta_\gamma{}^\nu & \delta_\kappa{}^\nu \\ \delta_\alpha{}^\rho & \delta_\beta{}^\rho & \delta_\gamma{}^\rho & \delta_\kappa{}^\rho \\ \delta_\alpha{}^\sigma & \delta_\beta{}^\sigma & \delta_\gamma{}^\sigma & \delta_\kappa{}^\sigma \end{vmatrix}$$

This indicates that the generalized kronecker delta changes sign on interchange of any pair of upper or lower indices, and that it vanishes if the same index appears more than once in either the upper or lower groups.

Most authors take $\varepsilon_{0123} = 1$ and $\varepsilon^{0123} = 1$. Care is required when employing both $\varepsilon_{\alpha\beta\gamma\delta}$ and $\varepsilon^{\alpha\beta\gamma\delta}$ in the same calculation. If we take the dual of $F_{\mu\nu}$ as

$$*F_{\mu\nu} = \varepsilon_{\mu\nu\alpha\beta}(-g)^{\frac{1}{2}}F^{\alpha\beta}/2$$

then

$$*F^{\mu\nu} = g^{\mu\iota}g^{\nu\kappa}\varepsilon_{\iota\kappa\alpha\beta}(-g)^{\frac{1}{2}}F^{\alpha\beta}/2$$

A straightforward reduction shows that to employ $\varepsilon^{\alpha\beta\gamma\delta}$ and remain consistent with the above expressions we must write:

$$*F^{\mu\nu} = -\,\varepsilon^{\mu\nu\alpha\beta}(-g)^{-\frac{1}{2}}F_{\alpha\beta}/2$$

These expressions may be employed to establish the following identity, valid for any two antisymmetric tensors in a four dimensional space:

$$A^{\nu\alpha}B_{\mu\alpha} - *A_{\mu\alpha}*B^{\nu\alpha} = \tfrac{1}{2}\delta_\mu{}^\nu A_{\alpha\beta}B^{\alpha\beta}$$

(footnote cont'd)

$$T_\alpha{}^\alpha = 0 \tag{9.1}$$

$$T_{00} > 0 \tag{9.2}$$

$$T_\mu{}^\alpha T_\alpha{}^\nu = \tfrac{1}{4}(T_{\alpha\beta} T^{\alpha\beta}) \delta_\mu{}^\nu \tag{9.3}$$

If the gravitational field equations are written in the form

$$R_\mu{}^\nu - \tfrac{1}{2}\delta_\mu{}^\nu R = \frac{8\pi G}{c^4} T_\mu{}^\nu$$

then contraction on the indices and the use of (9.1) leads to

$$R = 0 \tag{9.4}$$

so the field equations are

$$R_{\mu\nu} = \frac{8\pi G}{c^4} T_{\mu\nu} \tag{9.5}$$

The use of (9.3) and (9.5) lead to

$$R_\alpha{}^\beta R_\beta{}^\gamma = \tfrac{1}{4}\delta_\alpha{}^\gamma R_{\sigma\tau} R^{\sigma\tau} \tag{9.6}$$

The geometrical relations (9.4) and (9.6) apply to any gravitational field whose sources are a divergence-free Maxwell field. Another relation is needed to guarantee that the antisymmetric tensor out of which $T_{\mu\nu}$ (and $R_{\mu\nu}$) are constructed really satisfies Maxwell's equations. This additional relation is

$$\left[\frac{\varepsilon_{\beta\lambda\mu\nu} R^{\lambda\gamma;\mu} R_\gamma{}^\nu \sqrt{-g}}{R_{\sigma\tau} R^{\sigma\tau}} \right]_{,\iota} = \left[\frac{\varepsilon_{\iota\lambda\mu\nu} R^{\lambda\gamma;\mu} R_\gamma{}^\nu \sqrt{-g}}{R_{\sigma\tau} R^{\sigma\tau}} \right]_{,\beta} \tag{9.7}$$

(9.4), (9.6), and (9.7) are the formulation for gravity and electromagnetism, in the absence of charges. The expression (9.7) requires a somewhat lengthy proof which we outline, following Misner and Wheeler.

If we set $A = B$ and let A be the electromagnetic field tensor, the Maxwell stress tensor may be written

$$T_\mu{}^\alpha = \frac{1}{4\pi} \left[*F_{\mu\kappa}*F^{\alpha\kappa} + \tfrac{1}{4}\delta_\mu{}^\alpha F_{\iota\kappa} F^{\iota\kappa} \right]$$

Multiplying this by $T_\alpha{}^\nu$ as given by (4.15) then gives (9.3).

We shall require the dual of the electromagnetic field tensor $F^{\mu\nu}$, defined here by

$$*F_{\mu\nu} = (\sqrt{-g})\varepsilon_{\mu\nu\alpha\beta}F^{\alpha\beta}/2 \tag{9.8}$$

An operation $e^{*\alpha}$ is defined by

$$e^{*\alpha}F_{\mu\nu} = F_{\mu\nu}\cos\alpha + *F_{\mu\nu}\sin\alpha \tag{9.9}$$

We say that (9.9) constitutes a duality rotation on $F_{\mu\nu}$.[‡] The tensor $\xi_{\mu\nu}$ is defined by

$$\xi_{\mu\nu} = e^{-*\alpha}F_{\mu\nu} \tag{9.10}$$

corresponding to a duality rotation $-\alpha$.

By an appropriate choice of α we may obtain a tensor which is more simple then $F_{\mu\nu}$. Consider the invariants

$$\begin{aligned}
\tfrac{1}{2}\xi_{\alpha\beta}\xi^{\alpha\beta} &= \tfrac{1}{2}(F_{\alpha\beta}\cos\alpha - *F_{\alpha\beta}\sin\alpha)^2 \\
&= \tfrac{1}{2}F_{\alpha\beta}F^{\alpha\beta}\cos 2\alpha - \tfrac{1}{2}F_{\alpha\beta}*F^{\alpha\beta}\sin 2\alpha
\end{aligned} \tag{9.11a}$$

$$\tfrac{1}{2}\xi_{\alpha\beta}*\xi^{\alpha\beta} = \tfrac{1}{2}F_{\alpha\beta}F^{\alpha\beta}\sin 2\alpha + \tfrac{1}{2}F_{\alpha\beta}*F^{\alpha\beta}\cos 2\alpha \tag{9.11b}$$

We recall that (9.11a) is $H^2 - E^2$, and (9.11b) is $2E \cdot H$ in a Lorentz frame, with E and H the electric and magnetic fields associated with $\xi_{\alpha\beta}$. Select the angle α such that (9.11b) vanishes; the other invariant then becomes

$$\tfrac{1}{2}\xi_{\alpha\beta}\xi^{\alpha\beta} = \pm[(\tfrac{1}{2}F_{\alpha\beta}F^{\alpha\beta})^2 + (\tfrac{1}{2}F_{\alpha\beta}*F^{\alpha\beta})^2]^{\frac{1}{2}} = \pm\frac{c^4}{2G}(R_{\mu\nu}R^{\mu\nu})^{\frac{1}{2}} \tag{9.12}$$

The angle α is further restricted as to quadrant by requiring the sign in the right expressions of (9.12) to be negative. A field $\xi_{\alpha\beta}$ for which these requirements have been met is called an extremal field; it is a pure electric field, in the appropriate

---

‡ The dual of the dual of a tensor is the negative of the original tensor, in consequence of the fact that g is negative. The dual operation corresponds to a duality rotation angle of $\pi/2$. It is important to note that

$$*(e^{*\alpha}F_{\mu\nu}) = e^{*\alpha}*F_{\mu\nu}$$

Also, from the identity of the previous footnote,

$$F_{\alpha\beta}F^{\alpha\beta} = -*F_{\alpha\beta}*F^{\alpha\beta}$$

Lorentz frame. The extremal field is a convenient quantity to manipulate. For the remainder of this section $\xi_{\alpha\beta}$ will denote the extremal field. An arbitrary field may be obtained from $\xi_{\alpha\beta}$ by a duality rotation and a scale factor. It may be verified, using the formula (4.15) for the Maxwell stress tensor that all the components of $T_{\mu\nu}$ are unchanged by a duality rotation. Given an $R_{\mu\nu}$ which originates in a Maxwell field, we cannot uniquely specify the Maxwell field, but we can determine it up to a constant times a duality rotation. It will be convenient to write the Maxwell equations in terms of $\xi_{\mu\nu}$, then to write another expression quadratic in $\xi_{\mu\nu}$, in terms of $R_{\mu\nu}$, which then leads to (9.7). The Maxwell equations are expressed as

$$0 = F^{\mu\nu}{}_{;\nu} = \left(\xi^{\mu\nu}{}_{;\nu} + {}^*\xi^{\mu\nu}\frac{\partial\alpha}{\partial x^\nu}\right)\cos\alpha + \left({}^*\xi^{\mu\nu}{}_{;\nu} - \xi^{\mu\nu}\frac{\partial\alpha}{\partial x^\nu}\right)\sin\alpha$$

$$(9.13a)$$

$$0 = {}^*F^{\mu\nu}{}_{;\nu} = \left(-\xi^{\mu\nu}{}_{;\nu} - {}^*\xi^{\mu\nu}\frac{\partial\alpha}{\partial x^\nu}\right)\sin\alpha + \left({}^*\xi^{\mu\nu}{}_{;\nu} - \xi^{\mu\nu}\frac{\partial\alpha}{\partial x^\nu}\right)\cos\alpha$$

$$(9.13b)$$

These are rearranged to give

$$\xi^{\mu\nu}{}_{;\nu} + {}^*\xi^{\mu\nu}\frac{\partial\alpha}{\partial x^\nu} = 0 \qquad (9.14a)$$

$$ {}^*\xi^{\mu\nu}{}_{;\nu} - \xi^{\mu\nu}\frac{\partial\alpha}{\partial x^\nu} = 0 \qquad (9.14b)$$

The Maxwell field tensors satisfy the identity

$$F_{\mu\alpha}F^{\nu\alpha} - {}^*F_{\mu\alpha}{}^*F^{\nu\alpha} = \tfrac{1}{2}\delta_\mu{}^\nu F_{\alpha\beta}F^{\alpha\beta} \qquad (9.15)$$

Multiplying (9.14a) by ${}^*\xi_{\beta\mu}$ and (9.14b) by $\xi_{\beta\mu}$ and employing (9.15) gives

$$\frac{\partial\alpha}{\partial x^\beta} = \frac{-2({}^*\xi_{\beta\mu}\xi^{\mu\nu}{}_{;\nu} + \xi_{\beta\mu}{}^*\xi^{\mu\nu}{}_{;\nu})}{\xi_{\gamma\delta}\xi^{\gamma\delta}} \qquad (9.16)$$

The problem now is to express the Maxwell field tensor in terms of the Ricci tensor so that (9.16) can be written in terms of geometrical objects.

For convenience a fourth-rank tensor is introduced which is constructed out of the Ricci tensor so as to have the symmetry of the Riemann tensor. Such a tensor is $E_{\tau\sigma}{}^{\mu\nu}$, given by

$$E_{\tau\sigma}{}^{\mu\nu} = \tfrac{1}{2}(-\delta_\tau{}^\mu R_\sigma{}^\nu + \delta_\sigma{}^\mu R_\tau{}^\nu - \delta_\sigma{}^\nu R_\tau{}^\mu + \delta_\tau{}^\nu R_\sigma{}^\mu) \quad (9.17\text{a})$$

and

$$E^{\gamma\delta\beta\tau}{}_{;\tau} = \tfrac{1}{2}(R^{\delta\beta;\gamma} - R^{\gamma\beta;\delta}) \quad (9.17\text{b})$$

By considering the extremal Maxwell tensor in a Lorentz frame it may be verified that

$$\frac{c^4}{G} E_{\alpha\beta\gamma\delta} = -\,\xi_{\alpha\beta}\xi_{\gamma\delta} - {}^*\xi_{\alpha\beta}{}^*\xi_{\gamma\delta} \quad (9.18\text{a})$$

This is a tensor equation; therefore, it is valid in general. It may also be shown that

$$\frac{c^4}{G} E_{\alpha\beta\gamma\delta} E^{\gamma\delta}{}_{\mu\nu} = (R_{\sigma\tau} R^{\sigma\tau})^{\frac{1}{2}}(-\xi_{\alpha\beta}\xi_{\mu\nu} + {}^*\xi_{\alpha\beta}{}^*\xi_{\mu\nu}) \quad (9.18\text{b})$$

By solving (9.18a) and (9.18b) for $\xi_{\mu\nu}\xi_{\sigma\tau}$ we obtain

$$\frac{G}{c^4} \xi_{\mu\nu}\xi_{\sigma\tau} = -\tfrac{1}{2}E_{\mu\nu\sigma\tau} - \tfrac{1}{2}(R_{\alpha\beta} R^{\alpha\beta})^{-\frac{1}{2}} E_{\mu\nu\gamma\delta} E_{\sigma\tau}{}^{\gamma\delta} \quad (9.19)$$

Now define the tensor $F_{\alpha\beta\gamma\delta}$ by

$$F_{\alpha\beta\gamma\delta} = \tfrac{1}{2}(-g)^{\frac{1}{2}} \varepsilon_{\gamma\delta\mu\nu} E_{\alpha\beta}{}^{\mu\nu} = \tfrac{1}{2}(-g)^{\frac{1}{2}} \varepsilon_{\gamma\delta\mu\nu}(\delta_\alpha{}^\nu R_\beta{}^\mu - \delta_\beta{}^\nu R_\alpha{}^\mu) \quad (9.20)$$

and calculate $F_{\alpha\beta\gamma\delta} E^{\gamma\delta\beta\tau}{}_{;\tau}$ as

$$F_{\alpha\beta\gamma\delta} E^{\gamma\delta\beta\tau}{}_{;\tau} = -\xi_{\mu\nu}\xi^{\mu\nu}({}^*\xi_{\alpha\beta}\xi^{\beta\tau}{}_{;\tau} + \xi_{\alpha\beta}{}^*\xi^{\beta\tau}{}_{;\tau})\left(\frac{G}{c^4}\right)^2$$

$$= \tfrac{1}{2}\varepsilon_{\gamma\delta\mu\nu}(\delta_\alpha{}^\nu R_\beta{}^\mu - \delta_\beta{}^\nu R_\alpha{}^\mu) R^{\delta\beta;\gamma} \sqrt{-g} \quad (9.21)$$

$$= \tfrac{1}{2}\varepsilon_{\alpha\delta\gamma\mu} R^{\delta\beta;\gamma} R_\beta{}^\mu \sqrt{-g}$$

(9.5) and the relation for $T_{\mu\nu}$ in terms of $F_{\mu\nu}$ led to the relation (9.12); $-(G/c^4)\xi_{\alpha\beta}\xi^{\alpha\beta} = (R_{\mu\nu} R^{\mu\nu})^{\frac{1}{2}}$. Comparing (9.21) and (9.16) we see that (9.16), which is obtained from Maxwell's equations, can be written in terms of the Ricci tensor as

$$\frac{\partial \alpha}{\partial x^\beta} = \frac{\varepsilon_{\beta\lambda\mu\nu} R^{\lambda\gamma;\mu} R_\gamma{}^\nu \sqrt{-g}}{R_{\sigma\tau} R^{\sigma\tau}} \qquad (9.22)$$

Since (9.22) is the gradient of a scalar, its curl vanishes, so we obtain expression (9.7),

$$\alpha_{,\beta\iota} = \alpha_{,\iota\beta}. \qquad (9.7)$$

Given the Ricci tensor we may determine the Maxwell field (up to a duality rotation) in the following way. Use (9.22). Select some reference point and calculate

$$\alpha(x) = \int_p^x \alpha_{,\mu} dx^\mu + \alpha_0$$

Since the curl of $\alpha_{,\mu}$ vanishes, this is independent of the path. α_0 is arbitrary. This value of α may be used to obtain $F_{\mu\nu} = e^{*\alpha} \xi_{\mu\nu}$, since (9.19) may be used for the purpose of calculating $\xi_{\mu\nu}$, at each point. (9.22) does not exist for a null field. Another fundamental difficulty is that allowed geometric data on an initial hypersurface may correspond to more than one Maxwell tensor (45). This non-uniqueness exists, for example, when the initial Maxwell fields are localized in two separated regions. Duality rotation in one of the regions gives different physics but may not alter the geometric data for a finite time.

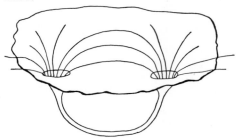

Figure 9.1

Wheeler notes that charges may be described by admitting regions with non-Euclidean topologies which are multiply connected. A schematic diagram of a pair of charges formed in this way is shown in Fig. 9.1. Such a theory is equivalent to a theory with charge and a Euclidean topology. Misner has noted that the total number of lines which thread such a "handle" is a constant of the motion. Wheeler has also discussed stable solutions of the combined Maxwell-Einstein equations. His "geons" (gravitational electromagnetic entity) are objects endowed with mass which are made up of fields, held together by gravitation (34).

9.2 Equations of Motion

It was noted by Einstein and Grommer (6) in 1927 that the equations of motion of a system of masses are contained within the gravitational field equations and therefore do not need to be postulated separately, as in electrodynamics. Bergmann has remarked that constraints on the possible motions appear as a result of relations such as the Bianchi identities; the nonlinearity then leads to laws of motion such as Newton's laws. An extensive literature exists on the deduction of the equations of motion and their connection with the problem of radiation and the conservation laws. We should like to stress that the proposed methods for detection and generation of gravitational radiation, given earlier, involve electrical as well as gravitational forces. Any conclusions derived from consideration of the equations of motion and the radiation problem for gravitation alone may not apply to the results of Chapter 8.

The following discussion of the equations of motion is due to V. Fock (7). In the zeroth approximation, space is considered to be flat, and a Lorentz metric is used. The stress energy tensor is then taken to be (Latin space indices)

$$T^{00} \approx \rho_M c^2 \qquad T^{0i} \approx \rho_M cv^i \qquad (9.23)$$

In this approximation, $T^{0\mu}{}_{;\mu} \approx T^{0\mu}{}_{,\mu}$, and

$$\frac{\partial T^{00}}{c\partial t} + \frac{\partial T^{0i}}{\partial x^i} = 0 \qquad (9.24)$$

The weak-field solutions (7.13) are

$$\varphi_{00} = \frac{4G}{c^4} \int \frac{(T'_{00})_{\text{retarded}} \, d^3x'}{|\mathbf{r} - \mathbf{r}'|}; \quad \varphi_{0i} = \frac{4G}{c^4} \int \frac{(T'_{0i})_{\text{retarded}} \, d^3x'}{|\mathbf{r} - \mathbf{r}'|}$$

$$\varphi_{jk} = \frac{2G}{c^6} \frac{\partial^2}{\partial t^2} \int \frac{(T'_{00})_{\text{retarded}} x'^j x'^k \, d^3x'}{|\mathbf{r} - \mathbf{r}'|} \tag{9.25}$$

For low velocities $v/c \ll 1$, and in this approximation only φ_{00} and φ_{0i} need be retained. Using (7.2) and (7.10) it then follows that

$$g_{00} \approx -1 + \tfrac{1}{2}\varphi_{00}; \qquad g^{jk} \approx \delta^{jk} \tag{9.26}$$

$$g_{0i} \approx \varphi_{0i} \tag{9.27}$$

In the next approximation we must consider $T^{\mu\nu}{}_{;\,\nu} = 0$; this gives, using (3.38),

$$\frac{\partial T^{\mu\nu}}{\partial x^\nu} + \Gamma^\mu{}_{\alpha\nu} T^{\alpha\nu} + \Gamma^\nu{}_{\alpha\nu} T^{\mu\alpha} = 0 \tag{9.28}$$

which we write as

$$\frac{\partial T^{00}}{c\,\partial t} + \frac{\partial T^{0i}}{\partial x^i} + \Gamma^0{}_{\alpha\nu} T^{\alpha\nu} + \Gamma^\nu{}_{\alpha\nu} T^{0\alpha} = 0 \tag{9.29}$$

$$\frac{\partial T^{ik}}{\partial x^k} + \frac{\partial T^{i0}}{\partial x^0} + \Gamma^i{}_{\alpha\nu} T^{\alpha\nu} + \Gamma^\nu{}_{\alpha\nu} T^{i\alpha} = 0 \tag{9.30}$$

The last expression, (9.30), will now be seen to be the equations of motion in the Newtonian approximation. Again, at low velocities, $T_{00} \gg T_{ij}$. Using this and retaining only first-order terms then leads to

$$\frac{\partial}{\partial t} (\rho_M v^i) + \frac{\partial T^{ik}}{\partial x^k} - \frac{G\rho_M}{c^2} \nabla \int \frac{(T'_{00})_{\text{retarded}} \, d^3x'}{|\mathbf{r} - \mathbf{r}'|} = 0 \tag{9.31}$$

ρ_M is the matter density when measured in the local rest frame of the matter. The first term on the left is the inertial term, the second is a force per unit volume due to the space derivatives of the pressure, and the last term is the gradient of the gravitational potential.

We may deduce the geodesic equation for a particle, following Papapetrou (35). First integrate the relation $T^{\mu\nu}{}_{;\nu} = 0$ over the entire three space, employing the form (3.76). Surface integrals may be dropped because the particle is localized, and we obtain

$$\frac{\partial}{\partial x^0} \int T^{\mu 0}(-g)^{\frac{1}{2}} d^3x = -\int \Gamma^\mu{}_{\alpha\beta} T^{\alpha\beta}(-g)^{\frac{1}{2}} d^3x \qquad (9.28\text{A})$$

Now integrate the product $x^\gamma T^{\mu\nu}{}_{;\nu} = 0$ over the three space, again dropping surface integrals, with the result

$$\frac{\partial}{\partial x^0} \int x^\gamma T^{\mu 0}(-g)^{\frac{1}{2}} d^3x = \int T^{\mu\gamma}(-g)^{\frac{1}{2}} d^3x - \int x^\gamma \Gamma^\mu{}_{\alpha\beta} T^{\alpha\beta}(-g)^{\frac{1}{2}} d^3x$$

$$(9.28\text{B})$$

Since these integrands are zero except for a small region it is appropriate to represent $\Gamma^\mu{}_{\alpha\beta}$ by the series

$$\Gamma^\mu{}_{\alpha\beta} = {}_0\Gamma^\mu{}_{\alpha\beta} + {}_0\Gamma^\mu{}_{\alpha\beta,\sigma}\,\delta x^\sigma + \cdots$$

The prefix zero refers to the value at the point which is taken as the position of the particle. Account must now be taken of the structure of the particle. Papapetrou defines a single pole particle as one which has only some of the integrals $\int T^{\mu\nu}(-g)^{\frac{1}{2}} d^3x$ not equal to zero. A pole-dipole particle has at least some of the integrals $\int T^{\mu\nu}\delta x^\rho(-g)^{\frac{1}{2}} d^3x$ and $\int T^{\mu\nu}(-g)^{\frac{1}{2}} d^3x$ not equal to zero. Extension to higher order multipoles is evident. For a pole particle only the first term in the series for $\Gamma^\mu{}_{\alpha\beta}$ is needed and the relations (9.28A), (9.28B) give

$$\frac{d}{dx^0} \int T^{\alpha 0}(-g)^{\frac{1}{2}} d^3x + {}_0\Gamma^\alpha{}_{\mu\nu} \int T^{\mu\nu}(-g)^{\frac{1}{2}} d^3x = 0 \qquad (9.28\text{C})$$

$$\int T^{\alpha\beta}(-g)^{\frac{1}{2}} d^3x = \frac{dx^\alpha}{dx^0} \int T^{\beta 0}(-g)^{\frac{1}{2}} d^3x \qquad (9.28\text{D})$$

In (9.28D) let $\beta = 0$, this gives in terms of the four velocity $U^\alpha = U^0 dx^\alpha/dx^0$,

$$\int T^{\alpha 0}(-g)^{\frac{1}{2}} d^3x = m\,\frac{dx^\alpha}{dx^0} = m_0 U^\alpha \qquad (9.28\text{E})$$

The rest mass m_0 has been set equal to $(U^0)^{-1} \int T^{00}(-g)^{\frac{1}{2}}d^3x$. Substituting (9.28E) back into (9.28D) leads to

$$\int T^{\alpha\beta}(-g)^{\frac{1}{2}}d^3x = m_0 U^\alpha U^\beta / U_0 \qquad (9.28F)$$

We may now employ (9.28F) in (9.28C). The result after using (9.28E) is

$$\frac{dU^\mu}{ds} + \Gamma^\mu{}_{\alpha\beta}U^\alpha U^\beta = 0 \qquad (9.31A)$$

which is the geodesic equation.

Extension of this procedure gives equations of motion for a pole-dipole particle. The spin $I^{\alpha\beta}$ is defined by

$$I^{\alpha\beta} = \int \delta x^\alpha T^{\beta 0}(-g)^{\frac{1}{2}}d^3x - \int \delta x^\beta T^{\alpha 0}(-g)^{\frac{1}{2}}d^3x$$

and the equations of motion for $I^{\alpha\beta}$ are

$$\frac{\delta I^{\alpha\beta}}{\delta s} + U^\alpha U_\rho \frac{\delta I^{\beta\rho}}{\delta s} - U^\beta U_\rho \frac{\delta I^{\alpha\rho}}{\delta s} = 0 \qquad (9.31B)$$

Again, as in chapter 8, $\delta/\delta s$ denotes covariant differentiation with respect to s.

Schiff (36) has employed (9.31B) to study the precession of a gyroscope which has a non gravitational constraining force $\mathbf{F}$, in the earth's gravitational field. His result to lowest order is that the spin vector $\mathbf{I}^0$ measured by a co-moving observer satisfies the equation

$$\frac{d\mathbf{I}^0}{dt} = \Big[\mathbf{F} \times \mathbf{v}/2mc^2 + (3GM/2c^2r^3)\mathbf{r} \times \mathbf{v}$$

$$+ (GJ/c^2r^3)(3[\boldsymbol{\omega} \cdot \mathbf{r}]\mathbf{r}/r^2 - \boldsymbol{\omega}) \Big] \times \mathbf{I}^0 \qquad (9.31C)$$

In (9.31C) $\mathbf{v}$ is the velocity of the gyroscope, J is the moment of inertia of the earth, $\boldsymbol{\omega}$ is the angular velocity of the earth, r is the radial coordinate. The first term on the right gives the special relativity Thomas precession, the second and third terms are effects of general relativity. For a spinning top on earth, a precession of $\sim 10^{-8}$ radians per day would be expected. Observation of such effects on earth or in a satellite experiment would provide a test of general relativity. Somewhat similar suggestions were put forth (unpublished) by R. A. Ferrell (Gravity Research Foundation Essay, New Boston, New Hampshire, April 1, 1959) and later by R. A. Pugh (Weapons Systems Evaluation Group Memorandum 11, November 12, 1959).

It is possible to deduce the equations of motion of isolated masses in a purely geometrical way (8, 9) using the left side of the field equations alone. Higher approximations to the equations of motion including effects of radiation have been obtained by a number of authors (10, 25, 27).

9.3 Mach's Principle

The Mach principle states that inertia is due entirely to the mutual action of matter. Thus a particle is considered to require force to accelerate it relative to the other matter in the universe. At least part of the centrifugal force appears as a mutual effect, in general relativity. Consider the geodesic equation for the space indices, keeping terms up to $(v/c)^2$:

$$-\frac{d^2x^i}{ds^2} = \Gamma^i{}_{00}\left(\frac{dx^0}{ds}\right)^2 + 2\Gamma^i{}_{j0}\frac{dx^j}{ds}\frac{dx^0}{ds} + \Gamma^i{}_{jk}\frac{v^j v^k}{c^2}$$

Here v is the ordinary velocity of the particle. To first order in $h_{\mu\nu}$ the Christoffel symbols are

$$\Gamma^i{}_{00} \approx -\tfrac{1}{2}h_{00,\,i} + h_{0i,\,0}$$
$$\Gamma^i{}_{j0} \approx \tfrac{1}{2}(h_{ij,\,0} + h_{i0,\,j} - h_{j0,\,i})$$
$$\Gamma^i{}_{jk} \approx \tfrac{1}{2}(h_{ij,\,k} + h_{ik,\,j} - h_{jk,\,i})$$

With these substitutions the geodesic equation becomes

$$c^2\frac{d^2x^i}{ds^2} = \left(\frac{dx^0}{ds}\right)^2\left[\nabla(c^2h_{00}/2) - \frac{\partial(ch_{0i})}{\partial t}\right]$$
$$+ c^2\frac{dx^0}{ds}\frac{dx^j}{ds}[h_{j0,\,i} - h_{i0,\,j}] - c^2h_{ij,\,0}\frac{dx^j}{ds}\frac{dx^0}{ds} - \Gamma^i{}_{jk}v^j v^k$$

$$(9.32)$$

We employ (9.32) to study the motion of a particle inside a hollow spherical shell of radius R and rest mass M. First let the shell rotate with angular velocity ω with respect to an observer within the shell. Let R_S, θ, and φ be the spherical coordinates of an element of the shell and let a, θ_0, and φ_0 be the spherical coordinates of the point within the shell at which the field components are calculated. U^μ will denote the four velocity of an element of the shell as seen by an observer within. The rectangular components are

$$U^1 = -\frac{\omega R_S \sin\theta \sin\varphi}{c\sqrt{[1-\omega^2 R_S{}^2 \sin^2\theta/c^2]}}; \quad U^2 = \frac{\omega R_S \sin\theta \cos\varphi}{c\sqrt{[1-\omega^2 R_S{}^2 \sin^2\theta/c^2]}}$$

$$U^3 = 0; \qquad U^0 = \frac{1}{\sqrt{[1-\omega^2 R_S{}^2 \sin^2\theta/c^2]}} \tag{9.33}$$

The mechanical stresses in the shell are assumed to be small, so the stress energy tensor is approximately $\rho_M c^2 U^\mu U^\nu$. The expressions (7.13) are then

$$\Phi_\mu{}^\nu = \frac{4G}{c^2} \int \frac{\rho_M U'_\mu U'^\nu d^3 x'}{|\mathbf{r} - \mathbf{r}'|} \tag{9.34}$$

We are using $\Phi_{\mu\nu}$ for the quantity $h_{\mu\nu} - \frac{1}{2}\delta_{\mu\nu} h$, reserving φ for a coordinate.

$$|\mathbf{r}-\mathbf{r}'| = [a^2 + R_S{}^2 - 2aR_S[\cos\theta\cos\theta_0 + \sin\theta\sin\theta_0\cos(\varphi-\varphi_0)]]^{\frac{1}{2}} \tag{9.35}$$

$|\mathbf{r} - \mathbf{r}'|^{-1}$ may be expanded in the series

$$|\mathbf{r}-\mathbf{r}'|^{-1} = \frac{1}{R_S}\left[1 - \frac{a^2}{2R_S{}^2} + \frac{a}{R_S}(\cos\theta\cos\theta_0 + \sin\theta\sin\theta_0\cos[\varphi-\varphi_0])\right.$$

$$\left. + \frac{3a^2}{2R_S{}^2}(\sin\theta\sin\theta_0\cos[\varphi-\varphi_0] + \cos\theta\cos\theta_0)^2 + \ldots\right] \tag{9.36}$$

Now ρ_M is the density in the rest frame of an element of the shell, while $d^3 x'$ is a three-dimensional volume element in the rest frame of the observer. In order to express the result in terms of the rest mass of the shell we note that a volume element d^3x'' in the shell rest frame covers a region d^3x' such that

$$d^3x'' = \frac{d^3x'}{\sqrt{[1-v^2/c^2]}} \qquad (9.37)$$

Utilizing (9.33) through (9.37) and carrying out the integrations then gives to order v^2/c^2 the values

$$\Phi_{00} = \frac{4GM}{c^2R_S} \left[1 + \frac{\omega^2 R_S{}^2}{3c^2} - \frac{2\omega^2 a^2}{15c^2} + \frac{\omega^2 a^2 \sin^2 \theta_0}{5c^2} \right]$$

$$\Phi_{11} = \frac{4GM}{c^2R_S} \left[\frac{\omega^2 R_S{}^2}{3c^2} + \frac{\omega^2 a^2 \sin^2 \theta_0 \sin^2 \varphi_0}{5c^2} - \frac{\omega^2 a^2}{15c^2} \right]$$

$$\Phi_{22} = \frac{4GM}{c^2R_S} \left[\frac{\omega^2 R_S{}^2}{3c^2} + \frac{\omega^2 a^2 \sin^2 \theta_0 \cos^2 \varphi_0}{5c^2} - \frac{\omega^2 a^2}{15c^2} \right]$$

$$\Phi_{33} = 0$$

$$\Phi_{12} = - \frac{4GM \omega^2 a^2 \sin^2 \theta_0 \cos \varphi_0 \sin \varphi_0}{5c^4 R_S} \qquad (9.38)$$

$$\Phi_{10} = \frac{4GM \omega a \sin \theta_0 \sin \varphi_0}{3c^2 R_S}$$

$$\Phi_{20} = - \frac{4GM \omega a \sin \theta_0 \cos \varphi_0}{3c^2 R_S}$$

$$\Phi_{30} = \Phi_{23} = 0$$

$$\Phi = \Phi_\mu{}^\mu = - \frac{4GM}{c^2 R_S} \left[1 - \frac{\omega^2 R_S{}^2}{3c^2} \right]$$

From these $h_{\mu\nu}$ may be calculated as

$$h_{\mu\nu} = \Phi_{\mu\nu} - \tfrac{1}{2}\delta_{\mu\nu}\Phi \qquad (9.39)$$

A study of (9.38) and (9.39) indicates that the last two terms on the right of (9.32) are of an order higher than $(v/c)^2$ and the factor dx^0/ds may be omitted from some of the remaining terms. For this case the geodesic equation then takes the form

$$c^2 \frac{d^2\mathbf{x}}{ds^2} = \nabla V - \left(\frac{dx^0}{ds} \right)^2 \frac{\partial \mathbf{A}}{\partial t} + \mathbf{v} \times \nabla \times \mathbf{A} \qquad (9.40)$$

where $V = c^2 h_{00}/2$ and $A_i = ch_{0i}$. If we now set $x^1 = x$, $x^2 = y$, $x^3 = z$ and write (9.40) in component form, the equations of motion for a particle inside the shell are

$$c^2 \frac{d^2x}{ds^2} = \frac{GM}{3c^2 R_S}\left[\tfrac{4}{5}\omega^2 x - 8\omega\frac{dy}{dt}\right]$$

$$c^2 \frac{d^2y}{ds^2} = \frac{GM}{3c^2 R_S}\left[\tfrac{4}{5}\omega^2 y + 8\omega\frac{dx}{dt}\right] \qquad (9.40a)$$

$$c^2 \frac{d^2z}{ds^2} = -\frac{8GM\omega^2 z}{15c^2 R_S}$$

It is clear from (9.40a) that we are observing centrifugal force on a body at rest inside the spinning shell. The effect is, in general, a small one — a factor $\sim GM/c^2 R_S$ times the value resulting from rotation relative to the other mass in the universe. This result was given long ago by Thirring.

If the shell does not spin but is given a translational acceleration in the x^i direction relative to a test particle inside, we have, from (9.34) and (9.37),

$$h_{10} = \Phi_{10} = cA_1 = -\frac{4GMv_S}{c^3 R_S(1 - v_S{}^2/c^2)^{\frac{1}{2}}} \qquad (9.41)$$

Here v_S is the velocity of the shell. (9.40) then gives for a particle momentarily at rest inside

$$\frac{d^2\mathbf{x}}{dt^2} = \frac{4GM}{c^2 R_S(1-v_S{}^2/c^2)^{\frac{1}{2}}}\left(1 + \frac{\mathbf{v}_S\mathbf{v}_S \cdot}{c^2(1 - v_S{}^2/c^2)}\right)\mathbf{a}_S \qquad (9.40b)$$

In (9.40b) $\mathbf{a}_S$ is the acceleration of the shell.

Consider a solid mass M instead of the shell and accelerate M relative to a small mass m. If m is momentarily at rest its acceleration may be calculated using (9.32) and employing the potentials of (7.13a). If we retain terms only up to v/c the acceleration of m is

$$c^2 \frac{d^2\mathbf{x}}{ds^2} = \nabla\frac{GM}{R_M}\left(1 + \frac{\mathbf{v}\cdot\mathbf{R}_M}{cR_M}\right) + \frac{4GM}{c^2 R_M}\left(1 + \frac{\mathbf{v}\cdot\mathbf{R}_M}{cR_M}\right)\mathbf{a}$$

$$+ \frac{4GM}{c^2}\left(\frac{\mathbf{a}\cdot\mathbf{R}_M}{cR_M{}^2}\right)\mathbf{v} \qquad (9.40c)$$

v and a are the velocity and acceleration, respectively, of M, and $\mathbf{R}_M$ is the radius vector from m to M. (9.40c) contains terms which depend on the direction of the acceleration relative to the radius vector from m to M. These are roughly v/c times the isotropic effect of the acceleration. From a consideration of (9.40) we may conclude that the term ∇V includes the centrifugal force associated with relative rotation, and the term $(dx^0/ds)^2 \partial \mathbf{A}/\partial t$ represents forces due to relative velocity and relative acceleration. The term $\mathbf{v} \times \nabla \times \mathbf{A}$ leads to Coriolis acceleration. For the rotating shell $\nabla \times \mathbf{A}$ gives an internal field similar to the magnetic field inside a spinning charged sphere. These considerations indicate that for the universe as a whole $GM/c^2R \approx 1$ if Mach's principle is a valid one.

This treatment shows that inertial effects depend at least in some degree on the mutual action of matter, according to general relativity. This does not satisfy the requirements of Mach's principle because with no matter present other than a test particle, inertial effects still appear. Special relativity is a limiting class of solutions, if no boundary conditions are imposed. We may always choose coordinates such that inertia appears as a local property of space and all terms on the right side of (9.40) are transformed away. It is evident from an equation such as (8.13) that inertia will be unequivocally isotropic‡ in consequence of the form of the stress tensor for

‡ Cocconi and Salpeter (29, 30) have considered the effect of anisotropy of inertia on the structure of spectral lines. For the gamma radiation of nuclei in crystals, the atomic magnetic field leads to $(2J+1)$ equally spaced components of the nuclear energy level. With the anisotropy of inertia ΔM, each component is shifted by an amount $(\Delta M/M)TP_2$, where T is the average kinetic energy of the nucleon and P_2 is a coefficient whose value depends on J, on the magnetic quantum number, and on the orientation of the magnetic field relative to the direction toward the galactic center. In the Mössbauer effect observations, the transition frequencies in absorber and emitter are compared. Relative motion is produced and the counting rate is observed as a function of the relative velocity of emitter and source. Resonance occurs successively as lines overlap, provided the selection rules permit excitation by the shifted lines. The number of peaks observed will then change if the relative spacing of the Zeeman components is altered and if the atomic fields

(footnote cont'd)

a particle with scalar type rest mass. For these reasons the experiment of Hughes, Robinson and Beltran-Lopez (39) must be regarded as providing strong support for the present formulation of the general theory of relativity, and no support for a strong form of Mach's principle.

Einstein (11) and more recently Wheeler have explored the possibility that Mach's principle is not a consequence of the field equations, but is a boundary condition. If we have an "isolated" system we should require that at large distances the metric join in the proper way to the metric of the remainder of the universe. Satisfying this boundary condition would represent the mutual action of the matter in the universe on the mass in the "isolated" system. Carrying through such a program might lead to relations between inertial properties and the far-distant nature of the universe.

Other points of view on Mach's principle have been presented by Dicke and by Sciama (37).

9.4   Remarks on Cosmology

The equations of general relativity have solutions which appear capable of giving a description of the universe and its evolution. Long ago Einstein considered the problem and concluded that the equations do not admit a static solution for the universe unless an additional "cosmological" term $\lambda g_{\mu\nu}$ is introduced into the field equations. Later it was shown by Friedman that nonstatic solutions exist, without addi-

---

are aligned. If the atomic magnetic fields are randomly oriented in emitter and absorber then the anisotropy of inertia broadens the lines. A Mossbauer effect experiment gave a negative result (38).

An elegant and much more sensitive test of anisotropy of inertia was recently carried out by Hughes, Robinson, and Beltran-Lopez (39). They observed the nuclear magnetic resonance frequency of the Li^7 nucleus in a solution of LiCl over a twelve hour period. The earth's rotation changes the orientation of the apparatus relative to our galaxy. This method is unusually sensitive because of the large kinetic energy which arises from a $P_{\frac{3}{2}}$ proton in the nuclear potential, and the great accuracy with which the absolute value of a nuclear magnetic resonance frequency can be measured. Their negative result establishes $\Delta M/M < 10^{-20}$.

tion of a cosmological term. The discovery of a red shift of spectral lines, increasing with distance, suggests that the universe is indeed nonstatic, in an expansion phase at the present time. A universe with positive curvature would be closed, finite, and unbounded. This is a very attractive idea. Other cosmologies have been constructed, notably by Bondi, Gold, and Hoyle. We limit our discussion to Friedman's solution (12).

The assumption is made that the universe is spatially isotropic. This is supported by the observation that the density of stars appears to be the same in all directions. An appropriate metric is

$$-ds^2 = dl^2 - dx^{0^2} \qquad (9.42)$$

$$dl^2 = g_{ij} dx^i dx^j = \mathscr{G}^2 a^2 (dx^{1^2} + dx^{2^2} + dx^{3^2}) \qquad (9.43)$$

In consequence of symmetry we can expect g_{ij} to have the same kind of space dependence at all times, so g_{ij} should be the product of a function $\mathscr{G}$ of x^0 alone and a function a of $x^{1^2} + x^{2^2} + x^{3^2} = r^2$. Here the coordinates x^1, x^2, x^3, and r^2 are dimensionless numbers. We need expressions for the g_{ij} in terms of the curvature invariant of the space. Suppose we have a curved space and we introduce at a given point a pair of vectors A^μ and B^ν; the quantity $R_{\alpha\beta\gamma\delta} A^\alpha A^\gamma B^\beta B^\delta$ is a scalar. Another scalar is $(g_{\alpha\gamma} g_{\beta\delta} - g_{\alpha\delta} g_{\beta\gamma}) A^\alpha A^\gamma B^\beta B^\delta$, and the tensor $g_{\alpha\gamma} g_{\beta\delta} - g_{\alpha\delta} g_{\beta\gamma}$ has been constructed to have the same symmetry as $R_{\alpha\beta\gamma\delta}$. The quantity K_R, given by

$$K_R = \frac{R_{\alpha\beta\gamma\delta} A^\alpha A^\gamma B^\beta B^\delta}{(g_{\alpha\gamma} g_{\beta\delta} - g_{\alpha\delta} g_{\beta\gamma}) A^\alpha A^\gamma B^\beta B^\delta} \qquad (9.44)$$

is also a scalar. Straightforward calculation shows that K_R is unchanged if A and B are replaced by any linear combination of A and B. K_R is called the Riemannian curvature. For an isotropic space, K_R will also be independent of the directions of A^μ and B^μ, so at a given point K_R has the same value for arbitrary A^μ and B^μ; therefore the Riemann tensor in isotropic space is given from (9.44) as

$$R_{\alpha\beta\gamma\delta} = K_R(g_{\alpha\gamma}g_{\beta\delta} - g_{\alpha\delta}g_{\beta\gamma}) \tag{9.45}$$

We employ (9.45) for the three space. The component R_{1213} is given by both (9.45) and (3.48). (9.45) gives zero for it and we write

$$R_{1213} = -g_{11,23}/2 + (3/4)g^{11}[g_{33,2}\,g_{11,3}] = 0 \tag{9.46}$$

We have made use of the fact that

$$g_{11} = g_{22} = g_{33} \qquad \text{Now} \qquad \frac{\partial}{\partial x^i} = \frac{\partial r}{\partial x^i}\frac{\partial}{\partial r}$$

(9.43) and (9.46) give

$$2\left(\frac{da}{dr}\right)^2 + \frac{a}{r}\frac{da}{dr} - a\frac{d^2a}{dr^2} = 0 \tag{9.47}$$

Expressions for components R_{1331}, R_{1221}, and R_{2332} may also be obtained by comparison of (3.48) and (9.45). These are combined and the term d^2a/dr^2 is eliminated using (9.47). The result is

$$\mathscr{G}^2 K_R\, a^2 + \frac{1}{a^2}\left(\frac{da}{dr}\right)^2 + \frac{2}{ar}\frac{da}{dr} = 0 \tag{9.48}$$

(9.47) and (9.48) express the requirements on a and $\mathscr{G}$ which are imposed by the isotropy of the space.

Solutions of these equations are of the form

$$a = \frac{c_1}{c_2 + c_3 r^2}\,; \qquad K_R = \frac{4c_2 c_3}{\mathscr{G}^2 c_1{}^2} \tag{9.49}$$

An adequate description will result if the constants are chosen so that

$$a = \frac{1}{1 + \alpha r^2}\,; \qquad K_R = \frac{4\alpha}{\mathscr{G}^2} \tag{9.50}$$

The metric therefore assumes the form

$$-ds^2 = \frac{\mathscr{G}^2}{[1 + \alpha r^2]^2}\left[dx^{1^2} + dx^{2^2} + dx^{3^2}\right] - dx^{0^2} \tag{9.51}$$

$$-ds^2 = \frac{\mathscr{G}^2}{[1 + \alpha r^2]^2}\left[dr^2 + r^2 \sin^2\theta\, d\varphi^2 + r^2 d\theta^2\right] - dx^{0^2} \tag{9.52}$$

we again note that $\mathscr{G}$ has the dimensions of length, r is dimensionless. The "radius" is given by $\mathscr{R}$, with

$$\mathscr{R} = \mathscr{G} \int_0^\infty \frac{dr}{1 + \alpha r^2} \tag{9.53}$$

For $\alpha > 0$

$$\mathscr{R} = \frac{\pi \mathscr{G}}{2 \sqrt{\alpha}} \tag{9.54}$$

From (9.54) we see that α is a factor related to our unit of length. Coordinates may be used in which $\alpha = 1$, when (9.54) applies. The use of (9.45) to calculate the curvature scalar ^3R gives

$$^3R_{ij} = 2K_R g_{ij} \tag{9.55}$$

$$^3R = 6K_R = 24\alpha \mathscr{G}^{-2} \tag{9.56}$$

We see from (9.54) and (9.56) that for $\alpha = 1$ we have a finite, unbounded universe with positive curvature. With $\alpha = 0$ we have a "Euclidean" open space and with α negative we have a curved open space with negative curvature. The assumption is now made that the stress energy tensor can be assumed, to a good approximation, to have only the one component $T_{00} = \rho_M c^2$, all others vanishing. The field equations are then

$$R_{00} - \tfrac{1}{2} g_{00} R = 3 \left(4\alpha + \left(\frac{d\mathscr{G}}{dx^0} \right)^2 \right) \frac{1}{\mathscr{G}^2} = \frac{8\pi G \rho_M}{c^2} \tag{9.57}$$

$$R_{11} - \tfrac{1}{2} g_{11} R = \left(4\alpha + \left(\frac{d\mathscr{G}}{dx^0} \right)^2 + 2\mathscr{G} \frac{d^2\mathscr{G}}{dx^{0^2}} \right) \mathscr{G}^{-2} = 0 \tag{9.58}$$

with identical expressions for $R_{22} - \tfrac{1}{2} g_{22} R$ and $R_{33} - \tfrac{1}{2} g_{33} R$. From subtraction of these equations there results

$$\frac{d^2\mathscr{G}}{dx^{0^2}} + \frac{4\pi \mathscr{G} \rho_M G}{3c^2} = 0 \tag{9.59}$$

Since both ρ_M and $\mathscr{G}$ are positive, (9.59) indicates that $\mathscr{G}$ cannot have minima, cannot have inflection points, and cannot be time independent. For "Euclidean" space, $\alpha = 0$; (9.57) gives

$$\left(\frac{1}{\mathscr{G}}\frac{d\mathscr{G}}{dx^0}\right)^2 = \frac{8\pi G\rho_M}{3c^2} \tag{9.60}$$

For $\alpha \neq 0$ (9.58) and (9.59) give

$$\left(\frac{d\mathscr{G}}{dx^0}\right)^2 = \frac{8\pi\mathscr{G}^2\rho_M G}{3c^2} - 4\alpha \tag{9.61}$$

(9.58) has assumed the pressure to be zero. The total mass M at any time is given by

$$M = \rho_M \int_0^\infty \left(\frac{\mathscr{G}}{1 + \alpha r^2}\right)^3 r^2 dr \sin\theta\, d\theta\, d\varphi \tag{9.62}$$

If the total mass is conserved, $\mathscr{G}^3\rho_M$ is independent of time. We may therefore set $8\pi G\mathscr{G}^3\rho_M/3c^2 = \mathscr{G}_0$, where $\mathscr{G}_0$ is a

Figure 9.2

positive constant, and obtain

$$\left(\frac{d\mathscr{G}}{dx^0}\right)^2 = \frac{\mathscr{G}_0 - 4\alpha\mathscr{G}}{\mathscr{G}} \tag{9.63}$$

For $\alpha = +1$ we have a closed universe with the time dependence of $\mathscr{G}$ as shown in Fig. 9.2. If $\alpha = -1$, $\mathscr{G}$ increases monotonically.

The most attractive possibility, $\alpha = +1$, can be tested by using Eqs. (9.60) and (9.61).

$$\frac{1}{\mathscr{G}}\frac{d\mathscr{G}}{dx^0}$$

can be calculated from astronomical data on the expansion

rate, and ρ_M may also be estimated from observations. If

$$\left(\frac{1}{\mathscr{G}}\frac{d\mathscr{G}}{dx^0}\right)^2 < \frac{8\pi G\rho_M}{3c^2}$$

then a positive value for α is allowed. Present observational astronomy data give too small a value of ρ_M, to give positive α. Wheeler and Ivanenko have both remarked that the idea of a closed positively curved universe should not be discarded before we are certain that our knowledge of ρ_M is sufficiently good to rule it out. Other presently unknown sources of energy may give values of matter energy density considerably in excess of what is indicated by observations using visible light alone.

9.5   Hamiltonian Formulation (14–17, 19–22, 26)

The theory which has been presented thus far is in Lagrangian form. The functions (6.5) and (6.10) were shown to lead to the field equations, and (6.10) permitted us to write the Lagrange equations (6.14).

In quantum theory the Hamiltonian form is the one which has been employed most successfully. In mechanics the Lagrangian L is a function of the coordinates q_i and velocities $\dot{q}_i$. The Hamiltonian is a function of the coordinates and momenta and is defined as

$$H = p_i\dot{q}_i - \mathrm{L} \tag{9.64}$$

The momenta p_i are given by

$$p_i = \frac{\partial \mathrm{L}}{\partial \dot{q}_i} \tag{9.65}$$

The equations of motion are

$$\frac{\partial H}{\partial p_i} = \dot{q}_i; \qquad \frac{\partial H}{\partial q_i} = -\dot{p}_i \tag{9.66}$$

For any other dynamical variable, say b,

$$\dot{b} = \frac{\partial b}{\partial q_i}\frac{\partial q_i}{\partial t} + \frac{\partial b}{\partial p_i}\frac{\partial p_i}{\partial t} = \frac{\partial b}{\partial q_i}\frac{\partial H}{\partial p_i} - \frac{\partial b}{\partial p_i}\frac{\partial H}{\partial q_i} = [b, H] \tag{9.67}$$

In (9.67) $[b, H]$ is the Poisson bracket, defined by

$$[u, v] = \frac{\partial u}{\partial q_k} \frac{\partial v}{\partial p_k} - \frac{\partial u}{\partial p_k} \frac{\partial v}{\partial q_k}$$

In order for this "canonical" formalism to be applicable the p's and q's must be independent variables in the following sense. No constraints, that is no a priori relations should exist to relate them.[‡] We have seen that several kinds of constraints do exist in general relativity. Expression (7.96) expresses some of them as a set of equations which must be satisfied by the initial values of the fields, and also at all subsequent times. The term constraint is used also to express the fact that there is some arbitrariness in the theory — for example the gauge group in electrodynamics or some aspects of covariance. Here we are following very closely the discussion of Dirac (16, 22).

When the Hamiltonian form is considered, the constraints may appear as soon as the momenta are defined by (9.65). We may find that the p's are not independent functions of the $\dot{q}$'s. Suppose there are a number of independent relations which appear as a consequence of (9.65), which we write

$$\varphi_m(p, q) = 0 \qquad (9.68)$$

Dirac calls all equations of constraint and equations which are valid in consequence of constraints weak equations and writes them as $f_m(p, q) \approx 0$.

The method of "Lagrangian" multipliers will be employ-

[‡] Such a requirement corresponds, in the Lagrangian formalism, to being able to solve for the $\ddot{q}_i$ in terms of q_j and $\dot{q}_j$. The Lagrange equations

$$\frac{d}{dt} \frac{\partial L}{\partial \dot{q}_j} - \frac{\partial L}{\partial q_j} = 0$$

may be written in the form

$$\ddot{q}_i \frac{\partial^2 L}{\partial \dot{q}_i \partial \dot{q}_j} - \frac{\partial L}{\partial q_j} = 0$$

The latter set of equations may be solved for $\ddot{q}_i$ only if the determinant with elements $\partial^2 L/\partial \dot{q}_i \partial \dot{q}_j$ does not vanish. If it does vanish, some procedure essentially equivalent to the one given here must be used.

ed. When the action principle $\delta I = 0$ is written to obtain equations of motion, we obtain first

$$\delta I = \int \delta L\, dt = \int \left[\delta p_i \dot{q}_i + p_i \delta\dot{q}_i - \frac{\partial H}{\partial p_i} \delta p_i - \frac{\partial H}{\partial q_i} \delta q_i \right] dt \quad (9.69)$$

Now let the Lagrange multipliers be u_m. We add

$$- u_m \delta\varphi_m = - u_m \left[\frac{\partial\varphi_m}{\partial q_i} \delta q_i + \frac{\partial\varphi_m}{\partial p_i} \delta p_i \right] \quad (9.70)$$

to the integrand of (9.69) and then set the result equal to zero. For variations which vanish at the end points, the equations of motion,

$$\dot{q}_i = \frac{\partial H}{\partial p_i} + u_m \frac{\partial\varphi_m}{\partial p_i}$$

$$\dot{p}_i = - \frac{\partial H}{\partial q_i} - u_m \frac{\partial\varphi_m}{\partial q_i} \quad (9.71)$$

then follow. The u_m are functions of p's and q's. The time derivative of any dynamical variable, say A, is given[‡] by

$$\dot{A} = \frac{\partial A}{\partial q_i} \dot{q}_i + \frac{\partial A}{\partial p_i} \dot{p}_i = [A, H] + u_m[A, \varphi_m] \quad (9.72)$$

Some of the functions φ_m represent real arbitrariness in the problem. For these, different choices of the arbitrary functions correspond to the same physics. Such "constraints" are called first class by Dirac and he provides a systematic procedure for singling them out. Other types of constraint may represent real restrictions, for example on the allowed initial values, and these are also taken properly into account by Dirac's procedure. Since φ_m vanishes for all time it follows from (9.72) that (letting $A = \varphi_{m'}$)

$$[\varphi_{m'}, H] + u_m[\varphi_{m'}, \varphi_m] = 0 \quad (9.73)$$

[‡] The constraint relations must not be employed anywhere in the calculation of Poisson brackets; that is, the p and q are considered independent in this instance.

If (9.73) can be solved for the u_m, the problem is finished, if not the equations (9.73) may give additional relations between the p_i's and q_i's such as

$$\chi_m(q, p) \approx 0 \qquad (9.74)$$

We may again write

$$[\chi_k, H] + u_m[\chi_k, \varphi_m] = 0 \qquad (9.75)$$

These expressions may be employed to solve for u_m, obtaining

$$u_m = U_m(q, p) \qquad (9.76)$$

A study of (9.73) and (9.75) indicates that any solution of

$$V_m[\varphi_{m'}, \varphi_m] \approx 0; \qquad V_m[\chi_k, \varphi_m] \approx 0 \qquad (9.77)$$

may be added to (9.76). The general solution is therefore

$$u_m = U_m + v_a V_{am} \qquad (9.78)$$

V_{am} is a set of independent solutions of (9.77).

Here the v_a are arbitrary coefficients, functions of time. By use of (9.78) we may eliminate the u_m, introducing the v_a as variables. These plus the independent p_i and q_i may be less than the initial number of p and q variables. (9.78) and (9.72) give for the general equations of motion

$$\dot{A} = [A, H'] + v_a[A, \varphi_a] \qquad (9.79)$$

with

$$H' = H + U_m \varphi_m; \qquad \varphi_a = V_{am} \varphi_m \qquad (9.80)$$

Formally a constraint is said to be first class if its Poisson bracket with the Hamiltonian and all χ_k and φ_m vanishes. The other constraints are called second class. Other authors have called the φ_m equations primary constraints and the χ_k equations secondary constraints.

(9.73) indicates that the Poisson bracket of φ_a with H' vanishes. Also

$$[H', H] \approx U_{m'}[\varphi_{m'}, H] \approx 0 \qquad (9.81)$$

(9.81) is seen to vanish in consequence of (9.77) and (9.78), after multiplying (9.73) by $U_{m'}$. Also (9.73), (9.75), and (9.78) show that the Poisson brackets of H' with χ_k and φ_m vanish. H' is therefore first class. The Poisson brackets of φ_a with φ_m and χ_k vanish in consequence of (9.77). The Poisson bracket of φ_a with H vanishes because of the vanishing of its Poisson bracket with H'. φ_a is therefore first class.

Equation (9.79) is seen to be made up of the first-class functions H' and φ_a. The v_a are arbitrary, not restricted by equations of motion. The number of arbitrary functions of the time v_a in the general solutions is seen to be the number of independent first class φ's. Dirac remarks that in practice we know what arbitrary functions there are in the general solution, in consequence of the invariance properties of the action function. This allows us to identify the first-class functions without calculating Poisson brackets. As we shall see later one may need to do this before the Hamiltonian is known.

For a field we may imagine all space to be divided into cells. (9.65) is still valid, but $\dot{q}_i$ is being varied only in a particular cell of volume $\Delta\tau$. The Hamiltonian is

$$H = \sum_{\text{cells}} \left(\frac{\partial L_F}{\partial \dot{q}_i} \dot{q}_i - L_F \right) \Delta\tau \qquad (9.64\text{A})$$

The momentum density π_i is given by

$$\pi_i = \frac{\partial L_F}{\partial \dot{q}_i} \qquad (9.65\text{A})$$

We may write (i is summed over all variables)

$$H = \int (\pi_i \dot{q}_i - L_F) d^3x \qquad (9.64\text{B})$$

and introduce the Hamiltonian density $\mathscr{H}$, by

$$\mathscr{H} = \pi_i \dot{q}_i - L_F \qquad (9.64\text{C})$$

From (9.64B) we have (j is summed from 1 to 3)

$$\delta H = \int \left(\pi_i \delta \dot{q}_i + \dot{q}_i \delta \pi_i - \frac{\partial L_F}{\partial q_i} \delta q_i - \frac{\partial L_F}{\partial \dot{q}_i} \delta \dot{q}_i - \frac{\partial L_F}{\partial q_{i,j}} \delta q_{i,j} \right) d^3x$$

$$= \int \left(\dot{q}_i \delta \pi_i - \frac{\partial L_F}{\partial q_i} \delta q_i + \frac{\partial}{\partial x^j} \frac{\partial L_F}{\partial q_{i,j}} \delta q_i \right) d^3x \qquad (9.64\text{D})$$

On the far right of (9.64D) we have omitted a surface integral. Employing the field equations (4.8) reduces (9.64D) to

$$\delta H = \int (\dot{q}_i \delta \pi_i - \dot{\pi}_i \delta q_i) d^3 x \qquad (9.64\text{E})$$

From (9.64E) it is apparent that $\mathscr{H}$ is a function of q_i and π_i so we may write

$$\delta H = \int \left(\frac{\partial \mathscr{H}}{\partial q_i} \delta q_i + \frac{\partial \mathscr{H}}{\partial q_{i,j}} \delta q_{i,j} + \frac{\partial \mathscr{H}}{\partial \pi_i} \delta \pi_i + \frac{\partial \mathscr{H}}{\partial \pi_{i,j}} \delta \pi_{i,j} \right) d^3 x$$
$$= \int \left[\left(\frac{\partial \mathscr{H}}{\partial q_i} - \frac{\partial}{\partial x^j} \frac{\partial \mathscr{H}}{\partial q_{i,j}} \right) \delta q_i + \left(\frac{\partial \mathscr{H}}{\partial \pi_i} - \frac{\partial}{\partial x^j} \frac{\partial \mathscr{H}}{\partial \pi_{i,j}} \right) \delta \pi_i \right] d^3 x \qquad (9.64\text{F})$$

Again surface integrals have been omitted on the far right of (9.64F). Comparing coefficients of δq_i, $\delta \pi_i$ in (9.64E) and (9.64F) then leads to the field equations

$$\dot{q}_i = \frac{\partial \mathscr{H}}{\partial \pi_i} - \frac{\partial}{\partial x^j} \frac{\partial \mathscr{H}}{\partial \pi_{i,j}}$$
$$\dot{\pi}_i = - \left(\frac{\partial \mathscr{H}}{\partial q_i} - \frac{\partial}{\partial x^j} \frac{\partial \mathscr{H}}{\partial q_{i,j}} \right) \qquad (9.66\text{A})$$

To obtain the time derivative of some quantity E, given as the three volume integral of a density $\mathscr{E}$ we write

$$\dot{E} = \int \left(\frac{\partial \mathscr{E}}{\partial q_i} \dot{q}_i + \frac{\partial \mathscr{E}}{\partial q_{i,j}} \dot{q}_{i,j} + \frac{\partial \mathscr{E}}{\partial \pi_i} \dot{\pi}_i + \frac{\partial \mathscr{E}}{\partial \pi_{i,j}} \dot{\pi}_{i,j} \right) d^3 x \qquad (9.67\text{A})$$

If $\mathscr{E}$ and $\mathscr{H}$ depend on higher derivatives of q_i and π_i these would also have to be included in (9.67A), (9.64F) and (9.66A). We now make use of (9.66A) in (9.67A), omitting surface integral terms, and obtain

$$\dot{E} = \int \left[\left(\frac{\partial \mathscr{E}}{\partial q_i} - \frac{\partial}{\partial x^j} \frac{\partial \mathscr{E}}{\partial q_{i,j}} \right) \left(\frac{\partial \mathscr{H}}{\partial \pi_i} - \frac{\partial}{\partial x^j} \frac{\partial \mathscr{H}}{\partial \pi_{i,j}} \right) \right.$$
$$\left. - \left(\frac{\partial \mathscr{E}}{\partial \pi_i} - \frac{\partial}{\partial x^j} \frac{\partial \mathscr{E}}{\partial \pi_{i,j}} \right) \left(\frac{\partial \mathscr{H}}{\partial q_i} - \frac{\partial}{\partial x^j} \frac{\partial \mathscr{H}}{\partial q_{i,j}} \right) \right] d^3 x \qquad (9.67\text{B})$$
$$= [E, H] = \int \left[\frac{\partial E}{\partial q_i} \frac{\partial H}{\partial \pi_i} - \frac{\partial E}{\partial \pi_i} \frac{\partial H}{\partial q_i} \right] d^3 x$$

This expression defines the Poisson brackets for fields. The functional derivative notation on the extreme right is employed by some authors. If E is not available as a volume integrated density, it may readily be converted into one by simply using a delta function.

If there are constraints relating the q_i and π_i, we may proceed as in the deduction of (9.71). The result is that the term

$$u_m \left(\frac{\partial \varphi_m}{\partial \pi_i} - \frac{\partial}{\partial x^j} \frac{\partial \varphi_m}{\partial \pi_{i,j}} \right)$$

is added to the right side of the expression for $\dot{q}_i$ and the term

$$- u_m \left(\frac{\partial \varphi_m}{\partial q_i} - \frac{\partial}{\partial x^j} \frac{\partial \varphi_m}{\partial q_{i,j}} \right)$$

is added to the right side of the expression for $\dot{\pi}_i$, in (9.66A). The equation of motion (9.67B) becomes

$$\dot{E} = \int \left[\left(\frac{\partial \mathscr{E}}{\partial q_i} - \frac{\partial}{\partial x^j} \frac{\partial \mathscr{E}}{\partial q_{i,j}} \right) \left(\frac{\partial \mathscr{H}}{\partial \pi_i} - \frac{\partial}{\partial x^j} \frac{\partial \mathscr{H}}{\partial \pi_{i,j}} + u_m \left[\frac{\partial \varphi_m}{\partial \pi_i} - \frac{\partial}{\partial x^j} \frac{\partial \varphi_m}{\partial \pi_{i,j}} \right] \right) \right.$$
$$\left. - \left(\frac{\partial \mathscr{E}}{\partial \pi_i} - \frac{\partial}{\partial x^j} \frac{\partial \mathscr{E}}{\partial \pi_{i,j}} \right) \left(\frac{\partial \mathscr{H}}{\partial q_i} - \frac{\partial}{\partial x^j} \frac{\partial \mathscr{H}}{\partial q_{i,j}} + u_m \left[\frac{\partial \varphi_m}{\partial q_i} - \frac{\partial}{\partial x^j} \frac{\partial \varphi_m}{\partial q_{i,j}} \right] \right) \right] d^3x$$

$$(9.67C)$$

and the result corresponding to (9.79) is

$$\dot{E} = [E, H'] + \int \dot{q}_a [E, \varphi_a] d^3x \qquad (9.79A)$$

In general relativity the field variables are those needed to describe the geometry of the three space at any given time. The field history is then a succession of curved three spaces. It is therefore reasonable to search for a canonical formalism which will end up with only six g_{ij} and their canonical momenta as the required variables.

Consider now the gravitational Lagrangian density[‡]

[‡] In this section we are using units for which $16\pi G/c^4 = 1$.

$$\mathcal{L}_G \sqrt{-g} = g^{\mu\nu}(\Gamma^\sigma_{\mu\rho}\,\Gamma^\rho_{\nu\sigma} - \Gamma^\rho_{\mu\nu}\,\Gamma^\sigma_{\rho\sigma})\,\sqrt{-g}$$

$$= (1/4)g_{\mu\nu,\rho}\,g_{\alpha\beta,\sigma}\{(g^{\mu\nu}\,g^{\alpha\beta} - g^{\mu\alpha}\,g^{\nu\beta})g^{\rho\sigma} \tag{9.82}$$

$$+ 2(g^{\mu\alpha}\,g^{\beta\rho} - g^{\mu\rho}\,g^{\alpha\beta})g^{\nu\sigma}\}\,\sqrt{-g}$$

The Lagrangian is $\int \mathcal{L}_G [\sqrt{-g}]\,d^3x$. The field variables are the $g_{\mu\nu}$; $g_{\mu\nu,0}$ are the velocities. The $g_{\mu\nu,i}$ are functions of $g_{\mu\nu}$ alone, independent of the $g_{\mu\nu,0}$. The momenta $\pi^{\mu\nu}$, canonically conjugate to $g_{\mu\nu}$, are defined by the statement

$$\int \delta\mathcal{L}_G[\sqrt{-g}]\,d^3x = \int \pi^{\mu\nu}\,\delta g_{\mu\nu,0}\,d^3x \tag{9.83}$$

A study of $\mathcal{L}_G\sqrt{-g}$ shows that it does not contain any terms which are quadratic in $g_{\mu0,0}$. It follows therefore that $\pi^{\mu0}$ will be a function of $g_{\alpha\nu}$ and $g_{\alpha\nu,i}$, which we denote by f^μ.

$$\pi^{\mu0} \approx f^\mu(g_{\alpha\nu}, g_{\alpha\nu,i}) \tag{9.84}$$

The f^μ functions are constraint relations. It can now be shown that the equations of motion in no way restrict $g_{\mu0,0}$ and that the constraints (9.84) therefore are "first class." If the infinitesimal coordinate transformation

$$x^\mu \to x^\mu + b^\mu$$

is carried out,

$$g_{\mu\nu}(x) - g'_{\mu\nu}(x') = \delta g_{\mu\nu} = g_{\mu\rho}b^\rho{}_{,\nu} + g_{\nu\rho}b^\rho{}_{,\mu} \tag{9.85}$$

Let $b^\rho = \frac{1}{2}(x^0 - c)^2\beta^\rho(x^i)$, where $\beta^\rho(x^i)$ is an arbitrary function. Then on the hyperplane $x^0 = c$ we have

$$\delta g_{\mu\nu} = 0; \qquad \delta g_{\mu\nu,0} = (g_{\mu\rho}\,\delta_\nu{}^0 + g_{\nu\rho}\,\delta_\mu{}^0)\beta^\rho$$

$$\delta g_{ij,0} = 0; \qquad \delta g_{\mu0,0} = \beta_\mu + \delta_\mu{}^0\beta_0$$

Since β is arbitrary it follows that an arbitrary change in $g_{\mu0,0}$ does not affect $g_{\mu\nu}$ or $g_{ij,0}$.

It is convenient (following remarks of V. Bargmann) to note that some variables of the four-dimensional manifold will not change their values on the given spacelike surface for coordinate transformations which do not affect the coordinates on the spacelike surface. Such variables are called intrinsic. More precisely, if we carry out the coordinate transformations

$$x'^\mu = F^\mu(x^0, x^1, x^2, x^3)$$

and F^μ satisfies the conditions

$$F^0(c, x^1, x^2, x^3) = c'$$
$$F^i(c, x^1, x^2, x^3) = x^i,$$

the variables which are intrinsic do not change their values. Thus the g_{ij} are intrinsic. The g_{00} and g_{0i} are not intrinsic and may be varied arbitrarily by choice of F^0 or particular coordinates.

We may expect that the intrinsic field variables will play the central role in the Hamiltonian formulation of general relativity.

The Poisson bracket relations to be employed here are (9.67B).

$$[g'_{\alpha\beta}, \pi^{\mu\nu}] = \tfrac{1}{2}(\delta_\alpha{}^\mu \delta_\beta{}^\nu + \delta_\beta{}^\mu \delta_\alpha{}^\nu)\delta_3(x' - x)$$

$g'_{\alpha\beta}$ is the value of $g_{\alpha\beta}$ at $x^0 = c$, x'^1, x'^2, x'^3.

Dirac notes that a study of $\mathscr{L}_G$ indicates that it can be modified to make $f^\alpha(g_{\mu\nu}, g_{\mu\nu,i})$ vanish, without affecting the equations of motion. This can be done by adding the expression

$$\triangle \mathscr{L}_G \sqrt{-g} = \{(\sqrt{-g}\, g^{00})_{,0}\, g^{i0}/g^{00}\}_{,i} - \{(\sqrt{-g}\, g^{00})_{,i}\, g^{i0}/g^{00}\}_{,0}$$

$$(9.86)$$

to $\mathscr{L}_G \sqrt{-g}$. $\int \triangle \mathscr{L}_G \sqrt{-g}\, d^4x$ can be written as a surface integral, so it will not affect the equations of motion. The new Lagrangian density function $\mathscr{L}_G{}^* \sqrt{-g}$ is obtained after a somewhat tedious reduction as

$$\mathscr{L}_G{}^* \sqrt{-g} = \tfrac{1}{4}\big[(e^{ra}e^{sb} - e^{rs}e^{ab})(-4\Gamma^0{}_{rs}\, \Gamma^0{}_{ab}$$

$$+ \{g_{rs,u}\, g^{u0} - (g_{r\alpha,s} + g_{s\alpha,r})g^{\alpha 0}\}\{g_{ab,v}\, g^{v0} - (g_{a\beta,b} + g_{b\beta,a})g^{\beta 0}\})/g^{00}$$

$$+ g_{\mu\nu,i}\, g_{\alpha\beta,j}\{(g^{\mu\nu}g^{\alpha\beta} - g^{\mu\alpha}g^{\nu\beta})g^{ij} + 2(g^{\mu\alpha}g^{\beta i} - g^{\mu i}g^{\alpha\beta})g^{\nu j}\}\big] \sqrt{-g}$$

$$(9.87)$$

with

$$e^{\mu\nu} = g^{\mu\nu} - g^{\mu 0} g^{\nu 0}/g^{00} \qquad (9.88)$$

Carrying out the operations listed in (9.83) with $\mathscr{L}^*$ instead of $\mathscr{L}$ gives

$$\delta\mathscr{L}_G^* \sqrt{-g} = (e^{ra} e^{sb} - e^{rs} e^{ab})\Gamma^0{}_{ab} \delta g_{rs,0}(\sqrt{-g}) \qquad (9.89)$$

So the momenta π^{rs} are

$$\pi^{rs} = (e^{ra} e^{sb} - e^{rs} e^{ab})\Gamma^0{}_{ab} \sqrt{-g} \qquad (9.90)$$

which may also be written

$$\Gamma^0{}_{ab} \sqrt{-g} = (g_{ra} g_{sb} - \tfrac{1}{2} g_{rs} g_{ab})\pi^{rs} \qquad (9.91)$$

Suppose that we have the hyperplane $x^0 = c$ and some intrinsic field variable η such that η depends on the g_{rs} and on the field variables for other than gravitational fields which may be present. Displace the surface $x^0 = c$ so that each point x^μ goes into $x^\mu + a^\mu$, with a^μ small and a function of x^i alone.

$$\delta\eta = \int \xi_\mu a^\mu d^3x \qquad (9.92)$$

with ξ_μ a function of x^i:

$$\frac{\partial\eta}{\partial x^0} = \int \xi_0 d^3x \qquad (9.93)$$

Let l^μ be a unit normal to $x^0 = c$:

$$l_i = l^\mu g_{\mu i} = 0; \qquad l^\mu l_\mu = -1 \qquad (9.94)$$

An expression for l^μ with these requirements is

$$l^\mu = g^{\mu 0}(-g^{00})^{-\frac{1}{2}} \qquad (9.95)$$

Let ξ_L be defined by the relation

$$-\xi_L = l^\mu \xi_\mu = g^{\mu 0}(-g^{00})^{-\frac{1}{2}} \xi_\mu \qquad (9.96)$$

$$\xi_0 = (-g^{00})^{-\frac{1}{2}} \xi_L - g^{i0} \xi_i/g^{00} \qquad (9.97)$$

Recalling (9.88) enables us to write

$$e^{rs} g_{s\alpha} = e^{r\mu} g_{\mu\alpha} = \delta_\alpha{}^r - g^{r0} \delta_\alpha{}^0/g^{00} \qquad (9.98)$$

$$e^{rs} g_{sa} = \delta_a{}^r \qquad (9.99)$$

$$e^{rs} g_{s0} = -g^{r0}/g^{00} \qquad (9.100)$$

Using these relations (9.97) becomes

$$\xi_0 = (-g^{00})^{-\frac{1}{2}} \xi_L + g_{r0} e^{rs} \xi_s \qquad (9.101)$$

and (9.93) becomes

$$\frac{\partial \eta}{\partial x^0} = \int [(-g^{00})^{-\frac{1}{2}} \xi_L + g_{r0} e^{rs} \xi_s] d^3x \qquad (9.102)$$

We want to have $\partial \eta / \partial x^0 = [\eta, H]$ and this is accomplished by writing for the Hamiltonian

$$H = \int [(-g^{00})^{-\frac{1}{2}} \mathscr{H}_L + g_{r0} e^{rs} \mathscr{H}_s] d^3x \qquad (9.103)$$

provided

$$[\eta, \mathscr{H}_L] = \xi_L; \qquad [\eta, e^{rs} \mathscr{H}_s] = e^{rs} \xi_s$$

$\mathscr{H}_L$ and $\mathscr{H}_s$ will have both matter and gravitational parts and depend only on the intrinsic variables. The standard definition of the Hamiltonian gives for the gravitational one, denoted by H_G

$$H_G = \int (\pi^{rs} g_{rs,0} - \mathscr{L}_G^* \sqrt{-g}) d^3x \qquad (9.104)$$

using (9.87) and (9.90) this is expressed as

$$H_G = \int \pi^{rs}(g_{rs,0} + \Gamma^0{}_{rs}/g^{00}) d^3x + \frac{1}{4} \int [-g]^{\frac{1}{2}} [(e^{rs} e^{ab} - e^{ra} e^{sb})$$
$$\cdot \{ g_{rs,u} g^{u0} - (g_{r\alpha,s} + g_{s\alpha,r}) g^{\alpha 0} \} \{ g^{v0} g_{ab,v} - (g_{a\beta,b} + g_{b\beta,a}) g^{\beta 0} \} / g^{00}$$
$$- g_{\mu\nu,i} g_{\alpha\beta,j} \{ (g^{\mu\nu} g^{\alpha\beta} - g^{\mu\alpha} g^{\nu\beta}) g^{ij} - 2(g^{\mu i} g^{\alpha\beta} - g^{\mu\alpha} g^{\beta i}) g^{\nu j} \}] d^3x$$
$$(9.105)$$

Using (9.91), (3.29) and (9.100) the first integral on the right of (9.105) is written

$$\int \pi^{rs}(g_{rs,0} + \Gamma^0{}_{rs}/g^{00}) d^3x = \int \{ (-g^{00})^{-1} (-g)^{-\frac{1}{2}} (g_{ra} g_{sb} - \tfrac{1}{2} g_{rs} g_{ab}) \pi^{rs} \pi^{ab}$$
$$+ g_{u0} e^{uv} [\pi^{rs} g_{rs,v} - 2(\pi^{rs} g_{rv})_{,s}] \} d^3x \qquad (9.106)$$

Dirac gives a procedure for eliminating the velocities and reducing the remainder of (9.105) to the canonical form (9.103). A study of the second integrand of (9.105) indicates that no term of the form $g_{r0} e^{rs} \mathscr{H}_s$, with $\mathscr{H}_s$ only a function of g_{rs}, $g_{rs,j}$ can originate there. It is therefore necessary to calculate only the contribution to $(-g^{00})^{-\frac{1}{2}}\mathscr{H}_L$. Since $\mathscr{H}_L$ also depends only on the intrinsic variables g_{rs}, $g_{rs,j}$ it may be calculated assuming $g_{i0} = 0$. The determinant g may be written in terms of ^3g, the determinant of g_{rs}, as $gg^{00} = {}^3g$. After omitting a surface integral the result is

$$H = \int \left[(-g^{00})^{-\frac{1}{2}} \{ (^3g)^{-\frac{1}{2}} (g_{ra}g_{sb} - \tfrac{1}{2}g_{rs}g_{ab}) \pi^{rs}\pi^{ab} \right.$$
$$+ \tfrac{1}{4}(^3g)^{\frac{1}{2}} g_{rs,u}\, g_{ab,v} \{ (e^{ra}e^{sb} - e^{rs}e^{ab})e^{uv} + 2(e^{ru}e^{ab} - e^{ra}e^{bu})e^{sv} \}$$
$$+ \{ (^3g)^{\frac{1}{2}} g_{rs,u}(e^{rs}e^{uv} - e^{ru}e^{sv}) \}_{,v} + \mathscr{H}_{ML} \}$$
$$+ g_{m0}e^{mv} [\pi^{rs}g_{rs,v} - 2(\pi^{rs}g_{rv})_{,s} + \mathscr{H}_{Mv}]] d^3x \qquad (9.107)$$

with $\mathscr{H}_{ML}$ and $\mathscr{H}_{Mv}$ the parts of the matter Hamiltonian corresponding to the parts $\mathscr{H}_L$ and $\mathscr{H}_s$ of (9.103). There are thus only six degrees of freedom corresponding to the g_{ij} left, since $\pi^{\mu 0}$ vanish in consequence of the modification of $\mathscr{L}_G$, which arranged for (9.84) to vanish. Also the relations (9.103) plus the requirement $[\pi^{\mu 0}, H] = 0$ leads to $\mathscr{H}_L$ and $\mathscr{H}_s$ vanishing in consequence of the constraints.

In the weak-field approximation the Hamiltonian which includes terms up to $(h_{\mu\nu})^2$ is given by

$$H = \int [\pi^{rs}\pi^{rs} - \tfrac{1}{2}\pi^{rr}\pi^{ss} + \tfrac{1}{4}g_{rs,u}\, g_{rs,u} - \tfrac{1}{4}g_{rr,u}\, g_{ss,u}$$
$$+ \tfrac{1}{2}g_{rs,r}\, g_{uu,s} - \tfrac{1}{2}g_{rs,u}\, g_{ru,s} + \mathscr{H}_{ML}] d^3x$$
$$- \int ([-g_{00}]^{-\frac{1}{2}} - 1)\, (g_{rs,rs} - g_{rr,ss} - \mathscr{H}_{ML})\, d^3x \qquad (9.107a)$$
$$- \int g_{r0}(2\pi^{rs}_{,s} - \mathscr{H}_{Mr})\, d^3x$$

For a particle of rest mass m the action is

$$I = -m \int ds = -m \int \left(-g_{\mu\nu} \frac{dy^\mu}{dT} \frac{dy^\nu}{dT} \right)^{\frac{1}{2}} dT$$

where y^μ are the coordinates of the particle.

$$L_p = -m \left(-g_{\mu\nu} \frac{dy^\mu}{dT} \frac{dy^\nu}{dT} \right)^{\frac{1}{2}}$$

$dy^0/dT = 1$ and is not a dynamical variable. The momentum P_r is given by

$$P_r = mg_{\mu r} \frac{dy^\mu}{dT} \left(- g_{\alpha\beta} \frac{dy^\alpha}{dT} \frac{dy^\beta}{dT} \right)^{-\frac{1}{2}}$$

The particle contributes a term

$$H_M = P_r \dot{y}^r - L_M$$

to the Hamiltonian.
This may be written in the form

$$H_M = -g_{s0} e^{rs} P_r + (- g^{00})^{-\frac{1}{2}} (m^2 + e^{rs} P_r P_s)^{\frac{1}{2}}$$

From (9.103) it follows that

$$\mathcal{H}_{ML} = (m^2 + e^{rs} P_r P_s)^{\frac{1}{2}} \delta_3(x - y)$$
$$\mathcal{H}_{Mr} = - P_r \delta_3(x - y)$$

A different approach to the Hamiltonian formulation of general relativity has been given by Arnowitt, Deser, and Misner. Their results are as follows.[‡]

A canonical form for general relativity involving only two pairs of unconstrained conjugate variables has been obtained. The action

$$I = \int [-g]^{\frac{1}{2}} R \, d^4 x$$

expressed in first-order form is

$$(-g)^{\frac{1}{2}} R = - g_{ij} \pi^{ij}{}_{,0} + (- {}^3 g g^{00})^{-\frac{1}{2}} ({}^3 g^3 R + \tfrac{1}{2} \pi^2 - \pi^{ij} \pi_{ij})$$

$$+ 2g_{0i} \pi^{ij}{}_{1j} - 2\{ ({}^3 g)^{\frac{1}{2}} ([-g^{00}]^{-\frac{1}{2}})_{,i} + (\pi_{ij} - \tfrac{1}{2} g_{ij} \pi) g_{0m} e^{mj} \}^{1i} \quad (9.108)$$

Here

$$\pi^{ij} = (-g)^{\frac{1}{2}} [\Gamma^0{}_{lm} - g_{lm} \Gamma^0{}_{pq} e^{pq}] e^{li} e^{mj}$$

e^{ij} is the matrix inverse to g_{ij}, ${}^3 R$ is constructed only of g_{ij},

‡ With minor alterations this section is essentially a reprint of the letter to the editor of *Nuovo cimento* by Arnowitt, Deser, and Misner (28). Reprinted by permission of the authors and *Nuovo cimento*.

π is the trace of $\pi_i{}^j$, and the bar notation is used for the covariant derivative with respect to the g_{ij} metric. Variation of this action gives rise to all the usual Einstein field equations in Palatini form. End-point variations give the generator

$$G = \int \left[-g_{ij}\delta\pi^{ij} + T^0{}_\mu{}' \, \delta x^\mu \right] d^3x$$

where the stress tensor terms, $\int d^3x \, T^0{}_\mu{}' \, \delta x^\mu$, vanish as a consequence of the constraint equations $G_0{}^\mu = R_0{}^\mu - \frac{1}{2}\delta_0{}^\mu R = 0$ (obtained from varying Eq. (9.108) with respect to $(-g^{00})^{-\frac{1}{2}}, g_{0i}$).

Now make use of an orthogonal decomposition of g_{ij} and π^{ij} according to the general scheme

$$f_{ij} = f_{ij}{}^{TT} + \tfrac{1}{2}\left(\delta_{ij}f^T - \frac{1}{\nabla^2}f^T{}_{,ij} \right) + f_{i,j} + f_{j,i} \qquad (9.109)$$

where $1/\nabla^2$ is the inverse of the flat-space Laplacian operator with appropriate boundary conditions,

$$f^T = f_{ii} - \left(\frac{1}{\nabla^2}\right) f_{ij,\,ij} \qquad (9.109a)$$

$$f_i = \frac{1}{\nabla^2}\left[f_{ij,\,j} - \tfrac{1}{2}\left(\frac{1}{\nabla^2}\right) f_{kj,kji} \right] \qquad (9.109b)$$

and the transverse traceless part of f_{ij}; i.e., $f_{ij}{}^{TT}$ is the remainder.

$$f_{ij}{}^{TT}{}_{,j} = 0; \qquad f_{ii}{}^{TT} \equiv 0$$

Such a decomposition is meaningful only when a set of coordinate conditions are imposed. The following are selected:

$$g_{ij,j} = 0; \qquad \pi^{ii}{}_{,jj} - \pi^{ij}{}_{,ij} = 0 \qquad (9.110)$$

General covariance is maintained, since imposition of these coordinate conditions is equivalent to using certain invariant functionals of the metric as independent variables in place of coordinates.[‡] Conditions (9.110) imply that the functionals [‡‡]

$$t = -\left(\frac{1}{2\nabla^2}\right)\pi^T; \qquad x^i = g_i \qquad (9.111)$$

are chosen. These ensure an asymptotically flat metric. Inserting the orthogonal decomposition into the generator we find after some partial integrations that

$$G = \int \left\{ \pi^{ijTT}\, \delta g_{ij}{}^{TT} + g^T{}_{,ii}\, \delta\left[\left(-\frac{1}{2\nabla^2}\right)\pi^T\right] - 2\pi^{ij}{}_{,j}\, \delta g_i \right\} d^3x \qquad (9.112)$$

since both the variation δ and the time derivative in the action commute with the decomposition. Here $g^T{}_{,ii}$ and $\pi^{ij}{}_{,j}$ may be expressed in terms of $g_{ij}{}^{TT}$ and π^{ijTT} by solving the four constraint equations[†] $G_\mu{}^0 = 0$ for them. We see, therefore, that the generator (9.112) is in standard canonical form $G = p\delta q - H\delta t$ with the additional momentum terms $T_i{}^0$ characteristic of a field theory:

$$G = \int [\pi^{ijTT}\, \delta g_{ij}{}^{TT} - \mathscr{H}\delta t + T_i{}^0\, \delta x^i]d^3x \qquad (9.112a)$$

Since x^i and t do not appear explicitly in the expressions for g_{ij} and π^{ij}, they do not appear explicitly in the equations $G_\mu{}^0 = 0$. Detailed calculation shows that they also do not

---

[‡] Thus, as is well known, the apparently noncovariant DeDonder conditions, $([\sqrt{-g}\, g^{\mu\nu}])_{,\nu} = 0$ are equivalent to the covariant statement that four linearly independent scalar functions h^α are to be used as the coordinates x^α, where $h^\alpha{}_{;\mu}{}^{;\mu} = 0$. Such an equivalence between coordinate conditions and covariant statements holds for this case and indeed for any other choice of coordinates which does not depend on the x^μ of some initial frame.

[‡‡] Appropriate boundary conditions have, of course, been imposed on the operator $(1/\nabla^2)$ in order to relate (9.110) and (9.111). A simple procedure making this operator manifestly nonsingular consists in rewriting (9.111) as $te^{-\alpha r} = -(1/2\nabla^2)\pi^T$, $x^i e^{-\alpha r} = g_i$ and subsequently taking the limit $\alpha \to 0$ at the end of the analysis.

[†] That $G_\mu{}^0 = 0$ has at least perturbation series solutions for $g^T{}_{,ii}$ and $\pi^{ij}{}_{,j}$ can easily be checked, as can the fact that these coordinate conditions are maintained in such an expansion. The Hamiltonian can thus be exhibited as an infinite series in powers of the canonical variables beginning with the linearized theory's $\mathscr{H}$.

appear in the solutions for $g^T{}_{,ii}$ and $\pi^{ij}{}_{,j}$. Thus the quantities

$$\mathcal{H} = -g^T{}_{,ii}(g_{ij}{}^{TT}, \pi^{ijTT})$$
$$\tfrac{1}{2} T_i{}^0 = -\pi^{ij}{}_{,j}(g_{rs}{}^{TT}, \pi^{rsTT}) \qquad (9.113)$$

do not depend explicitly on the coordinates. This coordinate independence allows us to derive the standard conservation laws. From (9.112a) and the fact that the action of Eq. (9.108) reduces to

$$I = \int \{\pi^{ijTT}(g_{ij}{}^{TT}){}_{,0} - \mathcal{H}(g_{ij}{}^{TT}, \pi^{ijTT})\} \, d^4x \qquad (9.108a)$$

it follows that the two independent pairs of canonical variables are $g_{ij}{}^{TT}$ and π^{ijTT}. These, therefore, obey simple Poisson bracket relations

$$[g_{mn}{}^{TT}(\mathbf{r}), \pi^{ijTT}(\mathbf{r'})] = \delta^{ij}{}_{mn}(\mathbf{rr'})^{TT} \qquad (9.114)$$

where the transverse traceless δ function, $\delta_{mn}{}^{ijTT}$, is defined as in linearized theory and is, of course, independent of the metric (31).

The energy E of the field is defined to be the numerical value of the Hamiltonian for the given solution of the equations of motion. Thus, in the evaluation of

$$E = -\int g^T{}_{,ii} \, d^3x \qquad (9.115)$$

$g^T{}_{,ii}$ need not be expressed in terms of the canonical variables and so E can be evaluated as a surface integral (even though the Hamiltonian cannot be reduced to this form). From Eq. (9.109a) we obtain

$$E = -\int g^T{}_{,i} \, dS_i = -\int (g_{jj,i} - g_{ij,j}) \, dS_i \qquad (9.116)$$

here $dS_i = \tfrac{1}{2}\varepsilon_{ijk} \, dx^j \, dx^k$ is the two-dimensional surface element at infinity in rectangular coordinates. We have assumed that the metric becomes asymptotically flat and the coordinates rectangular at spatial infinity. Coordinate transformations preserving these boundary conditions can there be rigorously treated by the linearized theory where g^T is a coordinate scalar (31). Thus, it is not necessary to express the metric in the canonical coordinate system to evaluate the energy; neither is it necessary to use rectangular coordinates provided we make the usual flat space tensor transformations to the desired (e.g., spherical) coordinates. This definition effectively states that the energy of a closed system may be obtained from the coefficient of $1/r$ in the asymptotic expansion of g^T. It is also the gravitational mass of the system as seen by a distant test particle (due to the boundary conditions). The constancy of the energy ensures that this coefficient is time-independent. Equation (9.116) holds without modification when a point particle is coupled to the gravitational field; E now represents the total energy of the coupled system. For the simple case of the Schwarzschild metric one of course finds that the energy is the mass parameter.

It is a desirable criterion for the energy and momentum of a closed system that they involve only those quantities required to specify the state of the system at a given time. For general relativity these variables are g_{ij} and π^{ij} when no coordinate conditions are employed but do not include $g_{0\mu}$, which serve to describe how the coordinates will be chosen at a later time. The expression (9.115) for the energy satisfies this condition. Analogous considerations to the above hold for the total momentum of the gravitational system where again π^i is a coordinate scalar in the asymptotic region. An example of an initial value problem where $g_{0\mu}$ is not determined is the "many body" spatial metric of Lichnerowicz (33):

$$g_{ij} = \delta_{ij}[1 + \sum \alpha_n/2|\mathbf{r} - \mathbf{a}_n|]^4 \qquad (9.117a)$$

$$\pi^{ij} = 0 \qquad (9.117b)$$

Here Eq. (9.116) yields unambiguously the value $\sum \alpha_n$ for the energy.

This formalism also allows us to establish criteria for the existence of gravitational radiation; these are in exact correspondence to those of electromagnetic theory. Thus, the condition for radiation escaping to infinity is stated in terms of the Poynting vector there. The energy flux across a surface element dS_i at infinity is

$$T_i{}^0 dS_i = - 2\pi^{ij}{}_{,j} dS_i \qquad (9.118)$$

where, again, the right-hand side may be evaluated in any asymptotically rectangular coordinate system. More generally, the criterion for the existence of gravitational waves at any point is the presence (in the canonical coordinate frame) of a nonvanishing $g_{ij}{}^{TT}$ or π^{ijTT} there. Alternately, such a situation means that there exists an excitation of the gravitational field in one of its canonical variables (which are independent of the source variables). This is identical with the electromagnetic definition of a wave, which requires the existence of $A_i{}^T$ or $E_i{}^T$, the canonical variables of the electromagnetic field. In the obvious case where no waves are expected to exist, namely, the Schwarzschild solution, one can verify that $g_{ij}{}^{TT}$ and π^{ijTT} vanish everywhere in the canonical frame, which justifies its being regarded as a "one-particle" solution. This has not been established for the "many body" initial conditions treated above.

9.6   Remarks on Quantization of General Relativity

It has been noted by Landau, by Klein, and by Pauli that quantized general relativity would have to be considered in elementary particle theory, at high energies. A cutoff momentum P for quantum electrodynamics is suggested, with

$$\ln P^2/m^2c^2 \approx 1/\alpha \qquad (9.119)$$

Here α is the fine-structure constant and m is the electron rest mass. The result (9.119) was given by Källén and by Pauli as a consequence of the requirement of mathematical consistency. Landau noted that for energies corresponding to the cutoff momentum, the gravitational interaction is already of the same order of magnitude as the Coulomb interaction. In other words, as the energy increases the mass and gravitational interaction increase. The charge, however, does not change.

The quantum principles are very well established. They

take into account the "granular" structure of nature and the interaction between measuring devices and the system being measured. As P. G. Bergmann has remarked, unquantized general relativity cannot peacefully coexist with quantum theory. The gravitational field is the metric tensor; in this sense it is the most fundamental field in physics. Its quantization may affect, in a profound way, our notions of space and time, particularly in the realm of small dimensions (high energy).

It is interesting that it is possible to construct a quantity having the dimensions of length, out of $\hbar$, G, and c, it is

$$L = \sqrt{(\hbar G/c^3)} \sim 10^{-33} \text{ cm} \qquad (9.120)$$

This is much too small to be directly related to elementary particle dimensions now known. If[‡] we consider quantization using Feynman's formulation we should write for the wave function for the field

$$\psi_{\text{later}} = \int K_E(c, c')\psi_{\text{earlier}}(c')dc'$$

where the kernel is given by

$$K_E = \sum_H e^{iI_H/\hbar} \qquad (9.121)$$

with H meaning a sum over all field histories. For the gravitational field,

$$e^{iI_H/\hbar} = \exp\left[\frac{i}{\hbar}\int (c^3/16\pi G)R\sqrt{-g}\, d^4x\right]_H \qquad (9.122)$$

The Feynman sum should in principle include all possible metrics and topologies as acceptable histories, consistent with the Lorentz signature. Since

$$R \sim \left(\frac{\partial g_{\mu\nu}}{\partial x}\right)^2$$

it follows from (9.122) that if we consider a region of four-dimensional space-time, L units on a side, the quantum

‡ This discussion follows the comments of J. A. Wheeler.

fluctuations would be expected to be of the order

$$\langle(\varDelta g_{\mu\nu})^2\rangle \sim \frac{\hbar G}{c^3 L^2} \qquad (9.123)$$

Also we might expect perhaps amelioration of the difficulties of quantum field theory (18). There are a number of functions employed there which are singular on the light cone. Consider two points which lie on a light cone in flat space. If the space is now curved the second point will no longer be on the light cone. If a Feynman sum is carried out, over all metrics, the difficulties associated with the light cone may turn out to have measure zero. This indicates, unfortunately, that any quantization scheme which starts with a flat-space linear approximation will immediately have all the divergences. To remove them, it may be necessary to quantize the nonlinear theory from the very beginning.

9.7   Spinors in General Relativity

We discuss briefly the formalism used by Bargmann[‡] to discuss spinor fields in general relativity. A field of γ matrices is introduced which satisfy the anticommutation law

$$\gamma_\mu \gamma_\nu + \gamma_\nu \gamma_\mu = 2g_{\mu\nu} I \qquad (9.124)$$

I is the unit matrix. The components of γ are assumed to be continuous functions of the coordinates, and to transform like a vector under coordinate transformations. Under a spinor transformation

$$(\text{Spinor})_{\text{new}} = S^{-1}(\text{Spinor})_{\text{old}} \qquad (9.125)$$

the γ transform like

$$(\gamma_\alpha)_{\text{new}} = S^{-1}(\gamma_\alpha)_{\text{old}} S \qquad (9.126)$$

It is more simple to deal only with real representations of the γ together with spinor transformations S whose matrix elements are real.

The following formalism is arranged to guarantee that

‡ As discussed by D. Brill and J. A. Wheeler, *Revs. Modern Phys.* **29**, 465 (1957). See also references 42, 43, 44.

tensors will transform like tensors, that the effect of a spinor transformation will be as given by (9.125), and that the effect of a spinor transformation on a spinor tensor will be

$$(T_{\mu\nu})_{new} = S^{-1}(T_{\mu\nu})_{old}\,S \qquad (9.127)$$

For covariant differentiation additional 4×4 matrices Γ_α are introduced. These Γ's are determined from (9.124) up to a multiple of the unit matrix by the relation

$$\gamma_{\mu,\nu} - \Gamma^\alpha{}_{\mu\nu}\gamma_\alpha - \Gamma_\nu\gamma_\mu + \gamma_\mu\Gamma_\nu = 0 \qquad (9.128)$$

The covariant derivative of an object with spinor transformation properties with respect to x^μ is written ∇_μ and has the properties

$$\nabla_\mu(AB) = (\nabla_\mu A)B + B(\nabla_\mu A)$$
$$\nabla_\mu(A^*) = (\nabla_\mu A)^* \qquad (9.129)$$
$$\nabla_\mu\gamma_\nu = 0$$

This * means transpose of the complex conjugate. Linear combinations of the γ matrices used in special relativity can be employed. These are written $\tilde{\gamma}_\mu$ and satisfy

$$\tilde{\gamma}_\mu\tilde{\gamma}_\nu + \tilde{\gamma}_\nu\tilde{\gamma}_\mu = 2\delta_{\mu\nu}; \qquad \tilde{\gamma}_i{}^* = \tilde{\gamma}_i; \qquad \tilde{\gamma}_0{}^* = -\tilde{\gamma}_0 \qquad (9.130)$$

A system of Vierbein is often used. A locally Lorentz metric is introduced at each point by writing

$$dx^\mu = a^\mu{}_\nu\,d\tilde{x}^\nu; \qquad d\tilde{x}^\mu = b_\beta{}^\mu\,dx^\beta \qquad (9.131)$$

Here the $\tilde{x}^\nu$ are the Lorentz metric coordinates and x^ν are the general coordinates.

A set of γ's satisfying (9.124) is

$$\gamma_\mu = b_\mu{}^\nu\,\tilde{\gamma}_\nu \qquad (9.132)$$

An expression for the Γ_μ which is a solution of (9.128) is

$$\Gamma_\mu = \tfrac{1}{4}g_{\kappa\alpha}\left[\left(\frac{\partial b_\nu{}^\beta}{\partial x^\mu}\right)a^\alpha{}_\beta - \Gamma^\alpha{}_{\mu\nu}\right]S^{\kappa\nu} + a_\mu I \qquad (9.133)$$

Here a_μ is arbitrary and $S^{\mu\nu} = \tfrac{1}{2}(\gamma^\mu\gamma^\nu - \gamma^\nu\gamma^\mu)$. If the Vierbein formalism is used, a similarity transformation of the spinors corresponds to a Lorentz transformation of the Vierbein.

The covariant derivative of a spinor ψ is given by

$$\nabla_\mu \psi = \frac{\partial \psi}{\partial x^\mu} - \Gamma_\mu \psi \qquad (9.134)$$

The covariant derivative of a spinor tensor $F_{\mu\nu}$ is

$$\nabla_\alpha F_{\mu\nu} = F_{\mu\nu;\alpha} + F_{\mu\nu} \Gamma_\alpha - \Gamma_\alpha F_{\mu\nu} \qquad (9.135)$$

The Pauli conjugate of ψ is written $\psi^\dagger$ and defined by

$$\psi^\dagger = \psi^* \beta \qquad (9.136)$$

with β a matrix which is Hermitian and which is selected so that $\beta i \gamma^\nu$ is also Hermitian. In the Vierbein formalism $\beta = i\tilde{\gamma}^0$. Real quantities such as current density can be written

$$J^\mu = \psi^\dagger i\gamma^\mu \psi \qquad (9.137)$$

The Dirac equation in general relativity is

$$\gamma^\alpha \nabla_\alpha \psi + \mu\psi = 0 \qquad (9.138)$$

with the arbitrary traces of the Γ_μ arranged to include the effect of the four potential. (9.138) may be obtained from the variational principle.

$$\delta \int [\psi^\dagger \gamma^\alpha (\nabla_\alpha \psi) + \mu\psi^\dagger \psi] \sqrt{-g}\, d^4x = 0 \qquad (9.139)$$

with $\psi^\dagger$ and ψ varied independently.

The assumption that the atom is a natural clock may be justified from these relations. We may introduce a Lorentz frame along the world line of the atom. The flat space (9.138) is valid since the atomic dimensions are too small for the Riemann tensor to affect the internal motion. To compare the radiation with that of a distant atom, a coordinate transformation is carried out so that only the time coordinate is changed, and the same time coordinates are employed for atoms in different places. From (9.124), $\gamma^0 = \tilde{\gamma}^0(-g^{00})^{\frac{1}{2}}$. The energy is associated with $\tilde{\gamma}^0 \partial/\partial x^0$ so the energy levels become $E^n = E^{n0}(-g_{00})^{\frac{1}{2}}$, in agreement with the red shift formula.

References

1. G. Y. Rainich, *Trans. Am. Math. Soc.* **27**, 106 (1925).
2. C. W. Misner and J. A. Wheeler, *Ann. Physics* **2**, 6, 525 (1957).
3. J. A. Wheeler, *Ann. Physics* **216**, 604 (1957).
4. B. Kursunoglu, *Proceedings of the Chapel Hill Conference on the Role of Gravitation in Physics*, 1957; ASTIA Document AD118180; WADC Tech. Rept. 57–216.
5. V. Hlavaty, *Geometry of Einstein's Unified Field Theory*, P. Noordhoff, N.V., Groningen, Netherlands, 1957.
6. A. Einstein and J. Grommer, *Sitzber. preuss. Acad. Wiss.* **1, 6, 235,** (1927).
7. V. Fock, *Revs. Modern Phys.* **29**, 3, 325 (1957).
8. A. Einstein, L. Infeld, and Hoffmann, *Ann. Math.* **39**, 65 (1938).
9. L. Infeld, *Acta Phys. Polon.* **13**, 187 (1954).
10. J. N. Goldberg, *Phys. Rev.* **89**, 263 (1953).
11. A. Einstein, *The Meaning of Relativity*, Princeton University Press, 1950, 3rd ed., p. 107.
12. A. Friedman, *Z. Physik* **10**, 377 (1922).
13. H. P. Robertson, *Proc. Natl. Acad. Sci. U.S.* **15**, 822 (1929).
14. J. L. Anderson and P. G. Bergmann, *Phys. Rev.* **83**, 1018 (1951).
15. P. A. M. Dirac, *Can. J. Math.* **2**, 129 (1950)
16. P. A. M. Dirac, *Proc. Roy. Soc. (London)* **A246**, 326 (1958).
17. P. G. Bergmann, R. Penfield, R. Schiller, and H. Zatzkis, *Phys. Rev.* **80**, 81 (1950).
18. S. Deser, *Revs. Modern Phys.* **29**, 417 (1957).
19. F. A. E. Pirani and A. Schild, *Phys. Rev.* **79**, 986 (1950).
20. F. A. E. Pirani, A. Schild, and R. Skinner, *Phys. Rev.* **87**, 452 (1952).
21. P. G. Bergmann, *Helv. Phys. Acta*, Suppl. IV, 79 (1956).
22. P. A. M. Dirac, *Proc. Roy. Soc. (London)* **A246**, 333 (1958).
23. See papers in *Revs. Modern Phys.* **29**, 5 (1957).
24. L. Witten, *Phys. Rev.* **115**, 1, 206 (1959).
25. A. E. Scheidegger, *Phys. Rev.* **99**, 1883 (1955).
26. P. A. M. Dirac, *Phys. Rev.* **114**, 924 (1959).
27. L. Infeld, *Revs. Modern Phys.* **29**, 398 (1957).
28. R. Arnowitt, S. Deser, and C. W. Misner, *Nuovo cimento* **XV**, 487 (1960).
29. G. Cocconi and E. E. Salpeter, *Nuovo cimento* **10**, 646 (1958).
30. G. Cocconi and E. E. Salpeter, *Phys. Rev. Letters* **4**, 176 (1960).
31. R. Arnowitt and S. Deser, *Phys. Rev.* **113**, 745 (1959).
32. R. Arnowitt, S. Deser, and C. W. Misner, *Phys. Rev.* **116**, 1322 (1959).
33. A. Lichernowicz, *J. Math. Pure and Appl.* **9**, 37 (1944).
34. J. A. Wheeler, *Phys. Rev.* **97**, 511 (1955).
35. A. Papapetrou, *Proc. Roy. Soc.* **A209**, 248 (1951).
36. L. I. Schiff, *Phys. Rev. Letters*, **4**, 215 (1960).
37. D. W. Sciama, *Monthly Notices*, **113**, 34 (1953).
38. Sherwin, Frauenfelder, Garwin, Luscher, Margulies, and Peacock, *Phys. Rev. Letters*, **4**, 399 (1960).

39. Hughes, Robinson and Beltran-Lopez, *Phys. Rev. Letters*, **4**, 342 (1960).
40. H. Bondi, *Cosmology*, 1952, Cambridge University Press.
41. O. Halpern and G. Heller, *Phys. Rev.* **48**, 434 (1935).
42. D. Ivanenko, *Trans. Acad. Sci. U.S.S.R.*, (1929).
43. V. Fock and D. Ivanenko, *Comptes Rendues*, 188, (1929).
44. V. Fock and D. Ivanenko, *Z. Physik*, **59**, 718 (1929).
45. L. Witten, *Phys. Rev.* **120**, 635, (1960).
46. H. Thirring, *Phys. ZS.* **19**, 33, (1918), **22**, 29, (1921).
47. P. Jordan, *Jubilee of Relativity Theory, Helvetica Physica Acta*, Supp. IV, 157, (1956).
48. O. Heckmann and E. Schucking, *Jubilee of Relativity Theory, Helvetica Physica Acta*, Supp. IV, 114, (1956).
49. O. Klein, *Jubilee of Relativity Theory, Helvetica Physica Acta*, Supp. IV, 58, 147, (1956).
50. G. E. Lemaitre, *Monthly Notices*, **91**, 490, (1931).
51. L. Landau, *in Niels Bohr and the Development of Physics*, edited by W. Pauli. McGraw Hill Book Company, 1955.
52. O. Klein, *in Niels Bohr and the Development of Physics*, edited by W. Pauli, McGraw Hill Book Company, 1955.
53. P. Havas, *Phys. Rev.* 113, 732, (1960).

Exercises

Just do the exercises diligently; then you will find out what you have understood and what you have not.

A. Sommerfeld (to W. Heisenberg)

1. Discuss the covariant and contravariant components of a vector in a plane in which oblique coordinates are employed.
2. Deduce expressions (3.30) and (3.31), the transformation laws for the Christoffel symbols of the first and second kinds.
3. Show that the number of independent components of $R_{\alpha\beta\gamma\delta}$ in a space of N dimensions is $(N^2/12)(N^2 - 1)$.
4. Discuss the embedding of a curved space of N dimensions in a flat space of a greater number of dimensions.
5. Derive expression (3.49) for $R_{\alpha\beta\gamma\delta}$.
6. Set up a coordinate system on a torus; calculate all components of $g_{\mu\nu}$, $\Gamma^{\mu}_{\alpha\beta}$, and $R_{\alpha\beta\gamma\delta}$.
7. Evaluate $\varepsilon_{\alpha\beta\gamma\delta}\,\varepsilon^{\alpha\beta\gamma\delta}$.
8. A contravariant vector is being parallel displaced along a small circle of a sphere. It has components $A^{\theta} = 0$ and $A^{\varphi} = 2$ at the point $\theta = \pi/4$, $\varphi = 0$. The path along which it is being displaced is $\theta =$ constant. Calculate the values of A^{θ} and A^{φ} as a function of φ along the small circle.
9. An observer in a uniformly accelerated frame measures time using the synchronized clocks fixed in an inertial frame with respect to which he is being accelerated. Calculate $g_{\mu\nu}$ for the accelerated observer.
10. Carry out the operations leading to (4.15).
11. Derive the expression (5.6).

12. Derive (5.13a) by starting with a four potential with $A_1 = A_2 = A_3 = 0$ and $A_0 = f(r)$.

13. Write the exact red-shift formula given in expression (5.21) as a series expansion, compare it with a series obtained using the relativistic Doppler effect in the equivalence-principle deduction of Chapter 1. To what order in the change in gravitational potential do they agree? Does this mean that general relativity is in disagreement with the equivalence principle?

14. Derive expressions (9.1), (9.2), and (9.3).

15. Show that (9.44) gives a value of K which is the same for any linear combination of A and B.

16. Given that the Lagrangian is

$$L = \dot{q}_0{}^2 - q_0{}^2 + b_1\dot{q}_1 + b_2\dot{q}_2 + b_3\dot{q}_3 + \dot{q}_4$$

with b_1, b_2, and b_3 functions of q_0, q_1, q_2, and q_3. Solve for the equations of motion.

17. Carry out the reductions leading to (9.87), (9.91), (9.95), (9.106), (9.107).

18. A satellite is equipped with a natural clock which is to be compared with an identical clock at rest on the earth's surface. If we compare elapsed intervals at the end of a given coordinate time, show that (Singer, Phys. Rev. 104, 11, (1956)).

$$\frac{ds_1 - ds_2}{ds_1} = \frac{GM}{2c^2r}\left(\frac{1-2h/r}{1+ h/r} - \frac{3\omega^2}{4\pi G\rho_M}\right)$$

s_1 is the interval for the earth clock, s_2 is the interval for the satellite clock, h is the height of the assumed circular orbit above the surface of the earth, M is the mass of the earth, ρ_M is the mean density of the earth, r and ω refer to the radius and angular velocity, respectively, of the earth.

19. Identify the terms in (9.107) which are the three dimensional scalar curvature.

20. Discuss theories of gravitation based on particles of spin 0, and spin 1 (Gupta, Revs. Mod. Phys. 29, 334, (1957), and explain why they are unsatisfactory.

Index